# More tea *less* Vicar!

*How to Survive in an English Country Vicarage*
*when you're not the Vicar!*

*For Sam, James, Charlie, Jo, Sophie, Olive and Ali*

## How to Survive in an English Country Vicarage when you're not the Vicar!

Jill Fraser

BREWIN BOOKS

First published by
Brewin Books Ltd, 56 Alcester Road,
Studley, Warwickshire B80 7LG in 2006
www.brewinbooks.com

Reprinted January 2007

ISBN 10: 1 85858 294 6
ISBN 13: 978 1 85858 294 8

A Cataloguing in Publication Record
for this title is available from the British Library.

Typeset in New Baskerville
Printed in Great Britain by
Cromwell Press Ltd.

# CONTENTS

**Acknowledgements**       **vii**

**1. January, February**       **1**
January Blues!       1
Aunt Lucy       8
The Day Of The Fog       12
The Aftermath       18
Judy       19
On The Move       22
Sorting Out       25
The Secret In The Garden       29
Getting There       33
Settling In       34
Early Days       37
The Church       42
Vicar Vic       45
The Accident       48

**2. March, April, May, June**       **59**
Mothering Sunday       59
The Vicarage       64
Faith, Hope And Charity       70
Peacocks And Pig       80
Past Times       85
Church Plays       93
Walking       96
Easter       102
Vicarages Again       104
The Floods       106
Cellars And A Secret Room       110
He Ascended Into Heaven       115
The Fete       119

**3. July, August, September, October**     **127**

Hay Fever     127

Animals     130

Leaflets     136

The Paper Chase     140

Starting School     146

Harvest     149

Flowers     156

Films     161

All Eyes     166

Boxes     171

Witches     180

Ghosts     184

**4. November, December**     **189**

Revelations     189

Uninvited Guests     195

Holly, Ivy And Mistletoe     199

Christmas Cake     202

Rudolph!     207

Christmas Chaos     211

Pins And Needles!     214

Carol Singers     217

Christingles     220

Preparations     225

The Nativity     228

Christmas Crackers     230

Christmas Morning     236

And Finally...     241

**A Very Important Acknowledgment**     **248**

# ACKNOWLEDGEMENTS

This book would not have happened without the support of the following people:

Carole Evans, Di Buckley, John Davis, Margaret Twigg, John Steed, Philip Woodfield, 'Bobby' Davis, Sue Robbins, Sue Green, Vernon Blackmore, Christine Blackmore, Georgina Isaac, Olive Fraser, Ali Fraser, The Aston Cantlow and District Local History Society, all the children who have taken part in the plays and, of course, Sam, James, Charlie, Jo and Sophie!

# Chapter One

# JANUARY, FEBRUARY

### JANUARY BLUES!

'You're brave.........coming up here without a coat.' George, the cameraman, pulled his fur-lined anorak tightly round him as if to emphasise the freezing January temperatures.

The three of us, George the cameraman, Sid the soundman and I were standing on the top of Wenlock Edge, Shropshire's highest escarpment. Crisp, clear skies that morning meant that we could see for miles across some of England and Wales' finest countryside. The shots we'd get from here would make a wonderful opening to our short film for television about the nineteenth century eccentric, Jack Mytton. MP, drunkard and general anarchist, the 'powers that be' in Shropshire had chosen to honour him by naming their county's longest bridleway after him. Their choice of 'Shropshire Lad' could have included the poet A.E. Housman and Clive of India, but Jack's long-standing reputation for charming the locals, even from the other side of the grave, meant that they didn't even get to the first fence.

The suggestion that we get to our starting point at first light, to capture the sunrise, had been a rash one given the treacherous state of the roads in the pitch dark in early January. Far worse, in order to make it there by 7.15am, I'd had to leave home at 5.30am! Now whose idea had that been? Oh, I remember...mine!

I'd been a reporter/researcher for a regional magazine programme for eighteen years but, ever since the children started arriving, I'd chosen to take the softer option and done part-time researching, only reporting when they were short. With my boss, Will, away in London for the week, today was going to be one of those days!

It had been a challenge to make this story about a dead drunk interesting enough to fill ten minutes of television time. God knows what young Jack discovered as he galloped across the hills nearly two hundred years ago. But had he made the journey today, he would have been surprised to pass a 'bed and breakfast' run by a former chef from Claridges, a pub serving genuine kangaroo burgers and a part-time ferryman who ran an internet café when he wasn't guiding passengers across one of the narrowest points of the river Severn.

As lunchtime approached, things seemed to be going to schedule. The only shot we had left to do, before we left the summit for our midday break, was the view of the glorious countryside around Wenlock Edge. As we pulled into the car park at its base, my 'phone rang. It was Josh, my nine year old, and he sounded fraught.

'Mum! Dad went off with my lunchbox in the boot of his car.'

'What?'

'He dropped me off at school and just as I was about to get my bag, he drove off.'

I 'tutted' in exasperation. 'I'll have to ring Granny to see if she can drop a sandwich in to you.'

There was a pause as he relayed the message to his teacher. A moment later I had Mrs Gates on the 'phone.

'If it's easier, I could organise for the catering staff to provide him with a meal…as it's only a one-off.'

'Well, that would be a help,' I admitted gratefully, feeling suitably chastened by her crisp tone. Clearly she didn't approve of working mothers, especially ones who allowed their children to starve while they 'swanned' off around the countryside. Given that I worked away from home no more than once a week, the criticism was hardly fair. Besides, she surely knew me well enough to know that I was perfectly capable of forgetting a packed lunch when I wasn't out working!

And that was why I managed to forget my coat. With an impatient cameraman and soundman keen to get to the pub, both glaring at me through the windscreen, I finished my call, grabbed my script and leapt into the back of their Range Rover, the only way of getting to the summit by car.

I could hear the wind howling round as we got to the top. It was hard to imagine a more exposed spot on this, the coldest day of the year so far. Down below I could see fields of sheep, woodland, winding rivers and clusters of farm buildings. As George tried to find a level surface to park, I realised I could also just make out my car…. and the corner of my thick, woolly coat on the back seat. But there was nothing I could do about it. Oh well, it shouldn't take too long to record a short introduction, should it?

But I was wrong. From the start, we had problems with the wind. As it whipped round the top of the hill, the noise was so loud it was difficult to hear my voice above it. And now, things were doubly hard because I was so cold I couldn't speak without my teeth chattering.

'It's a great view.' For a moment the soundman looked almost wistful. 'And you dying of frostbite adds to the atmosphere, bringing an even deeper sense of remoteness to the landscape.'

Ignoring the sarcasm, I gave it just one more go. It wasn't good, but it was going to have to do.

'It would have worked better if you'd been more appropriately dressed,' George commented as we walked back to his car. 'You looked really stupid with just a jumper on. Anyone watching will tell instantly that you're freezing!'

'You could have lent me your coat,' I reflected bitterly.

'Well, to be honest, I thought about that,' he said slowly. 'But, you see, I can't work properly when I'm cold!'

Half an hour later we were in the pub. But while the crew propped up the bar, I preferred to sit on a nearby radiator, happy to put up with the risk of piles and chilblains rather than make the effort to talk which, for the moment, was still not easy.

'Warmed up yet?' George shouted encouragingly across the room as he ordered his second pint.

Sadly, I could only shake my head in reply. Clearly, I was still a long way from a complete recovery.

\*　　\*　　\*　　\*

The temperature was still close to freezing as we left the pub. As I pulled my thick coat tightly round me, George dropped his next bombshell.

'According to your list, all we've got left now are shots of you walking along the Jack Mytton Way. I suggest we drop you off at various points along the route and get close-up and long distant shots of you strolling through some of the most scenic areas.'

I nodded without much enthusiasm. Some of the areas would be very exposed and, to add to my misery, I already had a nose which closely resembled Rudolph, and hair that was so windswept, it was often hard to see where I was going! This experience was bound to make Will realise that my days as a reporter were well and truly over!

'And don't forget to keep your coat off,' George reminded me as I climbed into my car. 'It's called continuity, remember,' he added unnecessarily. 'We've already got shots of you talking from the summit of the hill without a coat, so we can't really film you walking the rest of the way with one on. It would look stupid.'

'But it's even colder now,' I protested as the winter evening began to draw in.

'You should have thought of that when you delayed us with that 'phone call home this morning,' he said irritably. 'And you're lucky I pointed out this coat business,' he added accusingly. 'It's really your job to sort these things out.' He finished on a crisp note, keen to make it clear that he was very unimpressed that a man of his talents was working with such a moron.

I shrugged my shoulders and tossed my coat onto the back seat. It was at times like these that it was best to say nothing and just get on with it.

\*     \*     \*     \*

The long journey back with the car heater on, helped a little to thaw me out. I had just joined a long traffic jam on the outskirts of Worcester when a 'phone call marked the start of the next catastrophe of the day.

'Hi, darling!' It was Mac. Immediately alarm bells rang loudly in my head.

'You're on a mobile. Why aren't you at home with the children?'

'Don't panic,' Mac was using his irritatingly calm, slightly patronising voice. 'Everything's under control. Just had a bit of a problem with a late meeting. But I've managed to organise everyone. So, I thought I'd give you a quick ring in case you called home and were worried.'

'What have you done with the children?' I was deeply suspicious. If it had been that easy to sort, I wouldn't have bothered Mac to come home early.

'I asked Sue to pick Lizzie up from nursery and Archie from the child-minder's. She's going to give them tea.'

'Sue? God, not my completely perfect sister-in-law?' I groaned inwardly. 'Why on earth did you ring her? She normally flinches every time Archie goes within a mile of her immaculate home. I'll be repaying the favour for weeks,' I added darkly.

'Calm down for goodness sake,' I could detect a defensive note in Mac's voice. 'These things can't be helped. Anyway, I asked her if she minded and she said it would be no bother at all.'

'Mac, you're lying! Anyone who has Archie between the hours of five o'clock and bedtime and claims it's no bother at all is either a saint or mentally insane. She'll probably need therapy after the experience. Even his doting granny would think twice before agreeing to that one, especially when he's been at the childminder's all day. She probably just felt she had no alternative given that you were in town and I was stuck on the top of a precipice in the middle of nowhere. As far as she's concerned, it's just another example of our complete disorganisation. So, go on, now that I'm completely stressed, hit me with it. What have you done with the other two?'

'Mary collected them from school.'

'And is she giving them tea?'

'Well no. She had to take her children to some sort of ballet class. She just dropped them back at the house. But I've spoken to them and they're fine!'

'My God! So they're home alone. Mac, we'll have social services onto us if they find out.'

'Nonsense!' Mac was now sounding irritated. 'You do overreact. Claire's eleven for goodness sake. And Josh will be ten in a few months.'

'And they'll both be tired and hungry - a lethal combination. They'll have probably murdered each other by now,' I reflected bitterly.

'Kate, as we speak, they will either be slumped in front of the television or the play station. What can possibly go wrong?'

\*     \*     \*     \*

It was five minutes later when my 'phone rang again.

'Mum, how long are you going to be?' Claire sounded harassed.

'Hopefully not much longer. Are you alright?'

'We're fine, except....Mummy, Josh has just been into the lounge and there's water dripping through the ceiling?'

Mac's final words echoed in my head ...... 'What can possibly go wrong?'

'Have you left a tap running upstairs?' I asked without thinking.

'No. There isn't a room above the lounge. It's just loft space. Remember?'

Think fast. Okay.

'Right Claire, listen carefully. Go across to Mr Harper next door and ask him very politely if he'd mind coming to have a look at the problem. Then 'phone me back.'

The 'phone went dead and I drummed my fingers anxiously on the steering wheel as I awaited his verdict. A few moments later and the 'phone rang again.

'What does he think is the problem?' I asked nervously.

'Well Mummy, we did as you asked, and told him very politely about the drips. He was very kind and said he'd come across as soon as he'd finished his dinner.' Claire sounded relieved that something was being done.

'What are the drips like now?' I asked.

'Hold on.'

I could hear her put the receiver down and trot into the other room. She was soon back, running. In the background I could hear Josh crying.

'Mummy, it's pouring through. There's water everywhere.'

Swearing to myself that I would surely murder Mac when he returned, I shouted down the 'phone.

'Run across to Mr Harper again and tell him the leak's now much worse and can he come right now. Don't put the receiver down. I want to talk to him as soon as he's seen what's happened.'

After what seemed like ages I heard the noise of people coming into the house. Above the children's sobs, I could hear Mr Harper's loud booming voice. It wasn't reassuring!

'God Almighty, what a mess! This isn't a drip! This is a ruddy waterfall! Quick Josh, Claire, help shift some of the furniture before it's completely ruined!'

'Someone pick the 'phone up, please,' I yelled. But all I could hear above the expletives was the sound of furniture being moved at speed and Josh and Claire sobbing.

I continued to scream down the 'phone, but to no avail. After what seemed like for ever, Claire finally picked it up. She was inconsolable.

'Mummy, Mr Harper wants to know where he'd find the stop-cock?' she blurted out between her sobs. In the background I could hear Josh. He sounded hysterical.

Panic! Absolutely no idea. 'I'll ring Dad and ring you straight back,' I promised.

Excellent! Mac's 'phone was engaged. With vague memories of some metal contraption behind the washing machine, I rang home again. But that was also engaged. After several more attempts, light dawned. Oh God, the 'phone was still off the hook in the hall. Claire must have spoken to me from the kitchen when she asked about the the stop-cock. What now?

My last chance. I dialled Claire's mobile, praying that it had enough charge in it to take the call. A few seconds later, she answered. She sounded slightly calmer.

'Mummy, Mr Harper found the tap and the water's stopped now. But there's a terrible mess.'

Trying to sound as calm as I could, I spoke slowly and deliberately.

'Darling, you know Mummy's favourite little rug by the fire. Could you please pick it up and put it somewhere safe before it's too badly damaged.'

There was a short pause before Claire replied.

'Mummy, it's floating!'

* * * *

The problem turned out to be the header tank. The damage was considerable but a lot less than the damage I inflicted on Mac when he arrived home with the little ones later that evening.

'I ask you one little favour and end up with two traumatised children trying to sort out a problem that would have challenged Noah!'

Mac remained silent as he surveyed the damage. 'Of course,' he reflected, 'even if I had been here, I could have been in the kitchen with the children and never noticed a thing until it was too late.'

'However,' I added crisply, 'you might just have saved the children and me a lot of heartache. Claire's bound to have nightmares for weeks.'

But Mac was determined to keep a positive spin on it all.

'At least it's a step down to that room so there's no damage anywhere else.'

But I was not so easily pacified.

'The fire brigade said it was lucky the children noticed what was happening when they did, or else we'd have had an indoor swimming pool to deal with!'

* * * *

The 'flood' had two consequences. Firstly, in the short term, Mac became a lot more punctual. Secondly, as the lounge was our main living space, we struggled to live without it. We had moved into our little cottage thirteen years earlier, just the two of us and almost no furniture. At first it had seemed quite spacious. Then, at various intervals over the next eleven years, we had produced our brood. Claire first, creative and highly strung, Josh, never short of a one-liner and with enough energy to run a power station, four year old Lizzie, often prone to tantrums on an extreme scale and, finally, Archie, who at eighteen months could be either enchanting or dangerous. As they grew, they took up more space as did the endless clutter we bought to go with them. Over the years, we'd converted the cellar into a study and the roof space into two bedrooms for the older children. Three bedrooms on the first floor gave Mac and me a room, a playroom/bedroom which Lizzie and Archie shared and a little guest room. But, as none of the rooms was big, we were bursting at the seams. Either we needed to start moving children out into the sheds in the garden or we needed a bigger house. I'd mentioned it several times in the past but now I could see that Mac was beginning to listen.

## AUNT LUCY

'Mac, that was Aunt Lucy on the 'phone asking what time we want her here on Sunday. How could you possibly invite her after the week we've had?'

'I didn't invite her, she invited herself….as usual. She'd worked out there was a family service and she rang to ask if she could come across and see the children. It was a bit difficult to refuse really.'

'But we're in chaos. No lounge and furniture everywhere!'

'Calm down. She knows all that. She's not expecting you to roll out the red carpet. You know what she's like.'

'Well, make sure you tell her not to bring any of her 'stuff' with her. If we try and pack anything more into this house, I swear it will explode!'

Aunt Lucy was Mac's aunt on his mother's side. With no children of her own, we had become her 'surrogate' family.

For as long as anyone could remember, Aunt Lucy had collected anything old. While some pieces were undoubtedly valuable antiques, others were simply unusual bits of junk that she picked up in various second-hand shops across the country. While her husband had been alive, they had run an antiques business from their home in Somerset. They didn't bother with a shop or a showroom. Instead they furnished their house with their stock. Nearly everything in their rambling country pile was for sale and buyers were welcome at almost any time to come and have a browse. Not surprisingly, over the years they had had a few unwanted visitors. But with two Dobermans on site, they rarely got very far.

Before we had the children, we would sometimes go and stay with them in their eccentric home. It was not unusual to be having lunchtime drinks only to discover that the coffee table where you thought you'd left your drink, had unexpectedly been removed for a customer to see in a better light. Once, during the first course of a dinner party, Aunt Lucy suddenly handed a crystal water jug to a young woman who had just entered the room. We'd all thought she was a member of staff but, a few moments later, we saw her empty the contents of the jug onto the lawn and go off with it in her car. But the moment that made us seriously re-think our visits happened when we awoke one morning to find both bedside tables missing. An apologetic Aunt Lucy had stood at the bottom of our bed and explained that she hadn't liked to disturb us, but the gentleman had broken his journey to Scotland to make the purchase and was in a bit of a hurry.

'He didn't come in, did he?' Mac asked nervously as he pulled the duvet tightly around his neck.

'Oh no, dear,' she reassured him. 'I wouldn't allow him right into the bedroom. He could see all he needed to see well enough from the doorway!'

When Uncle Edmund died unexpectedly, Aunt Lucy reluctantly decided that the house and business were too much for one elderly lady to manage. So she sold up and moved to a smaller house not far from us. The family heaved a sigh of relief and hoped she might settle down to a quieter and more normal existence. But they were mistaken. Within months she was back on the prowl, this time buying up smaller bits and pieces which she sold, mostly with great success, at car boot sales across the country. She also took up knitting and supplemented her stock each week with a variety of colourful jumpers, hats and scarves. It was the greatest thrill for our elder three to be invited to help her run the stall whenever she visited sites in our area. Claire, a budding thespian, loved the idea of attracting customers by shouting out what was on offer that week from the bonnet of Aunt Lucy's car. Josh, who fancied himself as a bit of a wheeler dealer, soon learned how to 'haggle' a price, and Lizzie just liked to play with the goods and generally see what delights were on offer on the stalls around her.

The only problem was that Aunt Lucy would give as gifts to her relatives and friends anything she couldn't sell on the stall. And, to that end, she was very generous. She rarely arrived at our house without a car-load of what Mac described as 'junk'. It was hard to refuse it and even harder to know what to do with it.

So, despite Mac's efforts, she arrived on the Sunday with a standard lamp and a brass curtain rail poking out of the back window of her car. The children greeted her rapturously.

'Now, what have we here?' she enquired earnestly as she surveyed a line of 'Beanie Babies' in our already overcrowded hall.

'It's the animals for our Noah's Ark play,' Lizzie replied excitedly.

'Grrr!' Archie burst into the hall proudly wearing a stripy tiger mask.

'Silly idea of mine really,' I apologised, coming to greet her. 'What do they say about working with children and animals? It was the burst tank that inspired me. Having had a room full of water, I suddenly felt an empathy with Noah.'

'You should have told me your theme,' Aunt Lucy said reproachfully. 'Stuffed toy animals have become quite a successful line on my stalls recently.'

By the time I had stuffed my children, the props, the scripts and Aunt Lucy into the car, we were running late for the rehearsal. As we turned into the church car park, my face fell as I surveyed the group of children waiting patiently on the steps outside.

'Catherine, I made it quite clear when I spoke to your mother last night that I only wanted *toy* animals for my play. I cannot possibly use real ones. Apart from the chaos, it would only be a matter of moments before your hamster became some other animal's lunch! So, pop him back in his cage and put him on the table at the back of the church. And Simon, tie your dog up outside before he gets a sniff of that hamster.'

With a tearful Catherine at my side, we moved into the church. Ten minutes later and the rehearsal was in full swing.

'Ryan, you are not to throw the 'Beanie Babies' up into the air. I will say it one more time. When I nod my head, everyone holding a pair of animals is to solemnly take them up to the pulpit and place them on the steps as if they were entering the ark. Do I make myself clear? They are not to be thrown onto the steps or at your friend,' I finished, glaring at seven year old Alex.

'Yes, Mark, the animals would have done their 'pees' and 'poos' all over the Ark. It would have been Noah's family's job to clear it all up.'

'Yes, it would have been okay to simply throw it overboard.'

'No, Ben, nobody would have been swimming nearby and there were no Blue Flag beaches. The whole point of this story, if you remember, is that everyone, except Noah, his family and an Ark load of animals has been drowned in the flood! Now, if everyone is finished, can we go for this one more time.'

'For goodness sake, Josh, you're standing on the rainbow!'

\*　　\*　　\*　　\*

'Shame the hamster escaped,' Mac was trying not to smile as we left the church later that morning. 'Still I bet worse things happened on the Ark.'

'That's the last time I'm doing that,' I said bitterly as I crammed children and soft toys into my car.

'You always say that. Besides, the congregation loved it. Nothing like a bit of chaos to get them going.'

'I'm going home. Don't forget Aunt Lucy, will you. I think she's taken quite a shine to the vicar.'

'She's probably trying to sell him something.'

'In that case, if you get a moment, ask him if he wants a brass rail and a standard lamp!'

\*    \*    \*    \*

It was a challenge to fit everyone round the table at lunchtime. With the dining room stuffed full of the furniture from the lounge, I'd done my best to make room for Aunt Lucy in our already overcrowded kitchen. But that was before she had taken it upon herself to persuade the Vicar to join us.

'I hope you like your beef well done,' Aunt Lucy asked unnecessarily as she handed him a portion of my somewhat over-cooked joint.

'Anything would be lovely.' I could see that the poor man was looking distinctly embarrassed as he sat, slightly squashed, between Claire and Josh at the far end of the table.

'The flowers looked beautiful this morning,' I commented trying to lighten the conversation. 'The ladies on the committee must work so hard to create such a glorious effect.'

'Some of the vases are exquisite too,' Aunt Lucy chipped in. 'I was studying some of them carefully during your long sermon. I imagine some of them must be quite valuable?'

'You want to watch her, Vicar,' Mac warned. 'Given half a chance, she'd be trying to get you a good price for them on one of her stalls.'

'You must have quite a selection of antiques in your house,' the Vicar commented. 'Aren't you worried about security, now that you're on your own?'

'Indeed I am,' she acknowledged. 'Ever since the two Dobermans passed on, I've taken to going to bed with an old poker!'

'You kept that quiet!' Mac replied before I could stop him.

Over coffee, Mac talked about our current crisis. 'With the lounge out of action, we've got furniture piled up to the ceiling in our tiny dining room. I tried to find a book in there the other day. God knows how I managed it but, when I did, I felt I needed mountain boots and a rope to find my way out again.'

'The only good thing about all this,' I added trying to put a positive spin on it all, 'is that it has slowed down the endless stream of houseguests we've had recently. They often made use of the big sofa bed in the lounge and, at the moment, it's sodden covers are at the dry cleaners and the frame is buried under ten feet of furniture.'

'Mind you,' Mac added, 'most of our stuff isn't worth keeping. I reckon if we had a good clear out, we'd probably find we could manage with less than half of it. I think I'll order a skip next week.'

'A skip?' Aunt Lucy was clearly appalled. 'Why? I could sell half of it on my stall.'

'Wicked,' said Josh. 'Would we get to keep the money?'

'Josh, really!' Claire gave him a chilling stare. 'You're not supposed to say things like that in front of the Vicar.'

'We'll see,' I muttered cautiously. But I could tell from the expression on her face that Aunt Lucy's mind was already made up.

*     *     *     *

'The possibility of moving is getting more attractive by the minute,' I muttered as I crawled into bed later that night. 'No more embarrassing moments with the Vicar and the perfect reason for getting out of writing a play for the family service every month.'

'Well, I must say you made it particularly difficult for yourself with your choice of topic today,' Mac reflected as he climbed in next to me. 'I would have thought that, after the events of this week, Noah's Ark would have been your last choice of subject for the play. I thought you were after a couple of days rest and relaxation. The tale of the biggest flood in history was hardly destined to take your mind off things.'

'I think it made me feel better. After all, Noah was heralded a saint for managing a flood outside his home. We managed to survive one inside ours.'

But Mac's analysis was different. 'Personally, after a day with Aunt Lucy, I identified more with the idea of some poor chap being holed up with every member of his family in a confined space for all that time. If you ask me, he wasn't a saint for restarting the world's population. He was a saint for surviving forty days and forty nights on that boat without murdering any of them!'

## THE DAY OF THE FOG

'Oh no, that's all I need,' I exclaimed as I pulled back the curtains the following morning. 'Thick fog!' It was half past six and in just over two hours I was due to make a film about a family of stonemasons who lived about thirty miles away in a remote corner of the Cotswolds.

'On the Richter scale is that bad or calamitous?' Mac asked unhelpfully from under the bedclothes. 'I thought you said you were filming in someone's workshop for at least part of the day.'

'If the weather's the same down there, it's calamitous! I've organised a film about a group of craftsmen who spend their days carving Cotswold stone. Sure, we start indoors, but at least half the shots are supposed to be of the beautiful villages in the area, their golden stone buildings glinting in the winter sunshine. Snow would have been perfect. A hoarfrost even better. At least a strong wind would have cleared the skies. But fog??? We won't see a thing and it will be all my fault.'

'It may clear in a couple of hours,' Mac was trying to be optimistic, but he could see from my expression that he was wasting his time.

'Why do I do this to myself?' I grumbled, not for the first time. 'I've got four children and a house to run. I could have found myself a little part-time job selling jewellery or baby clothes in other people's nice warm homes. But instead I opt to freeze to death at the top of icy pinnacles or to lose myself in fog in the middle of nowhere! I might just as well have taken a job as a deep sea fisherman or a coal miner,' I finished dramatically. 'They might just have been easier!'

'You do it because you love it,' Mac reminded me. 'You do it because it keeps you in touch with the ever changing world of television and you do it because, as you said last night, it gives you a chance to escape from the madness of this house. And besides all that,' he finished, 'the pay's not that bad either!'

'Well, make the most of it,' I answered as I clambered into my warmest clothes. 'If today goes badly, I may be out of work by the end of the week!'

Half an hour later I was in the car with my thick coat tucked tightly round me. It was still dark and the fog was as bad as ever ....terrific!

With the thermometer registering just above zero, initially the roads seemed to be ice-free. But as I approached the Cotswolds Hills, it soon became obvious that the outside temperature was plummeting. And the fog, which for the first part of the journey had shown signs of clearing, was now getting worse by the minute. Within seconds of arriving at the Cotswolds borders, it seemed to grab the car and draw it into its swirling mists.

Driving at a snail's pace now, I crawled along the lanes, picking out signposts only when they were on top of me. Eventually I arrived at our first location – a remote churchyard halfway up a steep hill. How difficult would it be to meet up with the crew and our guests? Perhaps it would be easier when it was fully light.

I didn't need to worry. As I got out of the car, George, the cameraman approached me. At first I couldn't see him, but his voice, booming through the gloom like a fog horn, soon made him easy to identify.

'Ye Gods, I nearly felled a pedestrian and three sheep on my way here. Will's in an even worse mess. Apparently this fog's caused an horrific accident on the motorway and there's an enormous tailback. So it's anyone's guess what time he'll turn up.....if ever!' he added darkly. Scanning the churchyard with a menacing look in his eye, he continued. 'Did you know the weather was going to be this bad? How on earth we're going to see this church on camera is anyone's guess. At the moment I can't even see my hand in front of my face!'

Determined not to be riled so early in the morning, I simply sighed deeply. Given the unpredictability of British weather, George should have had a bit more tolerance. And, as for asking me if I knew it would be like this! Well, he had a radio in his car, didn't he? He could have listened to the weather forecast had he wanted to. And even if he had known, it wouldn't have made any difference. In this country, weather insurance costs a fortune so we didn't bother. Besides, what kind of realistic year round series would we produce if the weather was always perfect?

Peering through the fog, I could just make out the other person hovering behind him. I cringed. This rather anxious looking lady was our main guest for the day...the subject of our story. It had taken a great deal of encouragement on my part to persuade her to be part of our programme. Having assured her that our policy was always to be gentle, in order to coax the best performance from our guests, it didn't take a genius to work out that George's outspoken and irreverent behaviour had now cast serious doubts on my integrity. Hastily I moved forward to try and correct the damage.

'George,' I asked, 'have you met Mrs Heald?'

He straightened up and extended his arm. 'Good morning,' he said as politely as he could. And ignoring the ecclesiastical surroundings continued. 'Bloody awful weather, don't you think?'

It had seemed like a brilliant idea. Even my boss, Will, had thought so when I first suggested it. Why not spend a day looking at The Cotswolds through the eyes of a stonemason, better still a family of stonemasons, who spent their time carving stone from the local quarry into anything from simple bricks to ornate sculptures. I had been told about Mrs Heald and her family by a friend of mine who had recently had some work done by them. She had been impressed by their professional attitude, the quality of their work and their charm. So, I had approached them to see if they would be interested in my story. If we did it well, it would be huge publicity for their business. They jumped at the chance.

So, I'd planned a short film that would follow them through a typical day. We'd see the quarry where the soft honey coloured stone was cut, the family at work both in their studio and out and about, and we'd take lots of shots of some of the most beautiful Cotswold stone houses in some of the most idyllic villages in the area. I'd even found a local geologist who could tell us about the stone itself, its origins and how once, more than two million years earlier, the area was covered by a warm sea. That last bit, as it turned out, now being slightly harder to imagine than I'd first thought!

I turned my attention back to the poor lady in front of me. She still looked rather bewildered. Mrs Heald, a born-again Christian, had been carving stone since she was eleven. She'd agreed to make this film in good faith. She hadn't reckoned on my hysterical colleague. As we all looked up at the lintel she had so lovingly carved for the church in her own home village deep in the Cotswolds, I could see our problem. Thanks to the fog we couldn't even see the top of the door let alone its framework!

'Is your colleague alright?' Mrs Heald was clearly concerned by the sight of George pacing up and down in the graveyard like some demented chicken. 'Do you think a few quiet moments in the church might give him some comfort.'

I looked across at him. I could hear him muttering darkly about travelling half way across the country to film a pile of ruddy stones.

'Best leave him for the moment,' I advised. 'He's very temperamental I'm afraid. 'Comes of being frightfully creative,' I lied. 'If and when this fog clears, I'm sure he'll be absolutely fine.'

It turned out to be one of those days! The news that Will wouldn't be arriving much before lunchtime, leaving me temporarily in charge, only served to darken George's mood. And things didn't improve when he accidentally tripped over a pile of newly-cut bricks outside the workshops. As he fell to the ground, I could only look on in horror as a string of expletives rent the air. Across the courtyard, I watched helplessly as Mrs Heald simply crossed herself and then hastily disappeared inside her workshop, shutting the door firmly behind her. It didn't take a genius to work out that it was going to be a challenge to persuade her to continue.

And the journey cross country to the picturesque village of Naunton, (at least it would have been picturesque if we could have seen it), was even more fraught.

'What the hell are you playing at?' George yelled unceremoniously from his car when I signalled late at a crossroads. 'I nearly went right up the back of you.'

'I only saw the signpost when it was on top of me,' I replied defensively. 'Anyway, you shouldn't have been so close.'

'Unless I stay close, I cannot see the lights on your car.' His voice was bitter. 'Mind you, the way you drive, we'd all be better off going blindfold!'

Despite a break in the weather around noon, by the end of the 'shoot' I was exhausted.

\* \* \* \*

'Bad day?' Mac surmised later that evening as he watched me beating the life out of a lump of meat.

'Yes. By the time the fog cleared it was lunchtime, making everything terribly rushed. All my fault, of course! The only moment of relief happened at the quarry. With ice everywhere and a swirling mist, it looked more like the north face of the Eiger than a large hole in Gloucestershire. Then, out of the blue, a photographer turned up with a team of girls in fur coats. They were there to make a calendar. When George realised that they were wearing almost nothing underneath, he cheered up considerably. Persuading the young ladies that a television appearance would improve both their profile and the calendar's, he had the camera on before I could blink. His argument was that it would add an interesting twist to the idea of the hidden beauty of the Cotswolds, though quite how we're supposed to incorporate his shots into anything suitable for our early evening audience, is another matter!'

'So Will didn't make it at all?'

'Oh yes. Just as George was finishing his shots of the girls, he shot into the quarry. Quite why he hadn't turned back hours earlier was anyone's guess. As you can imagine, he wasn't in the best of moods having spent six hours in various traffic jams caused by the fog. The only thing that cheered him up was the sight of the glamour girls. I tell you, their unexpected appearance certainly made the day easier for me!'

'They didn't take your picture for the calendar then, did they?'

'Very funny! Actually, despite being well wrapped up, I was almost as cold by the end of the day as I was after that film in Shropshire. You can keep the sexy underwear I saw today. If this weather continues, I'm going to find my thermals!'

\* \* \* \*

So, the next morning with Mac at work and the older children either at school or nursery, I waited for Archie to take his morning nap and then dived into a long hot bath.

Half an hour later and feeling suitably refreshed, I wrapped myself in a large fluffy towel and set out to find my emergency winter underwear.

Padding gently across the landing to the guest room, I opened a large chest and started rummaging around inside. Somewhere in this higgledy-piggledy mess was a pair of thermal leggings and a vest. As I delved deeper, a cold draught wafted round me. Who on earth had left the window open? No wonder it was cold upstairs. I straightened up and moved across to shut it. A large bookcase and several cases blocked my way but, somehow, I managed to clamber over them. My towel fell off and I cursed as the cold wind stole round my naked body. I yanked at the handle but the ancient window refused to close. One more heave and it suddenly banged shut. Bother! Now I'd probably woken Archie up and he'd not long been asleep.

It was only then that I heard a movement behind me. I froze. Then a chill far worse than the cold weather outside slowly crept round me. Suddenly I knew exactly who had opened the window. It was the person asleep, or rather now pretending to be asleep, in the bed tucked behind the door only a few feet away from me. My twenty two year old nephew who had been using us as a base while he worked at a large firm of lawyers in town and, in reality, had been staying down the road with his new girlfriend for the past fortnight, had clearly taken it into his head to return for the night. How dare he!

And, oh God, here I was, stark naked in the full glare of electric light bending over a bookcase to shut the window. The poor chap, and me, had clearly both been damaged for life!

The thought was just too awful to contemplate. Without a moment's hesitation, I turned on my heels and fled.

Back in the safety of my bedroom, I quickly dressed and went downstairs. It was then that the 'phone rang. It was Mac.

'Hi darling. As you were asleep when I got back from the pub last night and I was in such a rush this morning, I forgot to say that I bumped into Tom and apparently he's had a fall-out with Lucy. So he's back in the spare room for a couple of nights if that's alright. Mind you, he's on a day off today, so I don't suppose he'll be up for a while. Don't have a heart attack if he appears unexpectedly, will you?'

'Too late,' I muttered weakly down the 'phone. 'Too late!'

It was about an hour later that Tom came into the kitchen. Smiling, perhaps too casually, he went over to the kettle to make himself a cup of tea. He'd seen me! But he wasn't going to say anything and neither was I!

*   *   *   *

The 'naked body incident' as it became known, had several repercussions. Firstly Mac unwisely relayed the story to a friend over the 'phone later that evening not realising that Claire and Josh were in earshot. They came rushing into the kitchen, clearly appalled by what they'd heard.

'Mum, you must wear your dressing gown whenever you wander round the house,' Claire advised crisply. 'You're far too old to run around naked.'

'I never run anywhere naked,' I protested.

'Did he really see you with nothing on?' Josh's face was a picture of horror. 'Oh yuk!'

But the saga brought a far more important issue to a head. Once the children were in bed, I turned on Mac. Blaming the whole incident on a lack of space, I argued that if we had had enough room in our own bedroom, I wouldn't have had to go in search of appropriate clothing in someone else's. Clearly the answer was simple. The time had come to move to a bigger house!

## THE AFTERMATH

'Did you really have nothing on?' Judy, who shared the nursery school run with me, was agog. 'How awful!'

'There's no need to sound so appalled,' I bristled. 'To be honest, I'd half hoped you might be sympathetic. But judging from your tone, I'm clearly wasting my time. You're almost as bad as the children!'

'Now, now, there's no need to get huffy! It's just that he's only twenty two and you're....' she broke off unable to contain her mirth any longer.

'Alright, alright... practically old enough to be his mother. Funnily enough I had thought of that.'

'And Mac? What did he think about it all?'

'Oh, he thought it was hysterically funny too. Despite my protestations, he's been living off the story ever since. Anyway, the news of the week is not supposed to be my naked body. Last night we made an important decision. We're going to move.'

'Move? Where to?'

'Don't know yet. But not too far from here. Too complicated with schools and things.'

'What sort of house are you looking for?'

'Not too fussy really as long as it's considerably bigger than the one we've got now.'

'You don't mean that. You know what Mac's like.'

'Of course I do! But we're not on any deadline. We're just going to start by having a gentle look around at what's on offer and then take our time until we find the one that's right for us.'

'I don't recall there being anything remotely gentle about buying and selling houses,' Judy commented wisely. 'But, as you haven't bought one for thirteen years, you've probably forgotten.'

On reflection, it was an odd thing for me to say. Over the years, I'd have struggled to use the word 'gentle' to describe any project we'd ever undertaken!

## JUDY

'Who was that on the 'phone?' Mac didn't take his eyes off 'Newsnight' as I came into the room. 'As if I didn't know.'

'If you know, why ask?'

'I thought you saw her yesterday. What on earth can you still find to talk about?'

I sighed. Why couldn't Mac just accept that, when it came to using the 'phone, men and women were different. He used it purely to pass on or accept information and frequently made calls that lasted less than thirty seconds. Me, well I liked to chat.

'Judy keeps me sane. She sees life the same way as me. You should be grateful that I have her to talk to sometimes. Since I've got to know her, I think we've probably had far less arguments about the children or anything else for that matter. Whereas you try to rationalize or dismiss all the minor disasters that happen in my daily life, she just listens, laughs and then empathises. She's become a soul mate,' I finished dramatically.

'You've only known her a couple of months. Bit soon to be a soul mate, isn't it? Anyway, I thought I had that role.'

'You do...for lots of things. But all women need a girlfriend to share all their 'girly' anxieties. You laugh at half the things I worry about ...either laugh or despair. Sometimes Judy laughs too, but in a different way. Because she's a woman, she understands in a woman's way.'

'So how did you manage before she came on the scene? Life 'BJ compared to Life AJ.'     .

'Pardon?'

"Before Judy' and 'After Judy'.'

'Don't be ridiculous!'

\*　\*　\*　\*

I'd first met Judy in the nursery school car park on a cold morning the previous November. It was her children's first day and she was looking extremely anxious. Within minutes I knew why.

'Expelled?' I cast an anxious look back at Lizzie who I could just see through the nursery school door. Thankfully she was happily playing with a tray of Lego. But how long would the tranquillity last now that it seemed that two juvenile delinquents had been sent to join her?

Judy Barton was a lawyer who, in her early forties, had been both surprised and delighted to find herself pregnant with twins. Having worked in a high profile job for most of her married life, she'd decided that now was the time to give it all up and indulge in motherhood. She had had no idea what she was letting herself in for.

'It's been hell,' she admitted. 'The boys cried for a year and now they've discovered their legs, they rampage around everywhere like a couple of mad chimpanzees. The house is ransacked, I'm on my knees and my husband's in permanent shock. So, when someone recommended a small nursery nearby, run by an older lady who was 'hot' on discipline, we leapt at the chance. We lasted six weeks!'

'What happened?' I asked, desperate to know how to help Lizzie cope with these two hooligans.

Judy paused for a moment. Clearly she hadn't intended to give so much away so soon.

'It all came to a head the week before half term. James, my husband, asked me to come up to the office for some charity 'do'. Most unusual, but I felt I had to do the 'wifely' bit. God knows, I've given him little enough time these last few years.

My plan was to drop the children off at their school and carry straight on to the city. But late the night before, I realised that I needed to clean the car to avoid it standing out a mile in his smart office car park. So I whipped it into the car-wash on the way to nursery.

God knows how the boys managed to open the back window! Five minutes later they emerged from the experience covered in foam and....more than a bit surprised!

I'd got no time to go home and sort them out. So, mumbling profuse apologies, ten minutes later I handed them over to their bewildered teacher explaining that I would be dealing with a divorce if I didn't get to my husband's office in time. Poor things, they looked more like poodles than children with white foam clinging to every part of their anatomy. 'At least you know they're clean,' I muttered apologetically as I kissed them goodbye. But she didn't see the joke.

Well the next day we had a letter explaining in no uncertain terms that it was *unacceptable* to bring children into school in 'that state' just as it had been *unacceptable* two weeks earlier to bring them in with full blown chickenpox. Well, I ask you? I didn't know. A degree in law doesn't mean you're an expert on childhood diseases. I just thought the rash was something they'd eaten. Apparently half the mothers had been apoplectic when they'd found out. People had had holidays booked for half term and, had their children caught our chickenpox, they'd have had to cancel.

The headmistress had finished the letter by saying life was all about making choices and, taking into consideration the two I had already made, coupled with the extremely unruly natures of my children, *she* had made the choice *not* to have them back after the half term break.'

'So in other words, they've not been expelled……… you have!'

'Is that any better?'

'Oh definitely. Making the wrong choices is what real motherhood is all about. We've all done it……loads of times. Anyone who tells you otherwise is lying!'

*     *     *     *

After that first meeting, Judy and I saw each other regularly. Just as she had said, her house was a bomb site. It even made mine look tidy. Claire and Josh were appalled. Initially, they refused either to eat or excrete on the premises.

'It's filthy,' Claire announced to Mac after the first visit. 'Mum had to remove two half-eaten biscuits and a beaker of what looked like really old milk from the toy box before she'd let Archie go anywhere near it.'

'I didn't.'

'You did. I saw you trying to whisk them out into the kitchen before anyone noticed.'

'You were rude to refuse a drink or anything to eat so bluntly. Archie and Lizzie both had clean cups and my coffee was delicious. Judy just can't cope with the day to day task of managing two very young children, a husband and a home. Don't criticise until you've tried it. Believe me, there's nothing on earth to compare with it!'

\*　　\*　　\*　　\*

Contrary to Judy's expectations, her two settled in well to their new school and Lizzie adored them. They were soon inseparable. When the new term started in January, they returned as full members of the gang. Judy, too, had enjoyed the small window of freedom that three hours a day can offer. Her house improved a little, though not enough for Claire and Josh's liking, and she showed signs, for the first time in nearly four years, of looking like a normal human being again.

So, she had greeted the news of our impending move with apprehension.

'I really hope you stay in this area. Fred and Eddie will be devastated if they can't see Lizzie any more.'

'We won't be moving anywhere until we sell our house and, as it is at the moment, no one would touch it with a barge pole. Our first task is to get it into some sort of order so that agents will want to show people round.'

'James says when the time comes for us to move, we'll have to have the house clearance people round followed by the fumigators. Only then will we be able to start to think about selling it to anyone else!' Judy sighed as she surveyed her own chaos. 'So when are you going to start looking?'

'Straight away. In fact I'm hoping to call in at the agents this morning before I pick Lizzie up from school.'

'Are you going dressed like that?'

'Why not?' I looked down and tried to brush the sticky biscuit crumbs off my jumper. The orange juice stain Archie had thoughtfully added to my sleeve proved more difficult to disguise. 'It's the house they're after. It doesn't matter what I look like, does it?'

## ON THE MOVE

I could tell that the agent wasn't impressed.

It hadn't been easy to negotiate my load up the high step and into his smart office. Dressed in old jeans and a jumper and with Archie asleep in the pushchair with several full carrier bags squashed into the basket underneath him, it wasn't the ideal time to start house hunting. But then again, since having children, I had learned that there was never an ideal time to do anything.

It was only when I was fully inside that I realised that Archie was wearing only one Wellington. How strange? I was sure he had had two on when we left the car. Slightly embarrassed now, I could only look on as the man in the tweed jacket transferred his gaze slowly from me to the bootless foot and back again. As I extended my free hand he seemed to flinch slightly. Perhaps he had also seen the rather 'tatty' shopping list in my other hand which said, quite simply, nappies, milk, baby wipes and....new house.

Gesturing me to sit down, he tried hard to be polite.

'How can we help you?' he enquired.

'I want to buy a house,' I replied simply.

He gave what I felt was a rather patronising smile.

'What kind did you have in mind?'

Now that was a good question. 'Bigger' seemed a bit of a flippant answer. So, I thought for a moment before blurting out a fairly random sounding list.

'Not too far from here, old, in a village with a shop, large garden, and enough space to accommodate, one husband, four children, the odd guest ...oh and me. The size bit is really important. If we live much longer in our current house, I fear we'll be in severe danger of murdering one another.' I laughed nervously but he didn't laugh back.

I waited while he wrote it all down.

'And are there any specifications you wish to avoid?'

I looked at him blankly for a moment. Then my face brightened. 'Oh yes. No water, please.'

'No water?' he repeated equally blankly.

'Well I want the 'mains' stuff but definitely no extras. You know, rivers, lakes, ponds that sort of thing. Some of my children are still very young.'

'Yes, I can see that,' he replied, eyeing my youngest offspring coldly.

I watched him as he slowly added 'no water' to the list.

'When do you want to start viewing?'

'Well there's no great rush. We haven't put our house on the market yet.' I could see his eyes roll at this point. 'But we are very keen to move,' I added encouragingly. 'Our little cottage is full of charm...at least it will be when I've tidied it up a bit. I'm sure it won't be that difficult to sell.'

Giving me one of his 'I've heard that one before' looks, he looked in his diary.

'We do have a few houses in your price range. If you're free at the weekend, I'm sure we could arrange for some of the owners to show you round.' He looked up. It wasn't difficult to work out from his expression that he wasn't convinced I was a genuine buyer.

I sighed. If Mac had been here, things would have been very different. This man would have liked him. Mac was a public schoolboy through and through. Quite why a lawyer from one of the most traditional firms in

Birmingham would want to marry a mad woman from television, would always be one of the world's great mysteries. No matter which way you looked at it, he was always smart whereas I was distinctly scruffy.

'Right,' he said, clearly relieved that our meeting was over. 'We'll be in touch as soon as we've contacted the various vendors. Thank you.'

And with some difficulty we left. This time he helped me get the pushchair down the step. The sooner he could get me off the premises, the better.

It was clear from the start that the gentleman had taken my 'brief' with a pinch of salt! 'No water,' I had said quite clearly. Yet the very first house we looked at required us to negotiate stepping stones over a pond just to get to the front door!

The second house, far from being in a village with a shop, was perched high on the top of a hill. The views would have been magnificent if the owner hadn't decided to plant a thick row of trees twenty feet from the front door. He clearly disliked exposed beams and, wherever possible had replaced them with what looked like glass tubes, prompting Lizzie to say out loud. 'Mummy, this house looks like Willy Wonka's chocolate factory!'

The third house might have been suitable until we worked out that all the main rooms pointed north.

We were getting more than a little despondent when we arrived in the pretty village of Lower Hadbury to view the fourth house that day. By now, Judy had taken the children off our hands, making the exercise considerably less fraught but, unfortunately, no more successful. Driving up a narrow lane beside the church, at the end we turned through a wide gateway into a drive dominated by the biggest horse chestnut tree I'd ever seen.

As I got out of the car, I could hear the sound of running water. Looking through a side gate, across a large garden awash with snowdrops and aconites, I could see a river bordering one side of the lawn and the stream that fed it across another. Threatening to jump straight back in the car, surprisingly Mac coaxed me towards the front door.

'Let's just have a quick look. We're here now. The more houses we see, the more we'll start to get a clearer idea of exactly what we're looking for.'

'I certainly wasn't looking for two rivers,' I retorted. 'Our agent is a complete waste of time.' But I went along with him all the same.

However, as it turned out, he wasn't quite the fool I had him for. Because, despite the raging torrent less than thirty yards from the kitchen window and the stream that fed it at the end of the garden, we took one look at The Old Vicarage and fell in love with it.

In many ways, the building was far from perfect. Built of mellowed red brick with a slate roof, it was a house of three distinct styles. Rising above the rest of the house, the oldest part of the building was Queen Anne and bore little or no similarity to the Georgian box attached to the front or, for that matter, the much lower Edwardian extension on the back. Different heights (the centre section had three floors), and different sized bricks gave a slightly chaotic look on the outside and created rooms on a variety of different levels on the inside. On the first floor it was quite possible to go up two stairs and round a corner to find one bedroom and then to go down three more to find another. In one of the rooms a walk-in cupboard turned out to be a walk-down cupboard and much to my delight, we opened one door on the landing and discovered a staircase.

Whilst I enjoyed myself peering into every nook and cranny, I noticed that Mac seemed to be taking things far more seriously, his eyes darting here and there, as if determined to take in every last detail.

\*     \*     \*     \*

'What do you think?' Mac asked as we drove out of the driveway more than an hour later.

'I loved it!' I replied. 'But isn't it far too expensive?'

'That's the trouble,' Mac sighed. 'We don't really know how much it's going to be. It's going to auction in three weeks. We still haven't put our house on the market.'

'Well, that's that then.' I sighed. 'Still it was fun to have a look.'

Mac was quiet for a moment. Then, with his eyes fixed firmly on the road, he spoke. 'I want that house,' he said. 'When we get home we have to make a plan that gives us the best possible chance of buying it. When the hammer comes down at the end of the month, we've got to be the highest bidders!'

## SORTING OUT

The next week passed in a flurry of activity. For, in order to stand any chance of selling our house, Mac and I both knew that our first job was to clear out thirteen years of chaos.

'There can be no family in the world capable of accumulating junk like we can,' Mac moaned endlessly. 'Look at that pile of clothes we've just sorted for the charity shop. I mean look at it. No one, however poor, would want to buy any of it. We've been dressing ourselves and our children in clothes that others literally wouldn't be seen dead in.'

'Nothing for Aunt Lucy's stall then?' Josh wondered, ever mindful of the chance to make a few quid.

'Good God, no,' I shuddered at the prospect. 'What if someone recognised any of it. How embarrassing would that be?'

'Only slightly more embarrassing than having to watch Aunt Lucy put a price on our junk,' Mac reflected. 'It wouldn't be worth more than tuppence!'

As if to highlight his point, he held up a pair of pyjamas that I'd removed from Lizzie's back only that morning. They had once had a Paddington Bear design on them. But that was years ago when they'd also been a favourite of Claire's. She, in turn, had been given them by a cousin who was now just finishing university.

'You can still make out Paddington's hat,' I argued, 'if you looked closely.'

Mac snorted and tossed them back in the pile. 'We'll burn them tonight before the neighbours see them and call the NSPCC!'

It didn't take long to fill a skip with the junk. Despite the rows we had deciding what was to stay and what was to go, everyone agreed, reluctantly, that the de-cluttering process had improved the house enormously.

'Do we still need to move now that we've got all this extra space?' Josh asked as he watched the skip being loaded onto the back of a truck the following day. But as he watched our rubbish disappear down the drive, none of us realised that someone else already had plans for the empty spaces.

*   *   *   *

'Only you could invite people to stay when we're in such chaos,' Mac reflected bitterly as I put the 'phone down on my old school friend from Devon.

'Well I didn't exactly invite her.' I said, defensively. 'She asked. Anyway it's only for one night. She's here for a conference. You'll hardly have time to notice her.'

'It's impossible not to notice Mary-Lou. Anyway, how come she's working? I thought she'd just had a baby.'

'She has, but her bit of the conference only lasts a morning. So she won't be leaving the baby for very long.'

'And who, may I ask, is looking after this child while she's away?' Mac was glaring at me now. 'Now, let me guess?'

Although he was genuinely fond of her, Mac had always been wary of Mary-Lou. Like me, she had four children and, also like me, she could never bear to throw anything away. Over the years I would regularly send Josh's hand-me-downs to her son and she would reciprocate by parcelling up her youngest daughter's clothes for Lizzie. Mac generally viewed these packages with disdain, but Lizzie always fell on them rapturously. Whenever she proudly paraded her new wardrobe in front of him, he would often be heard to mutter that we were clearly giving floor space to the clothes Oxfam had rejected! But he was never brave enough to stop the exercise.

\*    \*    \*    \*

The plan to empty our fridge and freezer before the move had been inspired by Mary-Lou's visit. Although she lived in a rambling house by the sea, inherited from an aunt not long after she'd married, she and her husband had never had enough money to care for it properly. For years, she'd kept her family warm in their draughty home by clothing them in layers of second-hand jumpers and fleeces. And she kept their stomachs full by ensuring that no food was ever wasted. Whatever was left at the end of a meal would somehow be incorporated into something equally delicious at a future date. It had been a system I had always admired but, to date, never managed to replicate.

So, with a huge new mortgage in prospect, I decided now was the moment to take a leaf from her book. However, if only I'd remembered to make time to label our leftovers properly, it would have been a lot better for everyone!

\*    \*    \*    \*

'I don't know what this is, but it definitely isn't custard!' With that, Mac dropped his spoon into his dish, grabbed the newspaper and disappeared into the hall.

Nervously, I leaned across and prodded the creamy contents of his bowl. A sliver of something silvery confirmed my worst fears. I had just managed to pour defrosted onion sauce onto his apple crumble.

From then on Mac was very suspicious of anything I served. He seemed to relish telling everyone that the only time he felt safe was when he made his own breakfast. But as it turned out, he spoke too soon.

Generally, whenever Mary Lou came to stay, her gifts would include a couple of bags of old clothes for me or the children, the odd bit of baby equipment depending on who was due the next offspring, and half the contents of her fridge. Within minutes of arriving, the hall would be cluttered with junk and our fridge would be filled with corners of cheese, yoghurts destined to expire while she was away from her own house, the remains of a couple of puddings and half a packet of bacon or ham. In fact, anything that she didn't want to go to waste!

\*     \*     \*     \*

So, when she arrived around mid-afternoon the next day we were prepared. And she didn't disappoint us. All my plans about fridge management were ruined as she carelessly pushed the remains of my stuff to one side and tossed a load of her leftovers into the empty space.

When several black bin-liners were carelessly dumped into our newly cleared hall, Mac 'tutted' and went outside to inspect the borders.

But the disaster, or near disaster, didn't occur until after she'd left for her conference the next morning. While I tried to amuse her baby, Mac, realising the coast was clear, came into the kitchen to snatch a quick breakfast before going off to work. He helped himself to some cereal and was about to pour on the milk when I stopped him.

'Hey, don't use that milk, it's Mary Lou's.'

'So what? She's eating all our food. Anyway I only want a little bit.'

'No, you don't understand,' I repeated grabbing the bottle from him. 'The milk in that bottle is her milk.....HERS!!!' I added pointing at my boobs just in case he hadn't grasped the enormity of what he was about to do. 'I'm supposed to feed it to her baby later on this morning.'

'Oh, my God!' Across the table, Mac had turned as white as a sheet. Slowly and deliberately he put the cereal bowl down on the table.

'Here, use this milk,' I said pushing a pint of full-fat across the table.

'No thanks.' I noticed he'd gone a nasty shade of green. 'Suddenly I'm not so hungry.'

And with that, he made a hasty exit.

\*     \*     \*     \*

When Mary Lou and her baby departed later that evening, Mac and I set about making a final effort to get the house fit for inspection. Tidied, polished and vacuumed, by the time we'd finished, we hardly recognised the place as our own. Threatening the older children with adoption if they messed anything up, the next day I confidently informed our agent that we were ready for his valuation.

Initially, I found it an odd experience to watch strangers looking around our home. And even more disconcerting was the fact that although most were genuine, others were either seriously odd or simply using the visit as a way of passing the time on a wet afternoon!

'Do you have a station in the village?' one lady asked.

'No,' I replied, 'but there's a bus.'

'Then you'll have to reduce the price to allow me to take a taxi into town each day!'

When I explained to another prospective buyer that 'fitted kitchen included' on the house details meant every single thing except the tiny cupboard on the far wall which had been a present from me to Mac just after we had moved in, her reply was quite simple.

'You can certainly take the cupboard. You can take the whole kitchen if you like. I think it's hideous!'

'Well, we're not selling the house to her,' I fumed as she drove out of the driveway.

'On the contrary,' Mac was in one of his superior moods. 'If she decides to buy the house, which I doubt, she can pull out every single fitting we have.'

And, unbelievably, despite endless moaning on my part, we did manage to keep the cottage tidy enough for someone to want to buy it. And after the most nerve-racking evening of my life, when the hammer finally came down at the auction, the Old Vicarage was ours.

## THE SECRET IN THE GARDEN

'The problem with having large families is that someone's always got a problem.'

'I assume you're talking about Lizzie?' Judy, on the other end of the 'phone, knew she was making a good guess.

'Right, first time.' It was 10.00 o'clock at night and I was having a late night moan to my best friend.

Lizzie had always had 'middle child' written all over her, even though, strictly speaking, she'd never been one. But then Lizzie had been proving the impossible possible ever since the day she was born.

\*    \*    \*    \*

'I'm not going to be here when we move,' she announced to us all over breakfast one morning.

'Excellent,' said Josh. 'When are you going?'

'Stop it,' I said glaring at him. 'Why don't you want to be here? It'll be fun.'

'It's not fair! You said we were moving house. But we're not. This house isn't moving. We're going to a new one.'

Josh rolled his eyes. 'You really are so stupid sometimes.'

'No I'm not. Am I Mummy?'

But Mac got in first.

'Why don't you want to move to the new house? You'll have a bedroom all to yourself and lots more space.'

'I don't want lots more space. I like it here. If we have to move, why can't we move to a house like Rebecca's? She's got Barbie wallpaper and a TV in her bedroom. Her house is really cool.'

'Her house is even smaller than this one. And it's right next to the maggot farm,' Claire reminded her, pulling a face.

'And it's damp,' added Josh. 'And it smells. I stayed the night there once after her brother's party.'

'I don't care. I want a house like Rebecca's. In fact I want Rebecca's house, even if I have to share it with her. It would be better than the one you've chosen……without even asking me,' she finished, bursting into tears for what she hoped was maximum effect.

'Oh please,' moaned Josh. 'No more. I can't stand it!'

'So where are you planning to go while we do all the hard work?' Mac enquired.

'Granny's!' Lizzie's reply was defiant.

'If she'll have you, which I doubt after you broke her best vase last week,' I reminded her.

'She will. I've asked her.' She said she'd love to have me, if it's all right with you.'

'Well that's a result.' Now it was Claire's turn to have her say. 'Let her go. She'll be a right pest hanging around here all day, getting in the way and annoying everyone.'

But, for once, Lizzie didn't retaliate. Instead she looked beseechingly at me. I was almost moved, although no one else seemed to be. After all, the idea was certainly appealing. Four year olds, especially our four year old, aren't generally a lot of help when you're trying to move thirteen years of clutter.

'I'll have to think about it,' I hedged. 'I'm not sure it's a good idea.'

'Good God! Why not?' Mac, by now, had been entirely convinced of the benefits.

'Go on, let her,' echoed Claire and Josh. From his high chair at the far end of the table, it even looked like Archie was nodding too.

But I stood my ground.

'Well don't blame us if she makes everyone's life hell on the day, as you know she's well capable of doing.' And with that Mac stomped upstairs to grab a shower.

We moved over two days. The afternoon before the upheaval started, Lizzie appeared in my room carrying an overnight bag with a pair of pyjamas, a toothbrush and a copy of 'Winnie the Pooh' crammed inside.

I sighed resignedly. 'Are you sure about this? It could be quite fun.'

But she was insistent.

But, by lunchtime the first day, I was anxious. Over coffee and a sandwich, and balanced precariously on two stools amidst a large selection of half filled bags, I tried to explain how I felt to Mac.

'She shouldn't miss out on the move entirely. She's got to face up to the fact that we're leaving here.' I could see from Mac's expression that he wasn't on my wavelength. Undaunted, I continued. 'At this rate she'll have left this house without properly saying goodbye to it. I don't think that's right.'

Mac looked at me blankly. As far as he was concerned it was all quite simple. We didn't have a whinging four year old under our feet. Surely it was much better to have Lizzie happily ensconced down the road in a warm, cosy house with granny when our cottage was missing most of its furniture!

He sighed resignedly. 'Do whatever you want or I'll never hear the last of it. Mind you,' he added darkly, casting his eyes critically around the room, 'before you make your final decision, I suggest you think about the desperate state of this house at the moment.' He kicked a half full carrier bag and several unmatched socks fell out onto the floor. He gave me one of his looks but, wisely, didn't comment. 'Anyway, as I was saying, if you bring her back here now, you may make her feel part of the move, but you also risk damaging her for life!'

\*     \*     \*     \*

It was an extremely reluctant Lizzie who was dragged back to our house later that evening. Irritatingly, I'd left it later than I'd meant and it was already dark when we arrived in the driveway. On the way, I'd tried again to make the new house, including her new, pink bedroom sound really exciting but, from the expression on her face, I could see I was wasting my time.

She shot out of the car and into the garden before I could stop her.

'Where are you going?' I called after her.

'I want to get something out of the Wendy House.'

My heart sank but it was too late.

Suddenly there was an ear-piercing scream. She was standing in the middle of a black rectangle of black grass. The Wendy House had gone.

'You've burned the Wendy House, you've burned the Wendy House!' she wailed jumping up and down in anguish. I tried to pick her up for a cuddle, but she wasn't having any of it. So, I knelt down beside her and tried to explain.

'We have not burned your Wendy House. It went on the van first thing this morning and, as it was so big and took up so much space, the kind delivery men took it over to the Vicarage and set it up at lunchtime. Although we can't really move into our new house until tomorrow, the owners didn't mind having your Wendy House in their garden overnight.'

She didn't look very convinced and was still sobbing as I led her back to the house. Once inside, the tears started again as her eyes fell on the dusty gaps where her beloved furniture had once stood.

Trying to ignore Mac's 'I told you so' look, I racked my brains for a solution to her misery. Suddenly I had an idea.

'I know,' I said, 'why don't we pretend we're detectives and go and search for your missing Wendy House. We could take torches and creep round the Vicarage to check that it's arrived safely in our new garden.'

Lizzie's eyes lit up. Mac's rolled in disbelief.

'They'll lock you up and throw away the key,' he muttered in my ear. But I was determined.

Five minutes later we were in the car....again.

As we drove up the driveway, the Vicarage was in darkness. The owners, I knew, had left earlier that afternoon. Lizzie was now bursting with excitement. But, looking into the blackness of the garden at the back, I was beginning to wonder if I was brave enough for all this. What did they say about Vicarages being haunted?

Pulling myself together, I grabbed my torch. In theory we were trespassing as we didn't officially gain possession until lunchtime the next day. Quite what I would say if any observant villager reported strange goings-on in the garden to the police, was a problem I would have to face as and when it happened. It was too late to turn back now.

As we crept round the dark shadows of the house, I did a great job of being Mrs Super-Sleuth. Lizzie was loving it. Please, no spectators, please!

And there it was, under the willow tree, nestling in a corner by the river. The look on Lizzie's face said it all. She'd found it. Moving tomorrow was not going to be so bad after all.

# GETTING THERE

'We should have moved under cover of darkness,' Mac muttered as we made our way to Lower Hadbury and our new home with a car full of children and clutter the following evening. 'As it is, Kate, you have made a mockery of the move that I'd so carefully masterminded. And I fear that half the village watched you do it.'

'What on earth are you talking about?' I shouted back at him. 'I'm not quite sure what *you* masterminded. As I recall, the only contribution you made was to order the removal men.'

'Precisely!' Mac was in full flight. 'And if you must know, I don't know why I bothered. Go on, admit it, exactly how many car journeys have you made here today? I mean, what was the point of booking a respectable removal company with respectable packing boxes if you were so determined to spend the day moving half the stuff yourself in a selection of tatty bin liners and carrier bags? We look more like a dysfunctional group of New Age Travellers than the charming young family the village were expecting.'

'These carrier bags are full of things we need for the next week. What with working and everything else, I didn't have the time to sort through our things properly. I simply couldn't face the fact that the removal men would simply toss everything into packing boxes and then I'd not find anything for a month. These bags contain the children's schoolbooks, sports bags, uniforms and everyday clothes. Earlier today I shifted all your important bits and pieces along with mine. The way things were organised, or not, at the cottage, they'd have ended up mixed up with the Christmas decorations and the camping equipment. It pains me to remind you that at the cottage, due to lack of space, my warm clothing had to be stored in the guest room along with our wine, some files, cake tins and a box of old curtains!'

'But if you had to do things this way, couldn't you at least have cleaned the car before you stuffed it full of plastic bags. Come to think of it, it wouldn't have looked quite so bad if you'd used some of our more respectable suitcases. We bought some quite decent ones just before our last holiday. We look a right load of scruffs turning up at our new home in this state.'

'Actually, I did think about the suitcases but, by that time, they'd already been put onto the removal van. And, as for cleaning the car before the move, that was definitely your job.'

Mac sighed and shifted slightly to remove Claire's hockey stick from his right ear. 'It just seems so insane to do it like this. I'm sure other families work to a plan. When my sister moved, everything was in its correct place by the end of the day. I seem to recall that, when we visited her that evening, it looked like they'd been there for months!'

Bristling visibly from the taunt, I gripped the steering wheel tightly. Josh's maths folder was painfully stabbing my left elbow, but it wasn't the moment to complain.

'Clearly, you should have married your sister, then,' I snarled. 'Though, come to think of it, Sue wouldn't have wanted to marry someone like you. She was sensible and chose a man who was willing to roll his sleeves up and offer serious help at times like these rather than endless criticism.'

Mac sighed deeply realising he was beaten. 'I suppose I was just hoping that my family could make a good impression on the day we arrived. As it is, it's likely we'll be the laughing stock of the village before we've even properly crossed the threshold.'

'Maybe no one has noticed us,' I suggested hopefully. 'I don't remember anyone waving or smiling at me when I arrived earlier.'

'They were probably hiding away for fear that someone from this mad family might want to talk to them. Thinking about it, it's highly likely that our previous neighbours sent them advanced warning of what to expect.'

'Mac, you really do talk nonsense when you're stressed,' I warned. 'Look what you've done to Claire. She looks really anxious.'

I looked in the mirror and sighed at Mac and Claire's glum faces. Archie and Lizzie were sound asleep. But, luckily, tucked away in the back of the car, half hidden under a pile of towels, Josh was in a philosophical mood.

'Well, the way I see it,' he reflected, 'we may not have given them a good impression today, but we've probably saved them a lot of time by giving them the right one!'

## SETTLING IN

'It's an awfully grown up house,' Judy observed as she sat at our kitchen table in our new home surrounded by packing cases. 'You're going to have to smarten up a bit if you want to survive here. No more odd socks and tatty T-shirts for you, old girl. From now on, it's twin-sets and pearls.'

Despite our chaos, it wasn't difficult to see that under the management of the previous owners, this had been a very well cared for home. With carpets, curtains and fittings all included, we were going to have to make a 'bit of an effort' to make our own clutter fit in.

'Have you had a chance to check the village out yet?' Judy asked peering through the window to see if she could see any locals wandering about in the churchyard.

'Yes. We all went to the Pub at the end of the lane for Sunday lunch. Apparently, it's more than five hundred years old – full of old beams and bursting with character. Legend has it that Shakespeare's Mum and Dad had their Wedding Breakfast there after marrying in this church. How's that for history on your doorstep?'

'And was Mac similarly impressed?'

'Yes, he really liked it. But that was mainly because he thought the beer was good. A pub could be falling down round his ears but he would only ever rate it by the quality of its liquid refreshment! Mind you, only time will tell whether it's good or dangerous to have that kind of facility less than a hundred yards from our front door! I don't think Mac's in any doubt, though.'

'And what did the children make of it?'

'Good question. Just as I was explaining its wonderful history, their eyes wandered across the road to an equally impressive building which is currently home to the Village Club. The sight of a wide screen television and a pool table in the games room sent all thoughts of Shakespeare out of their minds completely.'

'Were you introduced to any of the locals?'

'Yes, we met several, most of whom seemed to know quite a lot about us already!'

'How come?'

'It seems that dear Aunt Lucy took it upon herself to pay a visit to our new home for a quick 'nose around' last week and then simply couldn't resist a trip to the village pub to let the locals know what they were in for. I gather her tales of our various exploits over the years attracted quite a crowd!'

'Oh God!'

'Precisely! And knowing Aunt Lucy's amazing ability to embellish the truth, we dread to think what impression our new neighbours now have of us.'

'I bet Mac was thrilled when he heard what she'd done.'

'Well, what do you think? But it's actually far worse than that. During a rather heated telephone conversation, she accidentally let slip that some of the locals mentioned the price we'd paid for the house. Would you believe that a couple of them actually told her, that in their opinion, we'd paid too much for this place.'

'How on earth would they know something like that?'

'Apparently, several of them went to the auction, purely out of curiosity. When they told her what we paid, she was quick to point out that, as an experienced antiques dealer, she'd have had no trouble securing us a far better price.'

'So, are relations between aunt and nephew now at an all-time low?'

'Oh he's thrilled, as you might imagine! There's nothing like knowing that half the village thinks you're stupid! But to be honest, he's so used to his mad aunt and her loose tongue that he's almost resigned to his fate. The theory he's clinging to is that, like so many times in the past, it won't take long for the locals to see her in her true colours and then, with a bit of luck, they'll start to feel sorry for us.'

'I hope, for your sakes, he's right.'

'Oh, he will be. Believe me, although I haven't known her as long as Mac, it didn't take me long to get the measure of her. And I'm far more likely than most to give her the benefit of the doubt....except there isn't any!'

'So, despite your rather rocky start, do you think you're going to like it here?'

'I think I'm going to love it!' After lunch at the pub, we wandered across the road so that Mac could take a closer look at the sixteenth century Guild Room. But then the children spotted something they felt was far more interesting. Dragging us round the back of the building, we discovered a wonderful little playground and some tennis courts. For a few moments I had visions of us spending every summer teaching the older two how to play tennis, while the younger ones played happily on the swings behind them. Then the bubble burst as I realised that, in reality, Claire and Josh would probably argue endlessly over who scored what point, while Lizzie and Archie would have no trouble tipping themselves head first off the slide the moment my back was turned.'

'And what about Mac?'

'Oh, despite everything, he's in his element. He loves the village and, when we're at home, he keeps walking from room to room with a big grin on his face. And he's behaving very oddly in other ways too.'

'What do you mean?'

'Well, last night, after supper, we wandered into the garden and looked out over the churchyard. Then suddenly he gripped my arm and whispered in my ear.'

'And....'

He just said: 'I do hope you like it here because one day I want us to be buried together over there.'.

'You're joking!'

'No, I'm not. But then, when I'd thought about it, I decided that was probably one of the most romantic things that he'd ever said to me!'

## EARLY DAYS

Despite our efforts to clear out the rubbish at our old house, we still managed to arrive at the Vicarage with boxes of junk. Depressingly, furniture that had seemed, somehow, in keeping amidst the nooks and crannies of the cottage, looked plain 'shabby' in the bigger, brighter surroundings of our new home.

'We won't be entertaining here for some time,' Mac reflected as he tried to hide the holes in an old sofa with a collection of equally tatty cushions. 'Some of this stuff should have been thrown out years ago.'

'There's no point buying smart furniture when you've got a toddler in the house,' I argued. As if to prove the point, Archie waddled in carrying a beaker of blackcurrant juice in one hand and the soggy remains of a biscuit in the other. 'Once he becomes civilized, you can buy whatever you like.'

Mac stared down at his youngest offspring and shook his head. 'We're years off that one then.'

But despite the chaos, over the following days various friends and family members came across to view the new Arnold residence. Most ignored our less-than-perfect furniture and chose instead to make polite noises about our new surroundings. However, the visit from Mac's sister, Sue, and her family was slightly less successful.

'She literally turned her nose up as she entered every room,' I complained bitterly to Mac and the children after they'd gone.

'That's because she's allergic to dust. It makes her sneeze,' Josh explained. 'She told me when we were upstairs.'

But I wasn't convinced.

'She says that when she's at home she has to dust twice a day,' Clare explained. 'Otherwise her eyes and nose water so much she can hardly see.'

'Oh God,' I said despairingly as the winter sunshine emphasised the thick layer of dust on every surface. 'At this rate, I'm in danger of doing her in!'

Josh thought for a moment before replying. Then a grim smile crept across his face. 'On the other hand,' he said mischievously 'if you don't get to grips with the problem, the chances are we won't see her for dust!'

\*     \*     \*     \*

But, despite my misgivings, things gradually improved and, after a huge push on the cleaning front, I decided it was time to get to know my neighbours. So, I popped a note through the doors of all the people at our end of the village inviting them for coffee.

'I think that's a bit dangerous,' Stephanie, who helped at Lizzie's nursery school, was not encouraging. 'In a highly organised village like yours, you'll be asked to do something…. or to join something. If I were you, I'd 'suss' things out a bit before you jump in with both feet.'

'I don't mind doing something for the village. If I didn't want to get involved, I'd have moved into the town where you can be more anonymous.'

'Well, just watch out. Voluntary things can be more of a hassle than a full time job.'

'I know what I'm doing,' I replied haughtily. 'You don't need to worry.'

But any good impression I'd hoped to make was blown just a few days later. It happened at eight-thirty, one morning.

'For goodness sake, stop fussing me and get into the car!' I'd yelled at Lizzie. She was hovering by the car looking distinctly agitated.

'But mummy…'

'No arguments. Get in the car, NOW!'

'Morning!' I turned to look across to the churchyard and cringed. A lady in her fifties was out walking her dog. I recognised her immediately. It was Mrs Chapman who, as chairman of the Parish council, had her photograph on the notice board outside the village hall. It wasn't difficult to work out that she was thinking: 'Oh God, it's that woman from the Vicarage making a scene!'

Looking most unhappy, Lizzie climbed into the back whilst I returned to the challenge of 'bending' a screaming Archie into his car seat while he steadfastly arched his back in resistance.

Why did mornings have to be like this? No matter what time we got up, there was always a last minute rush, accompanied by a lot of shouting.

Two minutes later we drove out of the village. Slightly calmer now, I looked at Lizzie through my rear view mirror.

'What was your problem then?'

'I couldn't find my shoes,' she replied forlornly.

'Not again, Lizzie. Where had you hidden them this time?'

'I don't know.'

'Oh God! Don't tell me.' When we reached the T-junction, I turned round and was faced with two shoeless feet.

Infuriated, I turned the car round. When we arrived back in the driveway, Mrs Chapman was still in the churchyard. She smiled as I shot out of the car. Her face said it all…. 'Mad, completely mad!'

Then there'd been the time when we thought we'd lost Archie.

'Has anyone seen Archie?' was a much repeated cry those first few days. Our standard stair-gate failed to fit our non-standard stairway so, until we could get one made, we had to have eyes in the back of our head...and we didn't always manage that.

I'd been hopeful of a quiet Saturday morning. Mac had taken the older three into town for a few odd jobs, leaving me with Archie.

If only I hadn't started to clear out a few of the remaining packing boxes, a job that meant I had to temporarily take my eye off my youngest child, the incident could have been avoided. As it was......it wasn't!

'Mac, quick!' I yelled hysterically. 'I think Archie's escaped.' For a moment Mac, who was just getting out of the car with the children, could only look on helplessly as I shot past him in the driveway. Before he had a chance to reply, I'd flung the back gate open and was hurtling towards the river yelling 'Archie' at the top of my voice.

Seeing the horrified faces of his children, Mac moved swiftly to reassure them. 'It's alright everyone, she's overreacting. He won't have gone far. Claire, Josh, Lizzie, go inside and look for him please. I bet you anything he's in the house somewhere. You sort him out and I'll try and deal with your hysterical mother before she does something stupid.'

But, from the bottom of the garden, I was in no mood for calm words. As he ran towards me, my distraught face told the whole story.

'I've spent the last five minutes searching frantically for him,' I sobbed. 'I tell you, he's not in the house....and if he's not there, he must be out here somewhere. For God's sake, help me search. I'm terrified he may have fallen in either the river or the stream and drowned.'

'For goodness sake, Kate, look around you for a moment. When we first saw this house it had graceful lawns sweeping down to the river bank. Before we even set one foot on the property, you'd insisted on the whole lot being fenced with a wire mesh that makes the entire area look like the boundary of a high security prison. Short of having guards on the gate, we couldn't do more to protect the children. Think about it for a moment. Given that Archie is barely two feet tall, it's hardly likely that he's scaled the walls.'

But I wasn't convinced. 'Look, I'll search in the bushes over there and you check the fence back to the house. Oh, and stop looking so irritatingly calm. Mac. This is serious!'

As Mac made his way back up the garden, he heard a squeal of excitement from the house.

'Dad, we've found him.' A triumphant Claire and Josh were standing by the back door with Archie held firmly between them. 'He was under the iron bed on the top floor, fast asleep on the old cot mattress. He couldn't have heard mum shouting.'

Turning back to see if I'd heard, Mac could only look on helplessly as I slipped through a side gate, my high pitched shouts drowning any chance of his message getting to me.

Mac turned to his brood, his head in his hands.

'Oh my God, she's in the lane now. She'll have the whole neighbourhood out on the streets in a minute. Just in case they were in any doubt that we're not fit to care for our children, she's now gone and advertised it everywhere. Claire, quick, give me Archie. Seeing him in my arms is clearly going to be the only way to convince your hysterical mother that he's safe.'

And with that he shot off. A moment later an emotional mother and son were reunited.

\* \* \* \*

'Don't look so glum.' It was later that evening and Mac was still trying, unsuccessfully, to cheer me up. 'Look on the bright side. After your spontaneous performance this afternoon, you won't need to worry about the village kids running riot all over the house. Once word gets around that you are completely insane, their parents are bound to stop them coming anywhere near this place.'

I groaned. Then a sudden and obvious thought occurred to me.

'By the way, where did you find him? I could have sworn I'd been through the house with a toothcomb.'

Mac grinned. 'Aha, that's my secret. As there's clearly a hiding place you don't know about in this house, I'm planning to make good use of it the next time there's a scene of any sort. And, if past experiences are anything to go by, that won't be long!'

\* \* \* \*

So it was with a brave smile that I welcomed a gathering from the village into my new home the following week.

'I hear you work in television,' an elderly, smart lady I hadn't met before asked, slightly scathingly, as she appeared to scan the room for signs of illegal substances.

'Only part-time,' I admitted. 'And I work mostly from home so that I can fit things in around the children.'

She smiled, clearly only slightly reassured. It wasn't too difficult to work out that she'd heard about the incident the previous Saturday.

Hastily, I moved across the room to where a group of ladies were deep in conversation. As I approached, they turned to greet me.

'How well did you know the Campbell's when they lived here?' I asked, curious to know the kind of reputation we had to match.

'Oh, Clodagh and David were delightful. And so generous.... Whether it was the annual fete......'

'What annual fete?' I interrupted

'Surely you were told that the village fete is always held in your garden. At least it always has been....unless....'

'Oh, I'm sure that will be fine,' I said, picturing Mac's face when I told him.

'Then there's the carol singing.'

'Do I have to organise the carol singers?' My eyes widened in horror.

'Oh no. Louisa, the choir mistress, does that. Every year the Campbells and, come to think of it, the Brewers before them, would invite the carol singers in for mulled wine and mince pies. In return, the carol singers would perform a handful of carols. It was always a lovely occasion,' she added wistfully.

'And how many carol singers would you get in a small village like this,' I wondered. 'Half a dozen, or more than that?'

Rebecca laughed. 'More like fifty.'

'Fifty!' my voice was beginning to sound slightly strangled.

'And Clodagh's enormous talent for flower arranging really came into its own whenever it was her turn to do the church flowers.'

'The church flowers?'

'Oh yes, nearly all the ladies in the village take a turn at doing that. You'll probably just take over her slot. Joyce will tell you when it is.'

Joyce's face brightened. 'As I remember, it will be the week after you've tidied the playground. I seem to remember Clodagh saying that September was always a busy month.'

I was beginning to feel slightly faint.

'We all take it in turns to tidy the playground. So, your turn will only come up once or twice a year. You just take a big black bag and scour the grass for litter. You'd be amazed what we've found there....shocking really for such a rural village!'

'It's amazing that Clodagh found the time to fit it all in. She was so house proud as well.' The lady at the far corner of the sofa cast her eye around our lounge and sighed. 'Gosh, when she lived here it looked so different.' She turned to her friend with an almost dewy eyed look. 'Do you remember this room before? It was really lovely!'

Reeling slightly, I went out into the kitchen to get some more coffee. I didn't notice that Moira, the church warden, was right behind me.

'I know it's a bit of a cheeky question. But I understand you were very involved in the family services in your old parish?'

'Yes, that's right,' I said slightly nervously. I feared I could see exactly where this was leading.

She hesitated and then continued. 'It's just that our new Vicar is desperate to reinstate the family service here and, as you've got four children and live so close, I just wondered if we'd be able to count on your support?'

I nodded. It was a bit hard to refuse.

Later that evening, I told Mac about the conversation.

'You'll be running it before you know it,' he said knowingly. 'You just watch this space.'

## THE CHURCH

It was around eight o'clock one evening about a fortnight after we'd moved in. Lizzie and Archie, exhausted after an afternoon with friends, were already asleep. Claire and Josh were glued to the television and I was beginning to think about Mac's supper. Suddenly the peace was shattered by a cacophony of sound.

'What the hell's that?' Mac came in from the garden. 'Has somebody died?'

'I rather think it's bell practice.'

'My God, do they do this regularly? Nobody said anything about bell practice before we moved here?'

'They probably thought we'd work it out. I reckon you'd look a bit stupid if you complained. Actually I think it's lovely.'

'You won't say that when the children are kept awake half the night.'

'But have you noticed that they were asleep before they started and they're still asleep now. It would take a nuclear explosion to disturb them when they first go off.'

Mac grunted and went back outside to collect some logs.

Later that evening I flicked through the book on the village that the history society had recently written and that the previous owners had kindly left for us. It soon turned up a few gems.

'Listen to this Mac! It says here that there's been a church on this site since Saxon times, though it was probably wooden then. Would you believe that parts of this building date back to the thirteenth century.'

Mac looked suitably impressed.

'And it gets better! Apparently, in the 14th century, a priest who was once a Vicar in this parish, ended up a saint, canonised eight years after his death by Pope John XXII. That's not a bad claim to fame, is it?'

'And what about these bells?'

Mac waited as I flicked through the pages. 'Here we are. There are six bells up there. One is pre-reformation. Apparently they are all hung on an oaken frame. And... oh no!'

'What's the matter?'

'I only hope it's strong because it says here that the heaviest bell weighs 12.5 cwt! You'd know about that if it fell on you! And, by the way, you got off lightly this evening. When they rang a full peal to celebrate the marriage of Prince Charles and Lady Diana it lasted two hours and fifty four minutes!'

*     *     *     *

The children had all reacted in different ways to the idea of overlooking a churchyard. Claire, always the most nervous, kept her curtains tightly shut at night and generally tried to pretend it wasn't there. Lizzie, on the other hand, was enthralled by the idea of so many dead bodies being only a few feet from our front door. Josh regarded the entire area as an alternative adventure playground. Archie remained indifferent.

'If I catch you clambering over the tombstones one more time,' I warned Josh, 'there'll be serious trouble! It is both disrespectful and dangerous.'

'Mum's also worried that you'll be spotted by some member of the village and they'll realise that she's bred a hooligan.' Claire advised. 'And you know what Mum's like when we embarrass her.'

Josh nodded and for a while he left the tombstones well alone.

And it wasn't just our children who found the area fascinating. Aunt Lucy, Mac's elderly aunt, caused serious panic one afternoon when she called round unexpectedly. She dropped her bombshell at tea-time.

'Did you realise that victims of the Black Death are buried in a grave on the north side of the church.'

'What's the Black Death?' Josh, who loved anything macabre, was keen to know more.

'A terrible disease that killed millions back in the 14th century,' she informed him knowingly.

'From whom did you glean this devastating piece of information,' Mac, who was accustomed to his aunt's vivid imagination, was sounding unconvinced.

'Moira, your church warden, told me. She was in the churchyard when I arrived. Apparently there are signs up asking people not to walk on that stretch of grass, but recently she's become worried that they're being ignored.'

Mac gave Josh a knowing look. 'No prizes for guessing who she's talking about. She's obviously seen you running amok out there. What did we say about lack of respect?'

'Oh that's not why she's worried,' Aunt Lucy was quick to explain. 'Moira read an article recently about the possible dangers of walking on land where plague victims are buried. It said that if you disturb the soil too much, it's technically possible to inhale the spores that caused the fatal disease.' Pausing for maximum effect, she then added, 'Of course, if that happens, one shudders to think of the possible consequences.'

Across the table, I watched as the colour drained from Claire's face. Then she burst into tears. 'I cut across that piece of land every day when I go to school. Does that mean that I might die?'

Mac stared at his aunt in disbelief. When he spoke, his tone was crisp. 'Despite repeated warnings, once again you have proved that you have the sensitivity of a gnat. Look what you've done to Claire. She won't sleep for a week now.'

'I was only trying to help. You can't go through life ignoring possible dangers you know.'

'Aunt, as I have reminded my family on many occasions, one of the greatest dangers they face is having to listen to some of the rubbish you come out with on a regular basis. Given that there must be thousands of similar graves in churchyards around the country, could you give us some idea of the number of people who have died of the Black Death in recent years? I think you might find that the answer is ....none!'

Across the table, Aunt Lucy thought for a moment and then continued to munch her cake.

But despite our reassurances, at bedtime Claire's worries resurfaced. It was only a sharp reminder from Mac that his aunt had always been completely batty and would be locked away in some high security home sooner rather than later, if he had his way, that finally calmed her down.

Lizzie, on the other hand, remained completely unbothered about the possible threat that lurked a few feet from our front door. She was enthralled by the whole space and, whenever we were in the garden, she would try and grab an opportunity to clamber over the wall and sit on the headstones the other side.

'How many times do I have to tell you that you are not allowed here on your own,' I chastised her.

'I'm not alone,' she confided, 'I'm with Albert.'

I looked around but the graveyard was empty.

'Whose Albert?' Then I looked at the engraving on the headstone. Albert Brittan 1845 – 1924.

'You are so weird,' Josh warned when he heard the story later.

But Lizzie refused to be bated. He could choose his friends and she would choose hers.

But not long after we'd moved, I began to wonder if the location of our house was having some effect on the children.

We had been invited by the local farmer to peep inside his small barn at the end of the lane. Two tiny lambs had been born there the previous evening and, providing the children were quiet, they were welcome to pop their head round the door to have a peep.

With Claire and Josh at school that afternoon, I wrapped Lizzie and Archie up warmly and set out along the path. As we approached the barn, Lizzie ran ahead. Poking her head round the door, she gazed inside for some time at the tiny lambs lying in the straw. As we came up behind her, she turned to me, her eyes sparkling with excitement.

'Mummy, you have to look in there,' she whispered. 'I think I've found baby Jesus.'

*　　*　　*　　*

'Have you met the vicar yet?' Mac asked one evening.

'No. She's new. I think she arrived just before us. But she's in Upper Hadbury in the modern Vicarage there. I think I spotted her the other day. You can't miss her really. She's very thin with a mass of bright red hair.'

'She?'

'Oh yes. I gather it came as a bit of a shock to some of the community. Not only is she female, she also owns a Harley Davidson!'

### VICAR VIC

Victoria Marsden had come to our parish at the beginning of February. After a three year stint as a missionary in Africa, she'd decided it was time to come home and establish herself in a parish of her own. Tall and skinny with a bubbly mass of red hair she was, at first, referred to by some of the older members of the parish as the 'Girl Racer,' Scarlet O'Hara or simply 'The Lady in Red' as she shot round the village on her scarlet motor bike dispensing compassion and humour by the bucket-load. Her mission, she explained, was to do her bit to rid the world of poverty and prejudice (clearly, she had quickly clocked the 'anti women priest' gang). Her passions, she told everyone, were God, art, fine wine and Alan Rickman. There was little doubt that she was ready for whatever her rural band of parishioners had in store for her. The question was, were those parishioners ready for her?

The Vicarage at Upper Hadbury was a modern building, set back amongst the trees behind the Victorian church. With around a thousand inhabitants, the village was about a mile and a half from Lower Hadbury and roughly four times the size. With two other tiny hamlets nestling in the hills beyond, Victoria had some miles to cover on her bike if she wanted to keep an eye on her flock. So it was a few weeks before I first caught up with her.

However, when a large and intriguing parcel arrived at our Vicarage instead of hers, I decided the time had come for us to meet. So, I put Archie into the back of my car, and dropped it round.

As I pulled into her driveway, Victoria was outside, covered in oil and staring critically at the engine of her red vehicle. Hearing us, she looked up and, recognising the package, grinned widely.

'My new easel ....excellent. Hi, I'm Victoria, and who's this little treasure? Got time for a coffee?'

Casting an eye over the oily bike and its owner, I hesitated. 'We don't want to hold you up. You look rather busy.'

'To be honest, I could do with a break.' As she wiped her hands on a rag, her face clouded over and she sighed deeply. 'When I first arrived here, I decided a motorbike was the most effective way of getting about. With so many hills, I didn't fancy a pushbike. I felt I'd be far more in touch with my parishioners on something like this than driving around in a car. So, I trawled through all the various bike magazines. When I saw this one for sale, I thought I'd found a real bargain. However, it hasn't quite worked out that way. Much as I love riding it, it's costing me a fortune in maintenance. It's going to the garage this afternoon and if I get one more big bill, I'm afraid I'll have to sell it.' She paused for a moment and then continued. 'Actually, on that note, I wonder if I could ask you a big favour?'

'Go on. But I'm afraid I'm not much good when it comes to bikes.'

'Oh I don't need your knowledge, I need your faith.'

'Pardon?'

Patting the handlebars, she hesitated for a moment. 'Well, I know this is going to sound silly, but at around five o'clock this afternoon, would you mind saying a quick prayer for it.'

I laughed. 'Okay, but why?'

'Well I know, of course, that as a vicar, I should have faith in everything.... and I do try. It's just that, much as I love my bike, I fear I'm in danger of giving up on it. Later this afternoon it's having its M.O.T. and I desperately need it to pass. And, believe me, in order to do that, it's going to need all the help it can get. As I say to some of the waverers in this parish, you may not believe in the power of prayer, but when the chips are down, anything's worth a try.'

'I'll remember,' I promised.

Over coffee, she explained that she was still getting to grips with her new role. On the whole she'd been warmly welcomed, but some of the older villagers still struggled with the idea of a woman in her thirties taking their Sunday services. As the last vicar had been seventy five when he finally hung up his dog collar, she felt it was time to make a few changes and to drag the village church into the twenty-first century. To that end, she admitted, she was encountering some opposition.

'They've given me all sorts of nicknames, you know.' Bending down to give Archie a biscuit, she added. 'But if you want to know what to call me, just call me Victoria or 'Vicar Vic'...I rather prefer that.'

'Someone told me you were in Africa just before you came here.'

'Yes, that's right. It was wicked. I was shot at a couple of times, narrowly missed being mauled by a lion and brushed with death when a snake sank its fangs into my foot during a safari.'

'So life here is going to be a little dull after all that. What on earth made you come to this little quiet corner of the world?'

'You'd be surprised. To be honest, the idea of confronting a lion now seems tame compared to the mauling I got the other day from a certain Lady Henrietta Caldwell, self styled lady of the manor. Apparently she doesn't like motorbikes......especially red ones. She would claim to be a pillar of the church but I gather she's responsible for the worst nickname of them all!'

'What? Vicar Vic?'

'No. According to her I'm 'The Red Devil'.'

\* \* \* \*

'I've met the new vicar already,' Josh informed us all later that evening when I told everyone about my visit. She came to our school to talk to us. At the end, she made us all say a prayer…it was awesome!'

'I've never heard you enthuse about a prayer before,' Mac was clearly astonished by his enthusiasm. 'What on earth did she say?'

'It was so simple. She told us all to put our hands together and bow our heads.'

'Go on.'

'Then she said in a very serious voice, 'Dear God, England's playing France in Paris tonight…and we need to win. Amen.'

## THE ACCIDENT

'That was the hospital on the 'phone,' Mac walked back into the kitchen looking slightly bemused. The sister in casualty has just told me that Aunt Lucy fell off a bus earlier this afternoon and has broken her leg.'

'How on earth did she do that?'

'Apparently she tripped over a hat stand.' I could see that Mac was trying not to laugh.

'A hat stand? Why was there a hat stand on the bus?'

'I should have thought that was easy to guess. She'd just bought it and was trying to get it home.'

'But why didn't she take it in the car. She managed to bring an eight foot long curtain rail to our house not long ago, so why not a hat stand?'

'Well, apparently she'd just dropped her car off to be serviced and saw the hat stand in a second-hand shop as she was walking to the bus stop. Need I say more.'

'I'm surprised she was allowed to take it on the bus. You'd know about it if it fell on you.'

'That was the problem. She fell as she was being ordered off the bus with it. She and the hat stand are now on Washington ward. A rather giggly nurse informed me that the latter is in rather better shape than she is!'

'What's happening about her leg?'

'She's being operated on at the moment. At her age, they won't put it in plaster. The plan is to pin it back together and, if all goes well, she should be up and about again in a few days, though it will be weeks, if not months before she's fully mobile.'

'When can we see her?'

'Whenever we like. Though she won't be very awake tonight. Apparently she's given the nurse a list of things she wants brought in. Would you believe, she's asked for six knitted bed jackets and six pairs of woolly socks. I always thought hospitals were heated to boiling point. Anyway I'll pop the stuff in later.'

'And I'll get some flowers organised. I'm sure the children could make some 'get well' cards too.....if I twist their arms. Can you think of anything else?'

'Oh yes,' Mac suddenly remembered. 'I've been given strict instructions by the nurse to collect the hat stand!'

\*     \*     \*     \*

It was late by the time Mac arrived back in the driveway. It was another ten minutes before he'd managed to extract his cargo.

'The things I do for my dear aunt,' Mac muttered as he placed the hat stand in the corner of the hall and threw his coat at it. 'You should have heard some of the remarks I got from a gang of youths who were hanging around the car park as I tried to get the wretched thing in the car.'

'How was she?'

'Drowsy. At first I thought she was sound asleep. But as I tried to sneak the hat stand away from the bed without disturbing her, she stirred and said very clearly. 'Be careful with that. I've just sold it to the lady in the bed opposite!''

\*     \*     \*     \*

Over the next few days, Aunt Lucy began to make a steady recovery. Although slightly bemused by the experience, she quickly bounced back. The nursing staff, at first enchanted by the eccentric old lady, soon realised they'd taken on rather more than they'd bargained for. The fact that Aunt Lucy had nursed in a London hospital just after the war was quickly drawn to their attention. Standards, it appeared, had slipped considerably since she patrolled the wards back in the 1940s!

'I ask you,' she exploded as we went in to visit a few days after the operation. She was sitting up in bed but her face was as black as thunder, 'I woke just now from a short snooze to find that a buzzer, a drink and a slice of rather dry cake had been delivered to my bedside. But they were all out of reach,' she spluttered pointing to a bed table at the end of her bed. 'I've just had an operation that's left me temporarily immobile. It's hardly rocket science to work out that I have no way of reaching them. If you hadn't arrived when you did, they'd have probably been whisked away before I'd even had a taste.'

We nodded sympathetically and moved the table to within easy reach. But she hadn't finished.

'It was the same the other morning. I woke up to find a bowl of water, some soap and a towel on the table. But, having had the operation only the day before, I was hardly in a position to wash myself without help. By the time the nurse got back to me, the water was stone cold.' She paused for breath but, seeing the sister pass the end of her bed, she was soon off again. 'Excuse me,' she called out in a voice which we recognised as dangerously polite. 'I wonder if you could spare a moment?'

It was with somewhat bad grace that the nurses put up with Aunt Lucy's constant stream of complaints. By day five, they'd had enough and were looking for any excuse to remove her from the ward. They didn't have much longer to wait.

\*    \*    \*    \*

'I don't know what Aunt Lucy is doing with all those bed jackets?' I queried one morning a week after the operation. 'That was her on the 'phone asking for another four to be brought in this afternoon. It seems so warm whenever we go in to visit and I've never seen her wear any of them. Perhaps it gets very cold at night. But, to be honest, I'd be surprised.'

But as it turned out, it wasn't a chill on the ward that had prompted Aunt Lucy's strange requests. The chill in the voice of the ward sister as she demanded a meeting with us later that day told a very different story.

'It has been drawn to our attention,' she explained indignantly, 'that your aunt is running a business from her bedside. It appears that a large number of hats, scarves, socks and bed-jackets have been sold to various patients on the ward, not to mention the cleaning staff. We've discovered that she's keeping the stock under her bed. At a conservative estimate, we believe she has sold several dozen items already and many more patients have pre-paid for things she's promised to deliver as soon as she's discharged. May I point out that this is a hospital and not a satellite branch of Marks and Spencer!'

'But where did she get the stock from?' Mac was curious. 'We were surprised when she asked for so many bed-jackets and bed socks, but we certainly didn't bring her any hats and scarves.'

'Apparently her cleaning lady's been bringing them in discreet carrier bags. If you look under her bed now, you'll see what I mean.'

'So, why are you telling us all this? Aunt Lucy, as you can see, has all her faculties. Surely it's her you should be addressing.'

'She was given a warning yesterday and she assured us she would cease trading immediately. However, this morning she was caught trying to sell a horse to the hospital's Chief Executive whom she unfortunately mistook for a visitor.'

'Selling a horse? She doesn't have one to sell.'

'She was running a sweep stake for a race later this afternoon. £5 a go. We really cannot tolerate that sort of behaviour on the ward. So we've called you in to suggest you take her home. We understand that you live in a large Vicarage. Although we would normally keep her a few more days, the doctor is happy that, under your supervision, it'll be quite safe to allow her home to complete the rest of her convalescence. We can arrange for a district nurse to pop in at regular intervals to check her progress.'

'Well, I'm not sure about that?' Mac looked appalled. 'We've got four young children. She's not easy you know.'

'There is really no need to tell me that. But unless you want us to take the gambling issue or indeed the question of her illegal trading any further, I suggest you think about our proposal very carefully. We have to think of our vulnerable patients. At the rate she's going, before we know it, her various business ventures will have spread throughout the whole hospital.'

\*     \*     \*     \*

It was a slightly subdued Aunt Lucy who arrived back at the Vicarage later that afternoon. But within half an hour of taking up her new base on a make-shift bed in the dining room, she had regained her old spirit....or at least some of it.

'You can't leave books like this lying around where the children might see them,' Mac complained as he tossed a fairly racy novel onto his aunt's lap.

'You seem to have forgotten that due to my premature discharge from hospital, I am still relatively immobile. I need something to keep my mind active.' She cast a disparaging eye around the room. 'I must say I'd hoped you'd have showed a little more initiative with this place. The scope is huge. Your décor is decidedly dull!'

'Aunt, we have only been here a few weeks! Give us a chance.'

She sighed. 'All it takes… is a little imagination!'

It didn't take long for Aunt Lucy's 'imagination' to get to work. On Saturday morning, two days after her discharge, she chose to make the first of many profound announcements.

'Last night my suspicions were confirmed,' she cast her eyes round the kitchen table to check she had everyone's full attention. 'This house is most definitely haunted.'

Claire turned visibly pale. Josh and Lizzie's eyes brightened with expectation. There was a grunt from behind Mac's newspaper.

'What on earth are you talking about?' he enquired without taking his eyes off the sports section.

'I heard creaking floorboards.'

'That was me going to the loo. Our bathroom is just above your room.'

'Squeaking…'

'Me opening a window.' He still didn't look up.

'And how would you explain a series of extraordinary exploding noises in between?'

With a sigh of resignation, Mac put down his newspaper and eyeballed his aunt. 'Okay, okay. So, I had a curry last night and it didn't agree with me. Now that you have exposed my bodily functions to everyone, can we please move on. This is not a suitable conversation for the breakfast table!'

For a few moments there was silence. Then Aunt Lucy spoke again. 'How can you say this house isn't haunted when you have victims of the Black Death lying feet from your front door. I've already warned you about the danger of dormant spores from their diseased bodies. Now that your noisy family has moved into this hitherto quiet corner of the village, it is highly likely that their tormented souls have become restless!'

Claire pushed her half finished cereal to one side and left the room. I followed leaving Mac incandescent with rage.

'If you'd refrain from terrifying my children, I should be most grateful,' his voice was dangerous. 'Or let me put it more simply. Any more talk of ghosts, poltergeists or fairies at the bottom of the garden……..'

'That was only a bit of fun.' Aunt Lucy looked defensive. 'Lizzie was bored so I just planned a little adventure for her.'

'She could have drowned! Kate found her crawling along the river bank, searching for pixies!'

Aunt Lucy looked sheepish.

'So as I was saying, any more talk of the supernatural and you'll be spending the rest of your convalescence with my sister!'

'Not Susan. You wouldn't! Whenever I am invited to that ultra modern, super efficient, super sterile place of hers, she all but dusts me down before she lets me cross the threshold. And of all the lovely gifts I've given her over the years, I've never seen any on display. The one time I knitted jumpers for her various offspring, she took them out of the parcel as if my fingers had somehow contaminated them. I tell you, with all that cleanliness and tidiness, I wouldn't survive a moment if I had to stay there.'

'Then, you'd better watch yourself, Aunt. And that's my last word on the subject.'

But, sadly, it wasn't.

\*    \*    \*    \*

'BANG!' It was 3.00am when a loud explosion plunged the village into instant darkness.

'Good God! What on earth was that?' Mac was at the window in an instant. 'I should think half the village will have been tossed from their beds. Are the kids alright?'

Confirming my long held view that, once asleep, it would take a nuclear attack to wake our children, there was, initially, no sound from any of them. That was until Aunt Lucy intervened.

'Help, help…terrorist attack!' she yelled hysterically from the bottom of the stairs. Seconds later a pale-faced Claire flung herself into Mac's arms.

'What's happened Daddy? Are we all going to die?'

'No! Certainly not! As usual your aunt is grossly overreacting.' Mac turned an accusing glare in the direction of the culprit. 'Believe me Claire, of all the worries we considered when we moved into this remote village, terrorism wasn't one of them. I can assure you that the only person likely to suffer from this incident will be Aunt Lucy…. just as soon as I get my hands on her. For your information, we've just heard a bit of a bang outside but, whatever it was, there's bound to be a perfectly simple explanation.'

'So why is it so dark?' Claire sobbed. Thanks to her nervous disposition, she never went to sleep without a nightlight in her room and on the landing outside.

'Bit of a bang? An explosion, more like,' Aunt Lucy shouted up the stairs, clearly anxious not to lose face. 'And big enough to cause a power cut. Unlike your father, this is a scenario that is not unfamiliar to me having grown up in London during the Blitz. If I was him, I must say that I would want to find out what caused the incident so that I could take the appropriate action to protect my family.'

'Oh Daddy, do you really think it's a bomb?' Far from being upset, Josh's eyes were shining. 'Will we all have to be evacuated?'

'Don't be ridiculous!' Mac was now peering out of the window towards the river. 'Aha. Mystery solved. The explosion wasn't caused by a bomb. Judging by its charred remains on the lawn, the perpetrator was ….a swan.'

'A swan?'

'A 'suicide' swan by the looks if it. It appears that his flight path took him right to the sub-station at the end of the garden. As a result, he's managed to cut the power to this village and no doubt several others round here.'

'He's also managed to knock his own lights out!' Josh observed wisely.

'I must say he does look rather spooky lying there in the moonlight,' Aunt Lucy reflected as she stared forlornly at the casualty.

Claire shuddered and tightly gripped her father's hand.

'Don't start,' Mac's voice had an icy chill as he addressed his aunt. 'There's no need to get emotional. If he was a chicken or a pheasant, we'd be eating it.'

'Ugh!' Claire shuddered for the second time. 'Would anyone really want to eat him?'

'Well actually,' Aunt Lucy piped up knowingly. 'I think it's against the law. Officially, I think that swan belongs to the Queen.'

'Wicked,' Josh's eyes lit up. 'And to think he found his way to our garden.'

Mac's eyes rolled.

'So there definitely wasn't a bomb.' Claire was still not entirely satisfied with such a simple explanation.

'No. Not this time,' Aunt Lucy advised. 'Though one can never be too careful in these troubled times,' she added, anxious not to be proved entirely stupid.

'Bomb attack indeed! Who on earth would want to target this sleepy part of the world? Unless of course you have any guilty secrets that terrorist leaders across the world are anxious to share, aunt? Judging by your extraordinary outburst just now, you clearly have a guilty conscience.'

'Nonsense! The noise simply frightened me.' Aunt Lucy was indignant. 'I am a frail elderly lady. In the face of an attack, I'd be completely defenceless!'

'Is that why you screamed then?' Mac persisted. 'Did you fear that your dubious past had finally caught up with you?'

'I was just trying to signal a warning. For all I knew, you could have slept through it.'

'Sadly there wasn't much chance of that. Once again, through your thoughtless action, you have alarmed the more impressionable children in this household. Thanks to your outburst the other day, Kate and I lost a night's sleep trying to reassure Claire that there were no ghosts in the graveyard. Now that you've suggested that terrorists may be roaming the countryside round here, she probably won't sleep for a week. Trust me, aunt, you have now left me with no alternative. I shall be on the 'phone to my sister just as soon as it's light!'

'You wouldn't!'

'Believe me, I would!'

\* \* \* \*

'How dare my sister choose this week to work in Paris! I tell you, if I have to put up with my mad Aunt Lucy for much longer, I'll have a nervous breakdown.'

'She's not mad. She just suffers from a vivid imagination.'

'I don't doubt that! But, as she has demonstrated on countless occasions, that vivid imagination can make her very, very dangerous!'

'I think that's going a bit far.' I was trying to serve supper as Mac was pacing up and down the kitchen. 'She can be quite sweet.'

'Sweet?' Mac gave a hollow laugh. 'Excuse me! Who was the person who scared Claire witless? Who tried to drown Lizzie? Who, given half a chance, would have had me chasing imaginary terrorists round the house?'

'That's hardly fair.'

But Mac wasn't convinced. 'Things like that didn't happen before she arrived. Not content to wreak havoc in a hospital, she's now hell bent on bringing me and my family to the brink of collapse!'

'Rubbish! She's just...well....eccentric. Contrary to what you might believe, the kids love her. They think she's exciting!'

'Huh!'

'If you want my opinion, we need to find her something to do that would keep her out of mischief.'

The familiar clanking sound in the corridor brought the conversation to an abrupt end.

'Help! It's Marley's ghost!' Mac raised his hands in mock horror. A few moments later, Aunt Lucy and her Zimmer frame arrived in the kitchen.

'Don't think I can't hear you, Mac dear. I may be temporarily crippled, but my hearing is as sharp as ever!'

'Come and sit down, aunt,' I gestured to a comfortable chair in the corner. 'I was just saying that you needed a project of some kind to channel your boundless energy.'

'I know I do and I don't know why I didn't think of it earlier. I need to knit,' Aunt Lucy said dramatically. 'Despite the efforts of the hospital authorities to thwart my initiative, I managed to sell around forty bed-jackets, twelve pairs of woolly socks and several hats and scarves. However, some of my customers pre-paid and I promised to deliver them as soon as I was home. I am not one to let people down, so I need to get going. Not only does my stock need replenishing, it was clear from the enthusiasm of my clients that my range needs expanding. Once I have got my orders out, I shall be developing some new lines. All I need is a copious supply of wool and some knitting needles and you won't hear a peep from me.'

'Kate,' Mac was smiling for the first time for days, 'we must get on the case at once!'

\*     \*     \*     \*

For the next few days, Aunt Lucy stayed in her room and knitted. Bed jackets, bed socks, smart cardigans, fancy hats all flowed off the end of her needles with great speed. By the end of the week, an impressive pile of woollens lay on the bed ready for customers.

'More wool, more wool!' Mac urged, the moment he felt that stocks were dwindling. 'She mustn't stop. The peace it brings us is invaluable. She's not been any trouble since the project began!'

But he spoke too soon.

\*     \*     \*     \*

'I hope you don't mind,' Aunt Lucy looked up from her toils on the Friday, 'but I was hunting around for something to use as shoulder pads for a rather fancy cardigan I'd just finished and I took the liberty of taking a packet of your maternity pads from the back of the cupboard in your bathroom. I assumed, I hope correctly, that you no longer have any use for them!'

I stared at her in disbelief. 'How did you get into my bathroom?'

'With difficulty,' she replied almost proudly. 'But I managed it. The district nurse helped me up the stairs this afternoon and I must have accidentally taken her the wrong way. I told her you wouldn't mind,' she added innocently. 'It saved us having to move all those plastic toys that clutter up the children's bathroom so much. Look,' she added, 'if you fold the pads in half and sew them carefully, they work really well.'

When I told Mac what she'd done he was surprisingly philosophical.

'I did warn you,' he said smugly. 'Not just mad, but light-fingered too. For God's sake don't leave anything else lying around. She'll have sold it before you've blinked.'

'I didn't leave the maternity pads lying around. I didn't even know I still had any. Goodness knows what the nurse thought when she started hunting around in our bathroom. I dread to think what she may have cast aside before she found what she was looking for. Mind you,' I giggled suddenly, 'she's not the first person I've known whose managed to put such things to a more imaginative use.'

'What do you mean?'

'Years ago I had a friend whose aunt worked at the factory that made those pads and other similar women's things! All the women were given a supply each month as a perk, but she continued to claim them long after she needed to. She made them up into oven gloves, hats and tea cosies. Being so 'padded' they make great insulators. I even slept in a bed that had an eiderdown made of hundreds of them, all carefully sewn together! It was weird, but very warm.'

'You're joking!'

'No. She proved quite how versatile they could be. Mind you, she got a few funny looks when people realised what they were looking at. But it didn't seem to bother her. My friend found it slightly mortifying though. Even worse than the embarrassment that Aunt Lucy can inflict.'

'Oh, I don't know about that. When I was about ten years old, she came on holiday with us. Uncle Edmund was away on business and my mother felt sorry for her. There was this fancy dress competition and, against my mum's wishes, she decided to go as a witch. When she bounced into our room with the finished costume, mum nearly died.'

'Why?'

'She told us with great excitement that she had found a shop on the sea front that sold all sorts of things that were just perfect for her outfit...a wig, shaggy eyebrows etc.'

'So?'

'The problem was the long wrinkly thing she attached to her nose so proudly. You see, although it looked a bit like a nose... it wasn't a nose.'

'What do you mean? Oh my God, no, surely not?'

'Yes. You've guessed it. She'd been sold the wrong body part. It was the only time I've ever seen my aunt truly embarrassed! She didn't appear in public for the rest of the holiday!'

Our conversation was suddenly interrupted as Lizzie burst into the room.

'Guess what? I've just said goodnight to Aunt Lucy and I was wearing my red dressing gown and she was sitting up in bed in one of her new bed jackets. It was just as if I was Little Red Riding Hood and she was the granny.'

'Shame you couldn't complete the picture with the Big Bad Wolf,' said Mac reflectively. 'Then he could have brought the story to its natural conclusion.'

# Chapter Two

# MARCH, APRIL, MAY, JUNE

## MOTHERING SUNDAY

The sea of blank faces in front of me was not encouraging. I had hoped that, with Mothering Sunday only a day away, the gathering of seven to eleven year olds might have been able to give me the answer to what I thought had been a fairly obvious question. But when asked who Christians regarded as the most important mother in the world, they didn't seem to have a clue.

'Victoria Beckham,' Hatty said brightly.

'That's a really stupid answer,' Claire said smugly. 'I know exactly who you mean. It's Princess Diana, isn't it?'

'No it isn't,' I said desperately, 'Listen, this mother had a son who is world famous too. He spent his life trying to help people less fortunate than himself. But, as his methods were often a bit unusual, he sometimes got into terrible trouble, causing his mother great distress in the process.'

'I know, I know,' Cosmo shot his hand into the air. 'It's 'Marge,' Bart's mother from 'The Simpsons'.

'No,' I snapped bursting his bubble of enthusiasm in a second. 'You're miles off.'

'Is it the mother in the 'Just William' stories?' Josh suggested tentatively. I gave him one of my withering looks.

With an enormous effort, I resisted the urge to yell 'Don't be such morons!', and, taking a deep breath, managed to regain my enthusiastic, 'Let's be encouraging' Sunday school voice. 'Why don't you all look at the picture beside the altar for a moment?' I suggested, trying to keep any trace of sarcasm from my voice. 'The lady with the halo and the baby in her arms just might be a clue.'

They all followed my gaze. Suddenly light dawned.

'It's Mary, isn't it?' Lizzie said slowly.

\*    \*    \*    \*

'Kate, what on earth are you doing?' Mac was staring at me in disbelief. It was later that evening and I was hard at work at the kitchen table.

'What does it look like? I'm trying to tie ribbon into a pretty bow round forty tiny bags of sweets to make them look home-made.'

'May I ask why you've suddenly had the urge to be creative? Is it for someone's birthday party?'

'No, I'm doing this for all the ladies who turn up in church. In case you hadn't realised, tomorrow is Mothering Sunday.'

Mac was indignant. 'I certainly haven't forgotten the date and I must remind you now not to be disappointed when you don't get a present from me tomorrow. I'm not your mother, remember?'

'I know Lizzie's got me something. They all came out of nursery on Friday clutching little bags with 'To my mummy' written on the front. On the other hand, I couldn't help noticing that Claire and Josh looked distinctly sheepish when they saw the theme of tomorrow's service.'

'Trust me, I have everything under control.'

'That's exactly why I'm worrying. Oh, and while we're on the subject, have you bought anything for Aunt Lucy?'

'Aunt Lucy? Why should I? She's not my mother!'

'I know that. But ever since her husband and your mum died, she thinks of you as her closest relative. After all, she doesn't exactly have a good relationship with your sister and nearly all her other relatives live abroad. It would mean a lot to her if you bought her a little something. If you don't have any children of your own, Mothering Sunday can be ghastly unless someone special remembers you.'

'Well, I'm hardly likely to forget her at the moment seeing as she appears to have taken up permanent residence! So, unlike you, I don't feel any obligation to buy her anything. Actually, I rather feel it's us who deserve a gift. Not only is it costing us money to feed her at the moment, the cost to the emotional health of my family has been incalculable!'

'Well, I still think you should think about it. Traditionally, Mothering Sunday is all about families getting together at their Mother Church and exchanging gifts. So, in that sense, it would be entirely appropriate for you to buy her something.'

'Okay, I'll think about it,' Mac grunted. But he didn't look very convinced.

In an attempt to change the subject, Mac cast his eye over a pile of scripts that were on the table ready for the following morning. 'So, how are the preparations for the play going?' he asked casually, not realising that he had inadvertently jumped out of the frying pan and into the fire. 'I'd have thought it was a bit daunting to have Mothering Sunday as your first family service here. I bet you the church will be full.'

'Don't!' I muttered darkly. 'I was feeling really confident earlier, especially as Victoria had saved me loads of time by organising a group of keen children for my first play. So, I got them all together this afternoon for a quick rehearsal. All was going well until I came up against a young lady called Scarlet Broadwell. Apparently she's new to the village too. They only moved here last week. When her mother dropped her off, she told me in no uncertain terms that her daughter had had heaps of acting experience and was very confident. So, being the trusting soul that I am, I immediately cast her in one of the main roles.'

'And was she as confident as her mother made out?'

'Rather too confident! Within a few minutes, I wasn't quite sure which of us was in charge.'

'What do you mean?'

'Well, given it's Mothering Sunday tomorrow, I've done a play based on the story of Jesus disappearing for three days and then turning up in the Temple in Jerusalem. As an introduction, I've written a short piece about a child who breaks away from her parents in a big department store and is eventually found, several hours later, in the soft play area in the basement. In both cases, when asked by their fraught mothers why they just wandered off without any explanation, both children answer: 'Why were you worrying? Didn't you guess where I'd be?''

'And the point you are trying to make?'

'Well, the point was supposed to be that, like Mary, all mothers worry themselves sick when their children run away. However, unlike Mary, who appears from the bible story to shrug off the incident fairly quickly, the mother of the girl in the play area gave her an earful she wouldn't forget in a hurry. But the rehearsal had ground to a halt well before then.'

'Go on?'

'Before we'd even got to the point of the story, 'smarty-pants' Scarlet, who was playing the part of the little girl, puts up her hand.'

'I can't play this part,' she whimpered.

'Why not?' I replied irritated.

'This part is about a naughty child,' she announced boldly. 'And I am never naughty!'

'Silencing the smirks from the other kids, I explained as patiently as I could that I hadn't asked her to be naughty. I had asked her to act. I also made it clear that some of the best actors in the world often played parts that were far removed from what they were like in real life. But she wasn't convinced.'

'So, how was it resolved?'

'Well, I tried to persuade her, but when she burst into tears, I gave up and made her a narrator instead. Poor Josh was most indignant to find himself suddenly being shoved into her part.'

'I thought Josh had said he didn't want to act. He just wanted to narrate and maybe do a reading or a prayer for the first few services.'

'You're right. So, when he reminded me of his 'no acting clause,' I simply whispered in her ear. 'Read the part. It's about a naughty child. So, in your case, no acting required!'

*  *  *  *

By eleven o'clock the following morning, I'd had enough. The play with its revised cast was as ready as it was ever going to be. Lined up in neat rows on the table at the back of the church were my forty little bags, each tied with a ribbon and, as an afterthought, covered in some colourful glitter I'd found in the toy-box. Each contained a little Mothering Sunday present for the ladies.

'I thought you said you wouldn't have time to get the children to put them together?' Judy, whose twin boys were also performing that day, commented as she tried to find a seat that would give her the best view of the proceedings.

'I didn't ask them. I did them myself at about midnight last night. It nearly killed me.'

Suppressing a giggle, Judy surveyed my efforts. 'I'd keep quiet about your creative talents if those are anything to go by. If you want to retain any self-respect, I'd let the congregation give the credit to a bunch of uncoordinated but well meaning five year olds!'

Feeling rather indignant I went back to my seat, but my embarrassment wasn't over yet.

'Is your aunt coming to the service? Moira, the church warden queried when she came across to check that everything was in order before the service began.'

'No. I'm afraid not. Mothering Sunday is one of the church festivals she tends to ignore.'

'Well, I hardly think that's the case this year.'

'What do you mean?' Mac asked warily.

'Surely you've seen the advertisements.'

Mac bristled. 'What advertisements?'

'The ones for her hats and scarves. She's selling them as perfect Mothering Sunday gifts. She's placed a small advertisement in the local paper and a much larger one in the church magazine. I assumed you knew about it because your address is at the bottom.'

It didn't take a genius to work out from our horrified expressions that Aunt Lucy's latest initiative was completely new to us. Resisting the temptation to grab her from the house for an immediate show-down, I tried as calmly as I could to explain our ignorance.

'No. I'm afraid we didn't know anything about it. We've only just paid our subscription for the church magazine and we haven't got round to ordering the local paper yet. No wonder Aunt Lucy's had so much post recently. I just assumed they were 'Get Well' cards. But I can assure you we'll be discussing it with her at some length just as soon as the service is over.'

'How dare she use our address without telling us,' Mac fumed after Moira had moved on. 'I can't believe the nerve of that woman. If it hadn't been for us, she'd have been in serious trouble for trading when she was in hospital. Now she's trying the same trick with us. She clearly has no scruples whatsoever. I shall be serving her an eviction notice as soon as we get home. And to think, you wanted me to buy her a present to make up for her disappointment on Mothering Sunday,' he added bitterly. 'She's clearly milked the day for all it was worth.'

'Mac, keep your voice down, for goodness sake. The service is about to start. Save your anger for when we get home. But, remember, you've said that Aunt Lucy would be 'sussed' by the locals sooner rather than later. Judging by the intense conversation Moira's now having in the back row, her fall from grace has already started.'

Despite the unfortunate start, to my surprise the first part of the service appeared to go off without a hitch. As the children took their seats at the end of the play, I felt myself breathe a sigh of relief. But any complacency was short-lived. Five minutes before the end of the service, Vicar Vic announced that there was a surprise in store at the back of the church. But as the congregation turned to look, it wasn't the gifts that first attracted their attention.

'Stop that at once,' I hissed unceremoniously as a gang of children, led by Lizzie and Josh, hurled themselves at the tray of goodies in a race to get the job of handing them out.

From the pew next to me, I watched Scarlet's mother as she pointedly put her arm lovingly round her daughter's shoulders. But this elaborate show of affection didn't fool me. The move was not so much a gesture of friendliness, but an attempt to restrain her from joining the rebels at the back.

But, as she looked on smugly, she didn't realise that she, too, was about to get her comeuppance.

In an effort to divert everyone's attention from the commotion, Vicar Vic hastily asked the remaining children what they thought their mothers would ask for if they could have anything they wanted on Mothering Sunday. Scarlet's hand shot up into the air.

While her mother looked on proudly, Scarlet rose to her feet. But her pride was short lived.

'I know exactly what she'd want.' Thanks to those speech classes, Scarlet's voice was loud and clear. 'My Mummy would want a Porsche!'

As Audrey's face turned a dull beetroot, Mac turned to me and whispered, 'Clearly Scarlet needs to write to Aunt Lucy. I'm sure that 'Old Vicarage Enterprises,' or whatever she calls herself, will be able to dig up a suitable model for Mothering Sunday – complete with a woolly bonnet!'

## THE VICARAGE

'We live at the Old Vickerdidge' Lizzie would tell everyone who came to visit during the first few months. The name stuck for years.

'What's the difference between a Vicarage and any other old house?' Claire asked me one day over tea.

'Ghosts!' said Josh in his spookiest voice. Seeing Claire's eyes widen in horror, he continued: 'They float across from the graveyard on cold dark nights to spook you while you're in bed!'

'Oh, don't start that again,' I pleaded as I watched the colour drain from Claire's face. 'Ignore him. He's talking rubbish as usual. To be honest, I can't think of any differences between our house and any other of a similar age. But if you hunt round, you'll find plenty of things in this house that you wouldn't find in a modern one...like Auntie Sue's.'

'Like mess,' said Josh provocatively.

'No, not like mess.'

'Like cobwebs,' said Lizzie anxious to say her piece.

'No, not necessarily.'

'Well, what then?' Josh persisted.

'Lots of things,' I ended, now irritated that I had thought, of all places, to mention Sue's immaculate home. 'Why don't you go and look.'

* * * *

'Why do you let my sister annoy you so much,' Mac asked when I relayed the children's comments later that evening. 'Why can't you just accept you're different?'

'Sue makes me feel hopeless. And it's not just her perfect home that bothers me. It's also her pencil thin figure and all those immaculate suits she wears whenever she's in court. Remember when she was working near here the other day and popped in straight from work? I'd just come home from a day's filming dressed in tatty jeans and covered in mud. Then she turns up unexpectedly, dressed in a pin-striped suit. One look at her and I felt like Mr Blobby's big sister!'

'You'd look pretty silly in a field full of pigs wearing a suit. Anyway, she's a solicitor. It's part of her uniform.'

But I wouldn't let it go.

'Pin-striped would become pin-curved over my out-of-control body. And it's not just her figure that's perfect. She's also got a wonderful job, a perfect home and highly academic children, all of which she manages beautifully. You only have to glimpse me and my home to realise I don't control anything. Everywhere you look, it's chaos.'

'Kate, we've just moved house and we have four children, the youngest of which isn't two yet. She only has two children and they're both much older.'

'Last time they came to stay, she turned up with two casseroles and her own bedding. She probably thought she might catch something if she used any of our facilities.'

'Nonsense. She was just trying to be helpful. And, as I have just said, we have only just moved house.'

'It was worse when we lived in the cottage. Once we'd started producing children, they never came to stay again.'

'That's because we didn't have the space for a family of four to stay. Honestly Kate, I think you're being unreasonable. If you want my opinion, I think it's far more likely that's she's jealous of you.'

I snorted. 'Jealous of what?' My fat figure, my riotous children or my chaotic home? Where would you like to start?'

'All of them probably. She'd love to have the confidence not to care about her appearance and her home. But she's miles off that.'

'Yeah, right.'

'Give her a chance. If you want my opinion, I think she's terrified of you. That huge façade is just her way of dealing with her complete lack of confidence. Underneath it all, she's screaming to be liked.'

\*     \*     \*     \*

'I'm not so sure Mac's right,' Judy reflected when I spoke to her later that evening. I was thin once and had a tidy house and it did wonders for my confidence. It must have been about three years ago….on a Saturday. The twins were being christened the following day and I had to have all James' family back for tea afterwards. It took almost a week to get the house tidy enough to entertain in. The effort of all that cleaning took about two inches off my waist-line. When I finally finished I felt fantastic.'

'And did you keep it up?'

'No. Sadly not. The afternoon before the christening, I popped out to the supermarket to do the big shop, leaving James alone with the twins. By the time I got back, they'd ransacked the place. I was so depressed I ate three of the cakes meant for the 'tea'. The weight was back before I could blink. I tell you, as the pounds flew onto my hips, my confidence flew out of the window. Anyway, what on earth made you ask your children to compare her house with yours?'

'They were trying to work out if there was anything unusual about living in a vicarage. To be honest, I couldn't think of a thing.'

'Oh Kate, there are lots of issues to do with living in an old vicarage like yours. For a start, not many people arrive in their new home to discover that they're expected to hold the annual church fete in their garden and host a carol singing evening. You're also expected to take your turn at the church flowers, field the odd 'phone call about a christening, marriage or funeral. And, if that wasn't enough, there's the small matter of writing and producing a short play at the family service each month. Shall I go on? Funnily enough, most houses don't come with any of that baggage.'

'Yes, but I don't see it as baggage. In fact, I don't really mind any of that.'

'That's not the point. You asked if there was anything unusual about living in a vicarage. Oh, and while we're on the subject, I spoke to Mac earlier today. I gather your latest task involves closing the church at midnight.'

'Ah well, that's not quite true.'

'Well that's what he told me. He said he found you wandering around the churchyard in your dressing gown and 'wellies' dodging owls.'

'Now that bit is true,' I admitted. 'But to be fair to the church warden, I was actually asked to lock the church at six o'clock. The trouble was, that's a bit of a busy time in our household, so I forgot. I only remembered when I was climbing into bed around midnight. And I tell you, I won't forget again. I was scared witless!'

'Why on earth didn't you get Mac to do it?'

'He was asleep. He only woke when he heard the owl hoot and me scream. The wretched animal flew straight at me. To be honest, I was in quite a state when he found me. He calmed me down and took me back to bed, but I was awake for ages. And when I did sleep, I spent the rest of the night dreaming of shadowy gravestones. I've been walking around like a zombie all day. I'm completely exhausted.'

'Kate, you can't go on like this. You spend your life rushing around like some headless chicken. You'll catch yourself coming backwards one of these days. And now, on top of everything else, you've got Aunt Lucy to deal with and she's more trouble than the rest of your troupe put together. You're going to have to get some help if you want to avoid ending up with a nervous breakdown.'

'Do you think I'd ever find anyone mad enough to want to help sort out the chaos that is our home?' I queried.

'Your mess is nothing compared to mine, remember,' Judy was swift to point out.

'True,' I replied bluntly. 'We've far more space here compared to the cottage. But although I've always thought it would be far easier to be tidy in a bigger house, so far, all we've managed to prove is that the more space you give the Arnold family, the greater their capacity to trash it!'

*       *       *       *

But it was the extra space we had in our new home that proved the greatest delight to the children. Now with their own bedrooms, they soon adapted to the new layout in their own individual ways.

Claire had always adored the stage and we had encouraged this from a very early age with weekly drama lessons in a nearby church hall. From the age of four she had enlisted the help of her younger brother, and any local friends who were willing to be bossed about, whenever she fancied putting on a production of her own. Somehow she always managed to land the star part. Biting my lip, I tried not to intervene unless it was really necessary …and sometimes it had been.

'Josh is quite right,' I argued one day. 'He doesn't have to play the part of your broom in your version of Cinderella.'

Then there was the day she actually gave him the title role in her own re-write of Aladdin, only to kill him off in the first scene.

In our old house Claire had proved on countless occasions, against my better judgment, that it was possible to hurl yourself in dramatic fashion from the bend in the stairs and fall three steps down to the soft carpet at the bottom without sustaining any serious injury, whenever she fancied playing the 'damsel in distress' role. In the new house she learned, to her cost, that it was possible to hurl yourself from the bend in the stairs and fall ten steps down to the hard floor at the bottom and break your arm and all the ornaments on the hall table at the same time!

'It's a very simple fracture,' I assured Mac over the telephone from the hospital. 'The doctor says that after a few weeks in plaster, she'll be fine. No lasting damage.'

'And what's the prognosis for the ornaments?' Mac demanded unsympathetically. 'Not to mention the damage to the table. That was one of the few decent bits of furniture we have. I inherited that from my godmother,' he added bitterly. 'Our children are going to have learn to respect their new surroundings a bit better. Since we arrived at the Vicarage, you've allowed them to run amok!'

'Nonsense! Claire's learned her lesson now. It won't happen again.'

But I spoke too soon.

To this day the children maintain that only a blind person wouldn't have noticed the skateboard in the middle of the kitchen floor. Brightly coloured and fairly large, I only realised when it was too late.

The children had never heard me scream in fear before. As I slid helplessly and uncontrollably across the floor, I caught a fleeting glimpse of their horrified faces before my view was obscured by the pile of washing I was carrying. It must have been an amazing sight as I shot past them showering dirty underwear in all directions!

As I lay on the floor, with Josh's pyjamas across my chest and Mac's smalls across my face, for a moment I was lost for words. However, even in my semi-conscious state, I was vaguely aware of four sets of eyes looking down on me from their seats at the kitchen table. After a moment, I spoke. Too dazed to be angry I simply said: 'How many times have I said that skateboarding is an outdoor sport?'

I wasn't aggressive but the effect was no less devastating. Clearly, for a moment, they had all thought I was dead.

Then, as one, they burst into tears.

* * * *

It was over tea one day that I announced to the assembled company that I now knew the difference between an 'Old Vicarage' and other houses of a similar age.

'Actually, it was Judy who provided the answer,' I admitted.

'What's that?' Josh was curious.

'Responsibility. When you live in the Vicarage, it's hard to ignore the church and all that goes with it, even if you're not the vicar.'

'Claire looked puzzled. 'And what does that mean?'

'Just making sure we do our bit, really. It's a huge privilege to live here, overlooking a medieval church and glorious countryside. So, it's very important that we give something back.'

* * * *

'How did you get on with finding some help?' Judy asked as we scooped up our paint-covered children from nursery one morning.

'Success!' I replied grinning. 'I found an advertisement on the parish notice board. Dorothy Price lives in Upper Hadbury and has spent the last few months nursing her husband following a fall at work. He's a lot better now so she's been looking for some part-time work to get her out of the house for a bit each week. She seems delightful. And, even better, she's happy to do some babysitting too which would be wonderful as the kids adore her. She's a real character. I think Aunt Lucy's finally found her match.

'What do you mean?'

'Well, on her first morning, when I'd been up half the night tidying so that she didn't get the wrong, or rather right, impression from the start, Aunt Lucy suddenly shouted from her bed. 'Is that the new maid?'

'Oh God, no!'

'Yes. Not a good start! I had visions of her upping sticks and leaving before she'd even started.'

'What did she do?'

Well, luckily I had warned her about my eccentric relative. So, hearing her call, she goes into the dining room drops a quick curtsey and says: 'Begging your pardon 'ma'am,' only I'm new here. Is it anything that I can help you with or will you be wanting the butler?' Then she curtsied again and left, leaving Aunt Lucy, for once, lost for words. She hasn't bothered her since.'

'Good for her! Looks like you've found a gem!'

'I hope so. Mac's impressed too. Apparently she likes to cook. She arrived the first day with some home-made pickle and a fruit cake. She may be sixty but I think he's fallen in love!'

## FAITH, HOPE AND CHARITY

The fat, middle-aged lady stood in the hall and stared round critically.

'You'll be glad when you're straight,' she observed staring fixedly at the muddle on the dresser.

And there was me thinking we were!'

Lady Henrietta Caldwell and her husband were the major landowners in our area. She'd driven round to put a leaflet through my door and found me digging a flowerbed when she pulled into the driveway. Unwisely, I had invited her in for a coffee.

It didn't take long for the conversation to get round to fund-raising.

Remembering Mac's instruction not to leap in with both feet, I politely refused her offer to join the committee of a local children's charity she chaired. Not to be put off, she asked me if she could call upon my services if ever they were unexpectedly short of manpower.

It was hard to say no to that.

'Well then, I wonder if I could impose upon your culinary skills. I know it's very short notice. But you see we're a bit stuck.'

Bad start!

'It's just that Margery Cuthbert lost her husband last week and has had to drop out of the team who were cooking for our annual Barn Dance at the village hall on Saturday. She was due to make the salmon mousse.....'

I had to suppress the voice inside me that said: 'Anything but mousse!' Over the years, my battles with gelatine had been overwhelmingly unsuccessful!

'No problem!' I said almost too brightly.

'Oh how very kind,' she said gushingly. 'It really is very good of you. It's just that Margery's bereavement has made things rather difficult. Of course we were hoping that you and your family would be able to come along and join in the fun. So many people are dying to meet you. If you're sure it's alright, bring the mousse with you and I can put it straight onto the table. It really is terribly kind.....'

And with that she swept out of the house and into her car.

\*　\*　\*　\*

'You volunteered to do what?' Mac was giving me one of his 'I despair of you' looks as I told him what I'd done later that evening. 'Kate, we've only been here a few weeks and you're already on countless committees elsewhere, let alone your job and the small matter of four children. And, besides,' he added bitterly, 'you know I hate barn dances.'

'I didn't mean to get involved quite so soon. It was just that the lady was so persuasive. You know the type. I could have had six children and been pregnant with triplets and she still would have expected me to get involved. My guess is she took one look at the house and thought 'They're a fair cop' She probably thinks I spend all my day in the kitchen concocting delicious home-made pies and pickles for my family.'

'Some chance,' Mac whispered under his breath. 'So, what are you cooking?'

'Salmon mousse.'

Mac grinned 'Didn't know that was one of your specialities.'

'Very funny! But it wasn't my suggestion.'

'Do you know how to make it?'

'No. But I can find out.'

'So why didn't you ask to do something else?'

'I was worried that she might suggest something even more complicated and I could hardly turn her down twice. She'd think I was stupid.'

Mac raised his eyebrows but didn't disagree.

'Could you cheat and buy some?'

'No, that's the trouble. It's very hard to find home-made looking salmon mousse. If it was a cake, it would be different.'

'Serves you right!' Mac was unsympathetic. 'They see you coming.'

But despite Mac's misgivings, after a few practice efforts on the family which largely ended in the bin, I finally made a passable 'go' at it. At seven o'clock on Saturday night I marched confidently into the hall.

'Lovely,' said Lady Henrietta who was putting the finishing touches to an elaborate centre piece, 'Put it on the table there. Oh, and put your name on the container so that it doesn't get lost at the end of the evening.'

I thought about it for a moment and then decided against that idea. Better to sacrifice the bowl than risk the possibility of anyone associating my efforts with me!

\*    \*    \*    \*

If Lady Henrietta left with the impression that I was new to charity work, she was a bit wide of the mark. For the past two years I had been chairman of a local branch if the National Childbirth Trust. Along with five other committee members, we were supposed to oversee the well-being of around two hundred predominantly middle-class, thirty-something mothers across our part of the Midlands. At any one time they were all either pregnant, coping with a baby or were mothers of toddlers. Few organisations in the world deal with so many hormones!

\*    \*    \*    \*

It was eight o'clock in the evening, a week after the Barn Dance, and the entire committee were sitting round our kitchen table having our monthly meeting. On the table in front of us were two bottles of wine and a large packet of crisps. Item four on the agenda concerned Minnetta Harrid, mother of one and a complainer!

In fact in the six months since she had been a member she had complained so many times that she had become known as 'Moaning Min'. Having had one baby, she apparently knew everything there was to know about motherhood. According to her, we knew ........virtually nothing!

Her latest 'curt' letter concerned some 'naughty' toddlers who had attended a coffee morning at her own house. Was there, she wondered, any way in which I could ban certain members from bringing their children if they were not going to behave perfectly?

So I had discussed the matter with the other members of the committee before drafting my reply.

'How would you deal with her?' I asked Sally, our mentor and former chairman, who'd left the committee several years earlier when, with three children under five, she'd discovered she was expecting triplets. Two years on, she'd returned to the committee purely as a way of getting out of the house.

'I'd tell her to get lost,' was the swift response. 'So, when you send the letter, I suggest you also tell her that if she's going to take that attitude, I don't want her kid at my house. She's the worst of the lot!'

\*    \*    \*    \*

The Craft Fair was not my idea. Anyone who has ever known me knows that I don't make anything apart from the occasional bed. At primary school I was sacked as flower monitor after only two days in the job and later, at secondary school, I was strongly encouraged to give up sewing after I accidentally sewed the tablecloth I was hemming to my sleeve!

However, Barbara, a new and extremely enthusiastic member of our branch, had suggested the idea of a Craft Fair as a way of raising a great deal of money very quickly. That bit was appealing. Coffee mornings were all very well but raise only a few quid at best. The idea of making, perhaps, £1000 in one hit had to be a good one. Also, she was assuring us that she knew everything there was to know about Craft fairs.....it got better by the minute!

So it was agreed that Barbara would book all the stall holders to ensure an interesting mix of skills and we, the committee, would do all the boring bits...like booking the hall, arranging refreshments, publicity etc. Little did we realise that we were being led like lambs to the slaughter.

And we nearly stumbled at the very first fence. Finding a suitable venue soon proved to be far more difficult than we had imagined. All the obvious, affordable sites had been booked up for months!

'Well, that's that then,' said Sally resignedly. 'We could go further afield but I'm sure we won't get our members to travel to the next town for a Craft Fair, at least not the ones with a troupe of very young children in tow.' Suddenly, she looked out of my lounge window and her face brightened. 'Unless, of course, we could use your village hall. It would be perfect. It's right in the middle of our patch, it's big enough and it's got a run-down field next to it. I bet if you paid the local farmer something, he'd let us use it as a car park for the afternoon.'

'That rundown field happens to be the back end of our garden,' I informed her crisply. 'We've got great plans for it!'

But Sally was not to be put off that easily. 'Even better. A load of cars will plough it up nicely for you. And what's more, if you'll agree, any nursing mothers can use your house to breastfeed their babies. We'd need to be seen to provide somewhere comfortable for them to do that. We are the National Childbirth Trust after all. And,' she added unnecessarily, 'you are the Chairman!'

'Hey, slow down a minute. I'm not sure the locals are going to be too thrilled at the prospect of hundreds of people descending on their village on a quiet Saturday afternoon.'

'On the contrary, we shall be providing great entertainment courtesy of one of the best Craft Fairs they'll ever see.'

But I wasn't so sure. 'We've only been in the village a few weeks. I don't want to frighten them off before I've even got to know them.'

'Tell you what...if you're really that worried, why don't you talk it over with some of the 'local dignitaries'. Get a feel for how they'd react.'

'Even better, why not suggest that they open the church for the afternoon and serve teas and coffees from there.' Barbara chipped in. 'Your village hall isn't as big as some of the venues in the town so it will be helpful not to have to allocate a large area for refreshments. Besides, most of our members haven't made a decent cake in their lives, whereas I bet there are a stack of older ladies in your village who are a dab hand at a lemon drizzle or a walnut cream. They'd be bound to make heaps of money and it would free up far more space inside the hall for our stalls. If they agree to serve everything from the church, it would also mean that there'd be less chance of a rampaging toddler pouring a beaker of orange juice all over a stall holders precious wares.'

I was beginning to be convinced.

\*     \*     \*     \*

Later that evening I put the proposal to Mac. At first he was indignant.

'You can tell your fellow committee members that the field they referred to as 'run-down' has some great fruit trees in it. They may park in it but I shall be supervising them. I've seen how some of your friends drive, and I'd prefer to be on hand to ensure there isn't a massacre.'

'A massacre? I wasn't aware that any of my friends had ever killed anyone.'

'I don't mean people, I mean my trees!'

\*     \*     \*     \*

Barbara was right. The church desperately needed to raise money and this seemed a simple way for them to do it. Even better, two of the ladies admitted to making cake decorations as a hobby and asked to have a stall. We were in business!

But there was still a long way to go. After careful measurement of the hall, Barbara worked out we could have no more than twenty stall holders. Each one would need a table of specific proportions.

'It's always the same,' she explained. 'Not only will many of them mind a lot if they don't get the right amount of space, they'll also complain if they haven't got the best position in the hall. Some will be great, but others don't think of themselves as stall holders, they think of themselves as artistes and behave accordingly.'

'HELP!!'

As the day approached, the organization reached fever pitch. Although the refreshments were sorted, we still needed people to man the door, sell raffle tickets, make posters, organize the publicity, etc.... the list was endless. Also, as we couldn't sell tickets in advance, we had no idea how many people would turn up. The problem, we quickly realized, of staging the event in a small village, was that we were not going to benefit from the kind of passing trade a town location would offer. However, what we did know was that there would be one 'hell of a stink' from the stall holders if attendance was poor. Clearly we would have to advertise the event in the local press. But on a cold Saturday in March, we needed to offer something special if we wanted people to turn up.

Then I had a brainwave. I would telephone our local Post Office to see if there was any chance of borrowing Postman Pat (albeit in the form of a costume) plus 'Jess the cat' as our celebrity guest. After all, in the National Childbirth Trust the average age of the children is just under two and a half. That gives most mums a great reason for *not* turning up at all unless there's a real incentive........it was worth a try.

Whoopee! The Post Office said yes and, better still, offered him for nothing. All I had to do was collect him the day before and return him (intact) after the 'do' was over.

So, at the appointed time, I arrived at the depot located in a remote corner of town. Unfortunately I could only find a parking space several roads away. Still, not to worry, I was, after all, only collecting a costume!

'I've come for Postman Pat,' I said brightly to the man on the door. I was so excited I nearly burst into song. After all, 'the man with the black and white cat' never failed to raise a smile in our house.

Without looking up, the man picked up the 'phone on the desk and dialled a number.

'There's a woman here come to borrow 'Postman bloody Prat'.' He turned to me, 'Where's your car?'

'About four hundred yards down the road.' I wasn't smiling any more.

He laughed, but not, I thought, in a very friendly way.

He was right to laugh. A few moments later a large...very large box was dropped at my feet. Inside was a huge head, the costume and Jess the Cat. We would need to find someone with gigantic proportions to wear it.

'Do you want a hand?' asked the man without enthusiasm.

'I can manage, thank you.'

With some difficulty and a few peculiar looks, I started my perilous journey back to the car.

By the time I got there, my enthusiasm had returned. Lizzie would be beside herself with excitement when she saw who was travelling with her today. Carefully I removed the head from the box and placed it on the front seat. Tossing the rest of the kit in the back, I proudly drove my celebrity passenger across town to the nursery school.

Lizzie took one look at the front seat and was hysterical. It was soon clear that either Lizzie or Pat would come home with me….but not both.

In the end I had to get the teacher to distract her while I replaced Pat in the box and hid him in the boot.

The journey home was a subdued affair. As I arrived in the driveway, I was greeted by none other than 'Moaning Min'. What now?

'I've just received your latest newsletter, and there's a mistake on the back page. I was just passing and I was wondering if you had a few moments..'

'Oh what a shame,' I tried to sound disappointed. 'But, unfortunately, I've a lot to sort out today what with the Craft Fair tomorrow….'

'Can I help?' she asked. I was 'gob-smacked!'

'If you really want to do something, you could take a couple of these road signs and stick them on the verge at the end of our village. Sally and I have some for the junctions on the edge of town. But if you could take two off our hands it would be a real help.'

Without another word she chucked them in the back of her car and was off. Strange lady!

The signs had been provided by another member of the committee who had wisely worked out that there was no point having a Craft Fair at a remote country location if you didn't tell people how to get to it. I studied her instructions. Two for the lane (Moaning Min had those), two for the 'bypass' roundabout (I could do that) and two for the junction on the far side of town (that could be Sally's job). I'd give the children an early tea and then pop out. With a bit of luck it wouldn't take long.

At around six fifteen that evening, I arrived at the narrow lane just before the slip road to the bypass. Luckily Lizzie and Archie were asleep in the back. Both were securely anchored in their car seats, but it was awfully dark. Dare I leave them for two minutes while I planted my sign? I didn't really have a choice.

The roundabout at the junction was like a racetrack! Crossing it, with a huge sign in my hands, was not going to be easy … especially in rush hour traffic on a Friday evening! Looking like some crazed lollipop lady, I gazed at the roaring traffic and realised that getting across without killing myself would be a challenge. Admittedly the traffic at the overhead junction was going slower than the four lanes pounding underneath, but taking on two lanes of determined commuters was a daunting prospect.

Ignoring the drivers' bemused expressions, I 'went for it,' using up several of my 'lives' in the process. Once on the island, I looked for a suitable spot to plant my charge.

Oh God!!!! I'd got the wrong sign. As I stuck it into the ground, I realized that, however hard I tried, I couldn't make the arrow point in the right direction. I'd picked up the sign meant for the turning down the road, assuming, wrongly, that they were both the same. But, the only way my sign would work was if its back faced the traffic. Useful for anyone who happened to be taking a stroll on the island (unlikely!), but useless to anyone else!

The journey back across the road was no better than the journey there and wasn't helped by the fact that I knew I had to do it again in a few moments. The temptation to 'cut and run' was huge but this, after all, was the key sign. If I didn't do it, I'd be in real trouble!

Luckily the children were still fast asleep as I grabbed the right sign. I shot back to the roadside and, dicing with death again, braved the traffic a second time. Ignoring a surprised look from someone I half recognized, I hid behind my sign as I negotiated the cars.

Success! Someone else could collect it tomorrow. And it was definitely going to be someone I didn't like!!!!!

Back in the car, I drove to our next location. Luckily that was easy. Then home and a stiff drink.

As I entered the house the telephone was ringing. It was Sally, just back from placing her signs at the far side of town.

'Oh thank God, you're alive,' she sounded relieved. 'I narrowly missed death several times during that little expedition!'

I could only agree.

'By the way,' she added mischievously. 'I've had a 'phone message from 'Moaning Min'. She wants you to ring her....and she says it's urgent.'

Suddenly I knew exactly who I was going to ask to collect my signs for me tomorrow!

*   *   *   *

'That's the last time I ever volunteer to do anything like that' I moaned to Mac as I climbed into bed the following evening. 'I have been highly traumatized by the experience. Despite the National Childbirth Trust and our church taking loads of money, I seemed to be permanently in trouble. I made it perfectly clear to the church committee what was involved, so I don't feel I can be held responsible for a stray two year old who felt the need to wipe his 'chocolaty' fingers on the altar cloth. Neither should I be blamed for the shock old Mr. Baines got when he slipped, uninvited, into my house to use the 'loo'. Apparently the sight of five women breastfeeding in the lounge affected his pacemaker. The only light moment came when I was able to correct that pompous woman, Sylvia Beckenham. Sneering slightly as she held up a crumpled piece of cloth as she washed up in my kitchen, I could see she was trying to make a statement about the poor standard of my coffee coasters. It was with great delight that I was able to inform her that the warm, damp object in her hand was, in fact, a breast-pad which probably belonged to the lady currently breastfeeding her baby in the room next door!

And some of the stallholders were no better. If it wasn't bad enough to narrowly escape death on a roundabout last night, this morning I only just avoided losing an eye when I kindly offered to help lift a display stand off the back of someone's van. I opened the back doors, as instructed, and the damn thing slid straight out on top of me. As I fell to the ground, some woman behind me yelled, 'Careful with that, it cost two hundred pounds!'

So I escaped inside and immediately had to deal with a distraught woman with a table full of ornate candles who claimed that the neighbouring stallholder, manned as it turned out by a mother from Lizzie's nursery school, had stolen eighteen inches of her patch for her designer jumpers. So I did a quick measurement, realised that she was right, and politely pointed out the oversight. But instead of getting an apology, I got an outright refusal from the woman to do anything about it. I tell you, I was tempted to ignite her fancy jumpers with one of the exotic candles. It was only Barbara's calming hand on my shoulder that stopped me. And did you hear about Aunt Lucy?'

Mac groaned. 'No, go on. I can hardly bear to think……'

'Well, you know how 'miffed' she was when she realised she was too late to take a stall.'

'Yes, but we did explain that, when the idea was put forward, she wasn't fit enough to get involved.'

'Well, as usual, she took matters into her own hands. Once we'd left the house, she loaded up the kitchen trolley with her knitwear and then pushed it round to all the ladies who were quietly breastfeeding in the lounge. I gather she did quite well.'

'Oh God, I can just imagine the pressure they were under. Trapped in a seat, they were all sitting targets.'

'On the contrary, they loved her. Apparently while she was selling, she gave them a running commentary on our family history....warts and all.'

'It's like a bad dream.'

'Yes, and it doesn't end there. Flushed with her success in the living room, she restocked the trolley and then took herself and her self-styled Zimmer frame across to the church where she made another killing amongst the ladies who were having tea. By the end of the day she'd taken a cool three hundred pounds!'

'And ruined our reputation for ever. Before her head gets too big, I hope she realises that some of that money will have to go to the National Childbirth Trust.'

'Oh, she's already handed them a cheque. Barbara was delighted. She's even offered her a stall at her next event. Anyway, how did you get on?'

Again Mac groaned. 'Somehow I could cope with your friends who managed to spin their wheels in the mud as they parked, splattering me from head to foot. I'd expected that and they didn't let me down. However,' he paused looking completely defeated. 'I simply wasn't ready for a rather pompous woman and her friend who calmly drove in at the gate, got out of their car, handed me the keys and a pound coin and said: 'Park it somewhere where we can find it and leave the keys under the sun visor.' As I was reeling from the curt instruction, the woman swung round and added: 'Oh, and do be sure to keep a careful eye on it. We don't want it stolen!' She then calmly turned her back on me and marched out of the garden all set to enjoy the rest of her afternoon.'

I gave him a sympathetic hug. 'At least I didn't get to speak to Minnetta Harrid. When I saw her red Vauxhall turn into the village, I was expecting a load of trouble.'

'In a Red Vauxhall?' Mac's voice sounded strained. 'That was the lady who asked me to park her car!'

'Oh God! This has all been my fault. Since we moved here I've let things slip. People are rapidly getting the impression I've got loads of free time to volunteer for things. And it always seems to land us in trouble. It's time I made it clear to everyone round here that I am a serious career woman......even if I only work part-time!'

Mac snorted. 'I can just picture your boss's face if he ever heard you say that!'

## PEACOCKS AND PIGS

'So you don't mind them without feathers, then?'

'Pardon?'

'Peacocks don't have feathers at this time of year,' the man explained patiently. 'It's when they moult.'

'Well I think we'd better leave it then.'

'No worries,' the man was being very good about it. 'Must admit I was a bit surprised when you rang. Try us again in June. They'll look splendid then.'

Well, wouldn't that have made a novel feature for the programme! A bunch of bald birds!

It was always hard to find colourful stories in the winter. So the idea of filming the peacocks at Warwick Castle had seemed inspirational. In my mind I had already pictured close-up shots of their gorgeous feathers against a backdrop of magnificent castle walls. Thank goodness the peacock breeder had pointed out this minor point before I arrived with a crew. I'd have been a laughing stock…again.

As I turned back to the piles of newspapers and magazines strewed across my desk, I was suddenly aware that I had company. Standing in the doorway, balanced on her two new sticks, Aunt Lucy was staring down at me.

'I must say I was astonished to hear what you just said. I had no idea that you knew so little about birds. When you grow up in the country, those kind of things are generally taught to you on your mother's knee.'

'Being born on the outskirts of London was probably a bit of a setback, then.' I replied crisply. 'Aunt, it really isn't polite to listen into my telephone conversations.'

'I was only doing my morning constitutional in the hall, as instructed by my physiotherapist. If you choose to leave the study door open, it's a bit difficult to avoid listening. Besides, I was only trying to be helpful.'

'I'm doing fine on my own, thank you.'

'If that conversation was anything to go by, you're clearly not. But if you insist on being 'huffy,' I'll leave you to it. I'll be in the lounge if you want me.'

With an effort, she continued on her way. But, just as I thought I was finally getting a bit of privacy, she turned back.

'Oh, and on a more positive note, might I say that I'm delighted to see you back at work again. I was beginning to worry that you were frittering your life away in your new house. I have always believed that it's important for women to contribute financially to the upkeep of a home. This place, as you no doubt realise, needs to be treated with tender loving care. When the time comes, you'll need to find specialists who understand these old buildings. And they don't come cheap!'

Clutching the edge of the desk, I only just managed to take a deep, calming breath before replying.

'With the greatest of respect, I have not been frittering away my time these last few weeks. On the contrary I've been working my socks off trying to settle my family into their new home, getting to know my neighbours and generally trying to establish ourselves in the village. I hardly call that time wasting!'

'Call it what you like. But it doesn't take a genius to work out from your husband's unpredictable moods at the moment, that he's under a lot of pressure. I just see it as a wife's duty to support her spouse in any way she can.'

With an enormous effort, I resisted the temptation to tell her that she might just be the reason her nephew was heading for a nervous breakdown. Instead I replied, as politely as I could. But, the effort wasn't easy.

'If you've finished, it might be wise to let me get back to work. Clearly I've got a fortune to earn before Archie wakes from his morning nap.'

It took quite a while to regain my composure. But, as I began to browse the internet for possible ideas, I realized that, in part, Aunt Lucy was right. I wasn't the obvious person to work on a countryside programme. I was a Londoner and had only been in Warwickshire since I'd been married. Although some of my colleagues were experts in a particular field, I couldn't claim to be a specialist in any area. I simply loved it all and just hoped that some of my enthusiasm spilled out when I put together ideas. Over the years I'd learned an enormous amount from the people I met but, more than once, my lack of knowledge had got me into trouble. Mind you, there were always those occasions when a variety of directors had been able to turn my ignorance to their advantage! Take that honey fanatic from Matlock. Now that was a case in point....

\*    \*    \*    \*

It was a bright warm day last August and we'd come to the home of a bee-keeper in the depths of Derbyshire. His bees produced a wide range of flavoured honeys depending on the flowers they pollinated. It had seemed a straight-forward, gentle story when I first heard about it. To that end, I couldn't have been more wrong!

'The whole point of a bee suit is to stop you being stung,' George explained in his slow, patronizing voice. 'However,' he added unnecessarily, 'if you insist on getting here at the last minute and then changing hurriedly right next to the hive, there's bound be the chance that you'll end up sharing the outfit with some uninvited guests! Under those circumstances you cannot expect the outfit to be as effective!'

'I don't think you quite understand the seriousness of the situation,' I snapped, hurling my protective clothing onto the grass. As I yanked my trouser leg up above my knee, several sleepy looking bees grabbed the chance of a quick escape. The damage to my right knee was considerable.

'Look, I've been stung loads of times,' I shouted 'And I'm in agony! And for some reason, best known to yourselves, you both seem to think it's funny!'

'On the contrary,' Will smiled. 'We couldn't be more serious! The shots we got of you yelling and jumping around were award-winning! They'll make the perfect introduction to the programme. It won't need any voice-over. One look at you says it all!....Bee Careful!!' I'll probably run the sequence again over the closing credits. God, you do make a fuss when you're in pain. It was wonderful. George, get down here and get a few close-ups of her knee while I do a quick interview.'

'What on earth do you think you're doing?' I stared in disbelief as George moved in for his shot. 'Go away.'

'Oh don't be such a spoil sport. It won't take a second. Point to the stings while you explain what happened. Your injuries will be an excellent warning to anyone foolish enough to be equally reckless this summer!'

I opened my mouth to object and then thought better of it. Why did my best moments always have to be when I was being stupid!

And then there was that unfortunate incident in the bog.

It had seemed a good idea at the time. A group of countryside lovers had booked a holiday with the British Trust for Conservation Volunteers in a remote village not far from Stoke on Trent. Their five day break would include the task of clearing a local bog. Perfect, if the thought of wading knee deep in mud appeals! In my case, it didn't, which was why it made it all the more appealing to my boss!

The idea of introducing the piece from the centre of the bog wasn't mine. But once I'd got my new waders on, the task seemed less daunting.

If only George hadn't made that last minute decision to move me to the right. Slowly I eased myself into my new position, but he still wasn't happy.

'The tree behind you is casting a shadow over your face. If you could just move over a fraction more, I'm sure it'll be fine.'

But it wasn't! As I took, or attempted to take, a bold step sideways, I lost my balance and fell straight into the smelly mire.

'Keep rolling, George,' Will urged. 'Excellent Kate. Keep floundering for a moment. I need George to get in a bit closer. Can you turn your face a bit this way? I want the audience to see the mud dripping off your hair. Oh, and hold that expression Kate. That desperate look in your eyes is quite perfect!'

With an enormous effort, I turned my head towards the camera. But my dangerous eyes found Will first and he hadn't bargained for the onslaught!

'For God's sake, turn that ruddy camera off and give me a hand. Is anyone going to help me? Or are you waiting for the moment when I finally sink completely.'

But far from being upset, Will grinned widely. 'It gets better by the minute. You're a natural at this, Kate. Okay somebody throw her a branch. Keep going George, and don't stop until she's out.'

Ten minutes later, I heaved my muddy body onto the bank. As I struggled to get up, Will knelt down beside me.

'Well done! That was wonderful. From the moment you fell, you showed real passion. Our audience will love it.'

I stared at my boss in disbelief. 'I'm freezing, filthy, and I haven't brought a change of clothing. I've never felt so disgusting in my life!'

But, far from being sympathetic, Will simply turned to George.

'Did you get that? It'll make a perfect ending!'

\*     \*     \*     \*

As the church clock chimed the hour, I was roused from my day dream. With Archie certain to wake by midday, and with Aunt Lucy's advice still echoing round my head, I had no time for reflection. So, determined to prove my house-guest wrong, I launched my campaign to make a fortune. Okay, so my first effort had failed at the first fence. Never mind, there were plenty more fish in the sea... or should I have said pigs!

Ten minutes and a strong cup of coffee later, my mood picked up. By chance I'd come across a story about a couple in Gloucestershire who had given up their teaching jobs to pursue a dream. With their savings, they had bought a small farm and were living in a caravan on site until they had made enough money to restore the derelict farmhouse. To avoid the problems of milk quotas etc, they had bought a herd of wild boar and were planning to sell their low cholesterol meat to the local pubs and shops. They had to be worth a visit, so I 'phoned them up. Initially they seemed quite keen for the publicity.

'If you want to see the animals before you film them, you'd better come along to the farm on Saturday afternoon.' The man was brusque on the 'phone but I was not to be put off.

So at three o'clock on Saturday I was ready by the gate as arranged. A few minutes later my guide appeared in a Land Rover. However, as I got ready to hop in, he hopped out.

'They're through here,' he said gruffly pointing to a very overgrown track. 'I won't get the Land Rover through. The track's too narrow.'

So we started to walk. Very soon the track was reduced to a path and ten minutes later we were scrambling through clumps of bushes. As the branches caught my new fluffy jumper, I 'tutted' in exasperation. I hadn't been prepared for this kind of adventure.

'How much further?' I queried as we entered what seemed to be an even denser part of the woodland.

'Not too far now,' he reassured me. But, by now we were fighting our way through the undergrowth. A cold chill began to creep round me. What were his intentions?

It's very foolish not to 'cut and run' when all your instincts tell you that what you're doing is pure madness! I didn't know this man from Adam and here I was in a dark wood with him, miles from anywhere.....and he had organised it! But in true British fashion I decided I must go along with him for a little longer.

After all, it was all my fault. I'd actually suggested this meeting. Asking him now if he was planning to murder me seemed, somehow, rather rude. Next time, assuming I lived to tell the tale, I'd have to be more specific about the details!

So, wearing my stiff upper lip and trying not to breathe too deeply, I renewed my determination not to let him realise my darkest fears. But, as yet one more branch caught me unawares, I began to plan my escape.

Just as I was about to make a 'run' for it, we came to a clearing and there, before me, in a double wire fence, were around thirty wild boar, some still tiny babies.

'Ohhh' I exclaimed. 'Aren't they sweet!'

And they were. It was soon clear that my escort was infatuated too. 'This is Jessica and the little spotty one over there is Lulu,' he said fondly.

As I crouched down and peered through the wire at these delightful creatures, all my fears melted into thin air. The man had turned out to be a real 'softy.'

'You're going to have a problem taking them to market when the time comes,' I said, relieved that he clearly hadn't suspected my fears about him.

His face clouded: 'I know,' he said. 'We can't bear to think about it.'

As the animals bounded around their large enclosure in this idyllic glade, I reflected on what a brilliant film this would make. Their remote location was essential if this farmer wanted to avoid complaining neighbours. After all, wild boar are classified as dangerous animals, hence the double wire fence. But given the choice of living next door to these little creatures in their strong enclosure or rampaging bulls in an ordinary field, I knew which ones I'd choose.

The filming went well and it was about a week later that, by complete coincidence, I met Mike again. We'd all gone across to Cheltenham for the day to meet friends for a walk, followed by Sunday lunch in their 'local'. It was while I was sorting out some drinks for the children at the bar, that he turned and saw me. We chatted about his forthcoming debut on the television and then, when my drinks arrived, he went back to his friends.

However, as I returned to our gang, I noticed him nudge one of his mates and point to me. Making little or no attempt to lower his voice, I cringed as he said: 'That's the woman I've been telling you all about. You should have seen her face in that wood. I reckon she had me down as the next Jack the Ripper!'

## PAST TIMES

The wild boar story featured in the programme at the end of March. Much to my surprise it caught Josh's imagination.

'I'm doing a project at school about ancient forests. Would they still have hunted wild boar round here by the time this house was built?' Josh was curious to know.

'Good question. But I think probably not,' I reflected. 'By the time this house was built in the early 1700s, the Elizabethans had destroyed most of the Forest of Arden to build the ships for the Spanish Armada.'

'When Edmund and I lived in the New Forest, we owned a hunting lodge that was more than five hundred years old.' Aunt Lucy's eyes brightened. 'In those days it would have been used by the aristocracy who came to hunt the wild boar. Rumour has it that Henry VIII once stayed there. To celebrate this historic fact, every year we held a Wild Boar evening. The butcher would prepare the meat, sixteenth century style, and everyone dressed up. Edmund would always be Henry VIII and I was Anne Boleyn.'

'How lovely,' I enthused, gesturing to Josh to write it all down.

'The perfect costume for the host and hostess,' Mac agreed smiling at Aunt Lucy. Then, from behind his paper he whispered to me, 'Legless and headless!'

As Josh wrote furiously, Claire couldn't resist offering sisterly advice.

'You've spelt it wrong,' she sneered as she glanced over his shoulder. Aunt Lucy's parties were called Wild Boar evenings B-O-A-R, not B-O-R-E!'

'Freudian slip,' Mac muttered again as Josh corrected his mistake.

'Would you have liked to have lived here in the olden days?' I had a particular reason for asking the question, though I suspected I knew the answer.

'No television, no play stations, no DVDs or videos. What on earth would we have done all day?' Josh wondered.

'For a start you could have gone to school next door. The house next to ours was once the village school, so close that it actually shared our driveway. Think about it. No school buses and an extra half hour in bed each day.'

I could see the idea was appealing.

'Would we have had a horse and cart to travel to town in?' Claire wanted to know.

If we'd lived here before the Second World War, almost certainly. 'By your age, you'd have probably been driving it yourself.'

'Cool.'

'Why all this sudden interest in the old days,' Mac was curious.

'Because Vicar Vic called round last night and told us about her idea to form a Reminiscence group.'

'A what?'

'Apparently she's done it before. The idea is to get the oldest and youngest members of the parish together so that they can learn from each other.'

'What on earth are they going to tell us about a little village like this tucked away in the middle of nowhere?' Josh was clearly appalled by the idea. 'I don't want to go. I know about the old days now. As I just said, we're doing it at school.'

But over the next few days I dropped little hints about what might be in store. Apart from the obvious attraction of a good tea, there was also the chance to find out about the plane crash that shook the village and the annual 'killing'.

'What do you mean......killing?'

'You'd better come along and find out.'

* * * *

Our village of Lower Hadbury lay in a valley about 7 miles from Stratford upon Avon. The river that ran alongside it, little more than a stream for much of its course, would sometimes swell to a raging torrent when the heavy rains came in the spring and autumn. But we didn't know that yet! To the east, a small escarpment could be negotiated by foot in dry weather without too much damage to clothing, and led to a tiny but beautiful hamlet. And south of that, Upper Hadbury, the largest village in the parish, could claim its place in history by being home to many of Shakespeare's relatives. Around ten miles south of Stratford the land swelled to become the rolling hills of the Cotswolds, whilst to the south west it gradually flattened out on its way to the area known as the Marketplace of England, The Vale of Evesham.

Our village was relatively small. The school closed in the 1960s but the church, which dated back to the thirteenth century, and the Tudor pub were still thriving when we arrived. Of the three hundred odd inhabitants, many had family trees that showed relatives living here before the time of Shakespeare.

'Gosh, they must be really old by now!' Josh reflected when he heard this devastating piece of information after church one day.

'Take no notice,' Claire advised our friends as we made our way to the pub. 'He was born stupid.'

* * * *

It was a week after the Reminiscence idea had been floated. In the village hall, half a dozen of the oldest members of the village were sitting on comfy chairs arranged in a semi-circle, the children huddled together on a large rug in front of them. The mums could have left them had they wanted, but most stayed, curious to hear what the older generation had to say.

As promised, a delicious spread of cakes and biscuits had been thoughtfully provided by Vicar Vic. As we sat down to listen, I wondered how she was going to kick it all off.

'I thought we'd start with 'the killing'. Victoria gazed intently at eighty-five year old Bob. He'd lived all his life in the village and, along with his nine brothers and sisters, had been brought up in a tiny cottage close to our house. For the past sixty eight years he'd been the church organist. From his seat opposite me he was smiling broadly, confident that his memories of a bygone age were about to be brought sparklingly back to life.

It was a good start. The prospect of a story involving a death, and all that goes with it, had got most of the children on the edge of their seats.

'The killing. Oh yes. That was quite a highlight. We never liked to miss that,' Bob began. Matthew, also in his eighties and Verger for nearly as many, nodded in agreement.

'Who was killed?' Lizzie asked excitedly. She had always had a strange fascination for anything morbid.

'The pig. Nearly every house here owned one. When it was time for it to be slaughtered, the butcher would come, place it on the pig bench, stun it and then bleed it by cutting its jugular vein. Then he'd pump the hind legs to get the remaining blood out.'

'Wicked,' Cosmo, the village wild child, exclaimed. By now four year old Hatty was mesmerised too. Claire, I noticed, had gone very pale.

'What next?' Lizzie demanded, leaning forward with her head cupped in her hand, taking in every word.

'Next he would burn the outside of the pig to remove the bristles. Then he would cut it open and remove the intestines. Those would be boiled in salt and vinegar and fried for breakfast.'

As most of the children moved in even closer, I noticed that Claire's pale face was beginning to turn a nasty shade of green.

'Nothing was wasted. The layers of fat, known as the leaf and vale, were made into lard. Sometimes the bladder was blown up too. Then it would be covered in the lard and, when it had set, it could be used as a football.'

'Must have been a bit sticky,' Cosmo reflected. 'And smelly too.'

'But it was better than nothing.' Matthew interrupted. Glancing out of the window at the four or five balls of various sizes scattered across the playground, he added. 'We couldn't just nip to Woolworths every time our ball went in the river or had a puncture.'

'What about the meat?' I wondered.

'The butcher's final job for the day was to hang the pig in a tree until it had cooled down. Then, the next day, he would cut it into portions. With no fridges to keep it cool, parts of the pig would be given to neighbours on the understanding that they would return the favour when it was their pig's turn to be slaughtered.'

'Of course, we didn't have television in those days.' Agnes Bell was now keen to make her mark. For twenty years she had run the Bingo at the village hall on Friday nights and was used to having her say. 'But even in a small village like this, there was always loads to do. We'd spend whole days in the woods or on the tiny island in the river at the end of the village. And there were all kinds of regular events too. Bob, do you remember 'Rocky' Herbert? Well, once a year he brought his travelling fair here and we'd spend all our pennies on the swing boats, the carousel and the Hoopla. Oh, and sometimes we'd get a visit from the local cavalry unit and, occasionally, even the local brass band would turn up to entertain us.'

'Then there was the annual flower show, mainly for the ladies, and fiercely competitive,' Joyce Brown, who organised the flower rota in the church, chipped in. 'It could get very nasty sometimes. But the best entertainment was 'catching the pig'.'

'Was that when you had to kill it?' Know-all Jeremy from The Dower House wondered.

'Oh no,' Sidney Smith looked horrified. 'This pig was always young. And, thinking about it, it was horribly cruel. The idea was to cover an eight week old pig in grease and then release the frightened animal into the crowd. If you could catch it, it was yours. Terribly messy of course, but great fun as long as you weren't the pig!'

'And were there shops here in the old days?' Ten year old Sammy, whose dad owned the farm at the end of our lane, wanted to know. To my children's disappointment, the only place to get sweets nowadays was a tiny store on the nearby caravan park. But it was open only from March to October. In the winter, there was nothing.

Bob thought for moment. 'When we were young, there was a train that took you to town, but it was a bit slow. And, once a week, there was a bus. So we had to be able to get most things in the village. Nowadays there's only the shop in the caravan park but when we were kids there was a baker, carpenter, wheelwright, post office, grocer, joiner and shoemaker. Not that my mum had money for shoes. With ten children to look after, she could only afford to buy off-cuts of leather and then she made the shoes herself!'

Josh looked down at his smart new trainers and avoided my gaze. He knew I'd be giving him one of my 'see, you don't know how lucky you are' looks.

'The war was a strange time,' Matthew reflected. 'You'd have thought we'd have been safe here, but someone had the idea of creating a decoy landing strip in the next village. When it was lit up at night, the Germans dropped incendiary bombs.'

'And,' Bob interrupted, 'we were quite close to Coventry. One night when I was cycling back from my job at the munitions factory, I saw a glow right across the distant skyline. Suddenly I knew what it was. Coventry was on fire!'

'Then, another time,' Sidney continued, 'I was just going to bed when I heard a plane approaching. I looked out of the window and saw it. No more than fifty feet above my head, it was on fire. Moments later it crashed into some trees in the field next to my garden.'

Lizzie clutched her mouth in excitement.

'We rushed out to see if we could help. On the way I tripped over what looked like two metal tubes. For a moment I thought they were bombs, but luckily they turned out to be oxygen cylinders.

When we got to the wreckage, the plane was ablaze, its cargo of incendiary bombs exploding like fire crackers. But far, far worse was the smell....of burning flesh!'

He paused for dramatic effect. The children stared at him, agog. Claire had her eyes shut, her body tense with horror.

'And....?' said Jeremy after a moment's pause. 'Who was dead?'

'Oh, no-one,' Sidney looked surprised. When the fire brigade arrived they realised that the pilot and crew had already bailed out. The smell had come from the carrier pigeons trapped in cages at the back of the plane.'

'So, compared to your life, ours sounds quite dull,' Cosmo mused. Nothing like that happens in the village these days.'

'Well, we haven't got to deal with a war now,' admitted Matthew. 'But we do still get travelling entertainers. 'You want to watch what comes to the village hall. Some of the stuff's excellent.'

'And the playground behind the tennis courts is great too. We didn't have anything like that when we were kids.'

'It doesn't touch catching a greasy pig or a fairground right here on the village green,' Cosmo looked quite downcast.

'Or being allowed out by yourself all day long without anyone fussing about you,' Josh gave me one of his reproachful looks. 'What you did sounds brilliant!'

'Well it wasn't all good,' Agnes reflected. 'For a start, we were cold a lot of the time. No central heating when we were kids! And, if you needed the loo, you had to go to the bottom of the garden. In this village there was no mains drainage until the 1970s. At our school, the building that's next to your house, we only had a bucket and earth closet. No nice 'chain' on hand to flush it all away. The sewage was dealt with once a week. But the vicar was kind. He allowed the school to bury the waste in your garden.'

Suddenly Claire sat up. 'Whereabouts?' she asked accusingly.

'Between the two horse chestnuts trees, I think?'

Claire's eyes widened in horror. 'I hope you're joking. That's where my new flowerbed is. Dad gave it to me so that I could plant my own vegetables. I was planting seeds there on Saturday. And now you're telling me that the contents of the school loo are buried there? That's it then! I'm never going to eat any of it! Not ever! It's disgusting.'

'On the contrary,' know-all Cosmo was keen to have his say. 'Your vegetables should do very well...with all that added manure!'

'You'd better check your 'wellies' when we get back,' Lizzie added unhelpfully. 'They've probably got 'poo' all over them.'

'I wouldn't be too smug if I were you, Lizzie,' Mac had just wandered into the room and caught the last bit of the conversation. 'Now I come to think of it, your Wendy House is directly over the place where most of the sewage would have been buried. Claire's flowerbed is just to one side.'

Now it was Claire's turn to smile.

'At least we now know what to call your little house,' Josh joined in with a glint in his eye. 'You've been fussing about its name for so long and all the time it's been staring you in the face.'

'What's that?' Lizzie asked innocently.

'The House at 'Poo Corner,' of course. It couldn't be more perfect!'

Lizzie let out a wail of horror.

'I think that's enough for the moment,' Victoria interrupted hastily. 'Our speakers look quite worn out. Now, if you're all so worried about hygiene, why don't you go and wash your hands and then come and have some tea – cakes and sandwiches just as you would have eaten all those years ago with neither an e-number nor artificial preservative in sight! And if you've got any questions you want to ask, I'm sure our guests will be happy to answer them once we're all settled at the table.'

'There's bound to be lots of honey,' Josh said knowingly to Lizzie as they went to sit down. 'Food doesn't come much older than that.'

'And particularly appropriate in our case,' Mac added mischievously.

'Why's that, Dad?' Josh wondered. 'I don't like it much.'

'Now, that's a shame because they do say 'Where there's 'poo', there's honey!'

\*　　\*　　\*　　\*

'Why the glum face?' Mac enquired. We were back at the Vicarage and Aunt Lucy was sitting bolt upright in her chair.

'You could have invited me,' she fumed, clearly furious at being excluded from the proceedings. '*I have many vibrant memories of my childhood.*'

In Lower Hadbury?' Mac queried. 'This was a reminiscence project about this village, remember? If my memory serves me correctly, you were born more than a hundred and fifty miles away. And, besides, you couldn't have come to watch. Victoria made it very clear. This first talk was for the children and a few of their parents who'd come to help. Many of the older people would have been intimidated by a large audience. Some of them had never spoken in public before.'

But Aunt Lucy was not to be put off. 'I could tell stories about my childhood that you simply wouldn't believe possible,' she added, glaring round at us.

'I have no doubt about that, Aunt,' Mac grinned. Then, under his breath he added, 'Which was another reason why you didn't get an invitation!'

Luckily, the conversation was brought to an end by a 'phone call. It was Judy.

'Oh thank goodness I caught you. Is it too late to volunteer the twins for the play at the family service in the morning? I suddenly panicked that I'd missed the deadline. It's such a wonderful opportunity. I'd hate them to miss it.'

I was touched by her enthusiasm. 'No, it's not too late. If this family service turns out to be anything like the ones at our other church, I won't know the full cast until midnight tonight...and that's only if I'm lucky. Oh, and thanks for saying it's a great opportunity. I like to think the children get something out of it. Not just the 'churchy' bit, but also the chance to gain some confidence in front of an audience.'

'Well actually I wasn't meaning the children,' Judy sounded slightly sheepish. 'As far as I'm concerned you offer far more than that. The last time you did this, I got to spend almost an hour and a half of quality time with my dear husband while the children were a mile down the road rehearsing. No chance of interruptions and me awake. James couldn't believe his luck! Normally, we only do these things at midnight when I'm so exhausted I can hardly keep my eyes open and with the real risk that the slightest noise will disturb the boys and bring them rushing into the room. I'm sure loads of the other parents feel the same way. It's brilliant!'

'And what about my plays?' I added indignantly. 'Would you still bring the children if you didn't have this added bonus on a Sunday morning.'

'Of course! You know the kids love the service....and so do we. But don't knock what I've just said. For lots of the parents, you're also offering a brilliant form of marriage therapy! And that, in the end, is just as beneficial to the family than any church play!'

## CHURCH PLAYS

It was 11.00 on Saturday night. For three hours I'd been in the study, staring despondently at the computer screen. Suddenly Mac appeared at the door.

'Why the glum face?'

'Lent!'

'Aha, I knew it. I spotted the empty wine glass by the sink earlier! No self control! I knew you couldn't get to Easter without having a drink.'

'Well, if you were faced with seven children wanting a part in a play that only has two characters, you'd have hit the bottle too.'

'What on earth are you talking about?'

'Jesus in the Wilderness,' That's what 'Lent' is all about. Jesus' confrontation with the Devil in the desert is one of the most powerful stories in the bible. There's just one problem. There are only two people in the story – Jesus and the Devil and, until about ten minutes ago, I'd got five children wanting parts. Now, to make matters worse, I've just had a call from Audrey Broadwell asking if Scarlet, and her friend who's staying the night, can be in the play as well! I tell you, she's got a nerve. Only yesterday she assured me that her family would be away for the weekend.'

'Presumably you told her that it was too late to change her mind.'

I paused for a moment. 'Well, not exactly. You see I don't like to turn children away. After all, it's not as if I'm running a serious drama club. It's just a form of Sunday school...really.'

'So, what did you say to her?'

'I said she could be included......but that I'd have to make a few late adjustments to accommodate her.'

'And is it a case of a few minor adjustments?'

'As it happens......no. I'm going to have to re-think the whole thing to stand any chance of giving Scarlet and her friend anything to do.'

Mac shook his head in despair. 'I did warn you not to take this job on. To be honest, it beats me why you ever agreed to it in the first place.'

'You know perfectly well why, so shut up! Nobody else wanted to do it, unless you're planning to volunteer yourself....which I doubt! And living in the Vicarage, working in television and having children who everyone knows are heavily into drama, meant it was quite hard to refuse. Actually, if you must know, I rather enjoy it..... or rather I do .....most of the time!'

'But if it's only a play for two parts, how come you'd sorted out five?'

'Well, apart from Jesus and the Devil, I'd got two narrators, and a third one reading the lesson. But that's about as far as I can 'push' it. After all, when the action takes place in the desert, I can hardly solve the problem by casting anyone as a sheep, ox or a tree!'

'Well, that's that then. There's no other way out of it. You're going to have to ring Audrey back and explain.'

I groaned. Then suddenly the fog cleared from my brain.

'Mac, did John the Baptist eat locusts while he was in the desert?'

'What a weird question?'

'Did he?'

Mac screwed up his face, trying to remember. 'Yes. I think he did.'

'That's it then, I said triumphantly. 'I've cracked it.'

*　*　*　*

'Is Lizzie alright? Judy queried as she sat down in her pew the following morning. She looks a bit green.'

'What? Oh yes, she's supposed to look like that. She's a cactus! Late last night I finally solved the problem that's been haunting me all week. How to cast seven children in a play about Jesus in the Wilderness.'

'And?'

'Inspiration struck just before midnight when I decided to put together a little play about life in the wilderness of Judea. The younger ones are going to perform it at the beginning of the service as a way of setting up the confrontation between Jesus and the Devil. I've cast Josh and your two as locusts. Look, over there. Fred and Eddie are wearing antennae!'

'Locusts?'

'Yes. John the Baptist ate them when he was in the desert so I think there's a good chance that Jesus ate some too during his forty day ordeal. I gather they're quite tasty!'

'I wouldn't have thought that my two would have had any idea what locusts were.'

'They didn't, but they soon got the hang of it. Plenty of hopping, swarming and eating lots of food. They thought it was wonderful.'

'What's the matter with Audrey Broadwell?'

'She's probably just heard about Scarlet's part. She only told me late last night that she was coming, so I told her I'd have to re-write part of the play to accommodate her. I think she was hoping I'd cast her as Jesus.'

'You didn't make her the Devil, did you?'

'No. She's not in the main play at all. She's with Fred and Eddie.'

'Is she a locust too?'

'No. She's the vulture!'

\*     \*     \*     \*

'I thought the play went really well.' Mac seemed buoyant as we walked home after the service. 'The little ones were sweet and, as for Cosmo…..he made a brilliant Jesus. I've never seen him look so angry.'

'Yes. The moment when he slammed his fist down on the pulpit will stay with me for ever. I was convinced he'd broken his hand.'

'I was more worried about the pulpit! But you don't seem entirely happy?'

'Well, I could have done without the impromptu performance from Josh at the end of the service.'

'When he tripped over the carpet? Yes, that was rather spectacular.'

'Except I've just heard it wasn't the carpet he tripped over. It was Lizzie's foot! And if that wasn't bad enough, I've just been told that grumpy Margaret Saville has complained about me to Vicar Vic.'

'What about? The play or our unruly children?'

'Neither! It's me she's worried about.'

'Go on.'

'It was all a misunderstanding. She arrived very early for the service this morning. Unfortunately I'd just taken the younger children back to the Vicarage for a quick 'loo' break. I should have left something on the pew to mark Josh, Fred and Eddie's place. But I didn't. By the time I'd got back, she was sitting in their seat.'

'Does it matter where the children sit?'

'Not usually. But today I'd planned for them to jump along the pew, locust-like, at the start of the service so that the congregation could see them. I knew if I changed their positions at such a late stage, it was bound to cause confusion. Fred and Eddie are only three years old, after all.

So, very politely and nervously I asked her if she would mind moving along to allow the children some space. I explained about the play and apologised for the inconvenience. Looking slightly confused, she obliged and the children slid into the seats beside her. Giving them all my 'behave yourselves or die' look, they sat tight.'

'So why was that a problem?'

'Well I gather Margaret's a bit deaf and didn't really understand what I was saying. Apparently, she's just asked Vicar Vic in her most pompous voice if she was aware that 'the woman from the Vicarage' was now demanding her own seats!'

## WALKING

'Why do we always have to go for a walk on a Sunday afternoon?' Josh moaned as he tried to sort out his Wellingtons from the pile in the hall. 'I had to get up extra early for the church service this morning and today my part was exhausting!'

'All that jumping! Claire giggled unkindly. 'I never thought you'd make such a good locust!'

'It was the way you flew though the air so spectacularly at one point that really got the congregation going,' Mac added unkindly. 'For a moment, we all thought you'd grown wings.'

'Leave him alone,' I gave Mac a warning look. 'Lizzie's very sorry now, aren't you?'

But Lizzie's face showed no sense of remorse.

'Considering you're normally so clumsy, your timing was excellent,' Claire clearly couldn't bear to let the subject drop. 'Tripping Josh up like that when he was carrying a full offertory bag, was inspirational. Some of the coins rolled the full length of the aisle.'

'On the contrary, there was nothing inspirational about it. It was a very stupid thing to do and Josh could have been badly hurt. But Lizzie's learned her lesson now, haven't you?' I added glaring at her coldly. 'She's promised me that from now on she's going to learn to control that temper of hers.'

'I still say it wasn't fair!' Lizzie objected. 'It was definitely my turn to do the collection. When Moira handed the bag to Josh, he should have passed it on to me.'

'And you thought that attempting to break his leg would be a good way of doing it?' Mac queried. 'I suppose it would have been too much of an effort to ask him politely to give you a turn.'

'I did ask him politely.' Now it was Josh's turn to look sheepish. 'But he just stuck his tongue out at me. I only tripped him up because I thought that it would stop him being such a show-off.'

'Well, you certainly achieved that. By the time he'd picked himself up from the carpet, he was a broken man.'

'And his mother a broken woman,' I assured her. 'I was completely mortified.'

'Well, I wouldn't be if I were you,' Mac was trying to be consoling. 'The congregation loved it. Joyce said that loads of people thought it was the best bit of the service.'

'What? Better than my play? Well, if that's what they think, I shan't bother writing one next month. I'll just arrange a punch-up in the pews instead.'

\*     \*     \*     \*

A myriad of paths dissected Lower Hadbury. On sunny afternoons during term time, when the older two were at school, I often took Lizzie and Archie along the footpath that skirted our garden to the little caravan park at the end of the lane. At the back of the owners' beautiful house, part of the kitchen had been converted into a little shop for the campers, where basic groceries, newspapers, fresh bread, sweets and a selection of small toys could be bought. On fine days, as soon as lunch was finished, there'd be a cry of 'Can we go to the caravan park,' as if I was offering the ultimate outing. No more than four hundred yards from our front door along a tree lined path, our two youngest were perfectly happy to amble along and then sit on the grass outside the shop with a cheap lolly and a paper aeroplane before wandering home again.

Sometimes, at weekends, Mac and the older two would join us and then we'd venture into the next field where, in the far corner, the river divided making a small island. When the river was low enough, it was possible to wade across. For a small river, the island was quite big. Measuring approximately a hundred yards in diameter, it was covered in trees and bushes and visited so infrequently that any visitor disturbed the wildlife considerably. It was not unusual for an owl to flap its wings in your face or a swan to unexpectedly lift its head out of the undergrowth. The children loved it, particularly if they could fall over in the shallow waters on the way back or, better still, let the river trickle over the top of their 'wellies' if the water was high enough!

But today our walk had got off to a bad start. By the time the wellies, coats and hats had been sorted and we had set off down the lane, it soon became clear that there was considerable dissent in the ranks. While Mac and Claire were keen to get some exercise, the various upheavals that morning had left me desperate for a quiet afternoon by the fire. Josh, still smarting from the embarrassment of his fall, had decided to take his anger out on everyone and Lizzie was sulking. Archie, warm and cosy in a back pack, appeared indifferent.

We'd only been walking for five minutes when the complaints started.

'I don't think I can go much further,' Lizzie sighed. As if to demonstrate her complete exhaustion, she sat down on the ground and folded her arms.

'We've only done about four hundred yards,' I explained, gritting my teeth. 'You can't possibly be tired yet.'

'How much further then?' she demanded. 'How much further 'til we turn back?'

'Given how much trouble you've already caused, I'm surprised you're prepared to make even more fuss.'

'Glad to see you're enjoying it so much,' Mac sidled up beside her. 'Always a pleasure to take you anywhere, Lizzie.'

'Look,' I said desperately. 'If you can manage to be good until we reach the canal, I'll let you have some bread and then you can feed the ducks.'

'And then can we go home?'

'We'll see. Why don't you stop moaning and look around you. There's so much to watch out for at this time of the year.'

We carried on in silence for a few moments. After a while the footpath took us in an easterly direction, close to a small wood.

Suddenly Lizzie, who, despite my advice, had been determined to take as little interest as possible in her surroundings, stopped dead in her tracks.

'Mummy, look.'

'What's the matter?' My eyes followed Lizzie's gaze. Then I saw her too. A young girl, dressed only in jeans and a T-shirt and clearly distressed, was leaning against a tree.

'Stay there, I told everyone. I'll go and check she's okay.'

'Kate!' Mac hissed. 'Wait for me.' But I was on my way.

I got fairly close before she noticed me. She was staring fixedly at what looked like a photograph of someone. Her face was pale.

I moved a little closer, not wanting to frighten her. Then she looked up and, seeing me, fled into the wood.

'That went well,' Mac commented as he came up to join me. 'Clearly from the speed she was going, there's nothing physically wrong with her. She was probably just enjoying a quiet moment away from the rest of the world. But with the Arnold family in the vicinity, there was never going be any chance of that!'

'She'd been crying. And she was freezing. When I got to her she was as white as a sheet and shaking. She had a photograph in her hand, but I couldn't see what it was.'

'I'd have thought it was obvious. I bet you any money she's either had a row with her boyfriend or split up with him.' Turning to Claire he added wisely. 'Be careful when you're older. We men have an extraordinary ability to break a woman's heart!'

'I wonder if she's from the village? I don't remember seeing her before.'

'We've not been here that long. Mind you, given our various exploits in the short time we've been here, it's highly possible she recognised you and immediately took flight!'

'Shut up! I was only being concerned.'

'Mum, look, she's forgotten something.' Claire was holding a tiny wooden boat. 'I bet it belonged to that lady. It's beautiful.'

'Oh, and here's a knife. Oh Mac, you don't think....?'

'No, I don't! Look at the boat. She's carved it herself. If you look carefully, you can see some of the shavings amongst the leaves.'

'Shall we take it back with us before the rain spoils it?'

'No. Leave it under the tree. If it's special to her, she'll come back. We don't know who she is, so there's no point us taking it.'

So, leaving the tiny carving in the driest spot we could find, we moved on. It wasn't long before Lizzie started moaning again.

'How much longer, now?'

'If you don't stop moaning,' Claire warned 'You won't have to worry about walking home because as soon as we get to the canal, I shall push you in. Then you'll be able to float along in the freezing water where only the ducks will be able to hear your endless complaints.'

'I wish I could be like that man, Moses,' Lizzie said profoundly.

'I beg your pardon?'

'He had to go on a long journey too. Vicar Vic told us a story about him at the end of the service this morning. When he wanted to cross the sea, God made a hole in it so that he could get to the other side. He didn't get wet at all!'

'So are you expecting us to part the canal, when we get to it,' Mac enquired. 'So that you can get close to the ducks without getting wet?'

For the first time that afternoon Lizzie's face brightened. 'That would be cool, Dad?'

'It certainly would?' Josh's face had brightened considerably too. 'Especially if the water cascaded back just before you got to them.'

'Moses didn't get wet when he did it,' Lizzie informed Josh crisply. 'He stayed perfectly dry!'

'So, in that case, you're not a bit like Moses,' Josh replied. 'Because you're perfectly wet!'

Doing what she always did when she was beaten, Lizzie burst into tears. Archie, firmly attached to Mac in a backpack, decided to join her.

'Excellent,' Mac's voice was dangerously crisp. 'What with that girl, and now you two, I reckon Victoria chose the wrong subject to talk about at the end of the service. She should have told you about the Wailing Wall!'

\*  \*  \*  \*

As our gloomy little group trudged back to the Vicarage, I broached the subject of the young girl to Mac.

'There was something about her that was familiar. I don't think I've met her before, but I'm sure I've seen someone round here who looks similar.'

'Kate, think about it. This is the middle of the countryside. There are several large families in our village. Albert at the end of our lane is one of fourteen and Bob is one of ten and most of their siblings still live round here. So, there's every chance that this girl is related to one of them. So, whatever you do, please don't start staring at everyone in the village until you find a match. They'll all think you're mad and, yet again, they'd be right.'

'I can't stop thinking about her. She looked so sad.'

'Well, please try. She is not your problem. I've never known anyone capable of making a worry like you can. You don't even know her. Anyway, what's so unusual about a woman crying? From my experience, they do it all the time and mostly over nothing. I should know, I live with three of them!'

I sighed. But I knew I wouldn't be happy until the mystery was solved.

\*  \*  \*  \*

It was a muddy, moody gang who arrived back at the Vicarage later that afternoon.

'Tea, bath and bed?' Mac suggested hopefully to the younger two as he turned the house key in the lock.

But his mood changed when he saw what was on the other side. Piled high in the hall were a number of bags containing Aunt Lucy's various possessions.

'It's time I was on my way,' she said emerging from the downstairs cloakroom with one of her more eccentric woolly hats perched jauntily on her head and a long purple scarf tied tightly round her neck. 'I'm afraid I've taken up far too much of your time with this ghastly business. But now I'm ready to resume my independent life once again. Kate, you've been a saint to put up with me and I shall miss the children dreadfully. Mac dear, I fear we have spent far too long under the same roof! If this experience has taught me anything, it is that we get on far better in short bursts, I'm sure you'll agree. In short, we are just too similar!'

Mac opened his mouth to object and then changed his mind, fearful of saying something that might jeopardise her imminent departure.

'So, with my bags packed and my latest knitwear collection ready for dispatch, I shall be off. The taxi should be here shortly.'

And half an hour later she'd gone. Claire and Lizzie burst into tears as the taxi disappeared down the driveway. Mac resisted the urge to skip round the dining room.

'We'll miss her, you know,' I reflected as I went to make the tea.

'I shouldn't get too downcast, if I were you,' Mac was looking less cheerful now. 'She'll be back before you know it!'

*   *   *   *

'Has an air of calm descended on the Arnold household now that Aunt Lucy has departed?' Judy wondered as we chatted on the 'phone a couple of weeks later.

'Hardly calm,' I mocked. 'But Mac and I are probably feeling a lot more relaxed. 'It wasn't so much what she did, it was the fear of what she might do that made us so anxious all the time.'

'Are you all set for a quiet Easter weekend,' Judy asked with not much expectation of the answer.

'Actually I might have a little bit of a problem there,' I replied hesitantly. 'But I'm sure I can sort it.'

'What have you done now?'

'It's just that the Church Warden rang me this afternoon, begging a favour and it was, well, hard to refuse.'

'Go on.'

'She's been let down at the last moment. So she's asked me to host the Easter workshop.'

'And you agreed?'

Well, what would you have done?'
'Does Mac know?'
'Not yet.'
'Well I wouldn't like to be in your shoes when you tell him.'

## EASTER

Mac's eyes were wide with horror.

'You've done what?'

'Well, it was hard to refuse. The Church Warden sounded desperate. The village hall is booked for a party and nobody else seemed to think they had the space to do it. It's only for a couple of hours. The Campbells did it for years when they lived here.'

'And what exactly does an Easter Workshop on Good Friday involve in this parish? How many children will come? What sort of help do we get? Did you think to ask any of these rather important details?'

'We haven't exactly discussed details yet,' I said defensively. 'I just thought it would be fun for our children. Anyway, with a bit of luck it will be sunny and we can have the whole thing outside.'

'In April?' Mac gave a derisive laugh. 'I wouldn't hold your breath!' And I'll tell you something else too. You'll get loads of children turning up. When parents realise that they can park their kids here for a morning while they put their feet up, there'll be no stopping them!'

I was shocked by his cynicism but I was not to be put off. When I told the children, at first they were thrilled.

'Wicked!' said Josh. 'Can we do pass the parcel?'

'It's not a party. It's an Easter Workshop. You'll be painting eggs and making Easter Gardens............. that sort of thing. Actually I think Vicar Vic's volunteered to do the eggs. She's got a bit of ground to make up with some of the more traditional churchgoers after last week's service. I don't think I'll ever forget Mrs Beale's face when she started the Palm Sunday service with a 'Pin the tail on the Donkey' competition. I thought she was going to have a heart attack.'

'It was brilliant,' said Josh. 'So, this workshop isn't too serious then?'

'Well,' I hesitated. 'I gather she plans to end the session with a talk to you all about the significance of the Easter celebration. It is a hugely important date on the Christian calendar. She won't want you to go without telling you a bit about it.'

Josh pulled a face. Claire was more direct.

'Well I'm not doing it,' said Claire decidedly. Mac winked at her and then gave me one of his 'I told you so' looks.

'Well don't come then. But I shall be doing an Easter Egg hunt and there'll be stacks of warm buttery hot cross buns for all those who plan to stay the course.'

I could see she was wavering.

In the end the entire family showed up as did around fifty children from the village and beyond. Several creative friends came along to 'blow' and paint eggs and miraculously turn a pile of moss, stones and 'lolly' sticks into fifty Easter gardens. I stood at the gate and managed to persuade several reluctant parents to stay and lend a hand including one granny who tried to leave me her eight grandchildren. Meanwhile Mac looked on astonished that something I'd organised could appear to run so smoothly. By the end of the morning all the chocolate eggs had been found including the two that had clearly been there since the year before!

Feeling fairly pleased and immensely relieved that we, and the house, had survived our first village event intact, at midday I helped Vicar Vic take the children across to the church. I watched as she explained the 'Stations of the Cross' and followed the children's gaze as they looked at the various paintings of Jesus carrying his cross to Calvary. When she asked if anyone had any questions, I was both pleased and surprised when Lizzie's hand shot up.

'I know what this is now,' she said brightly as she looked up at the different pictures of Jesus in agony. 'It's a spot the difference competition!'

Later, back at home, as we watched the last of the children gather their belongings, the Church Warden came across.

'That was lovely,' she said enthusiastically. Then, casting her eye over the staggering amount of mess the gang had created in our kitchen and hall she added, 'the children were so enthusiastic. And you and your husband have such a lovely attitude.' (She clearly hadn't seen me nearly murder one of the ten year old boys an hour earlier.)

I smiled and said nothing. I didn't realise Mac was behind me.

'Yet another job we've got for life,' he whispered. 'Two down and no doubt several more to go!'

Later over a cup of coffee, I braved the question to Victoria that had been bugging me ever since we'd first met.

'Do you mind that we live in what really should be your home?'

'No. Why should I?'

'I don't know really. It just makes me feel awkward every time you come here.'

'Oh, don't worry about me. One day I plan to be the Archbishop of Canterbury, then I'll have a whole palace all to myself! Or, better still, I'll marry Alan Rickman and then he'll be able to keep me in the style to which I shall easily become accustomed. Besides, what on earth would I do as a single woman with all this space, except perhaps be persuaded to fill it with hoards of marauding children like you seem to do. And quite frankly, looking at the mess they've just made, I can quite easily resist that at the moment. No, you can keep your Old Vicarage. For the moment, I'm far better off in my warm, modern one down the road.'

But not everyone agreed.

### VICARAGES AGAIN

'Kate, you're going to have to do something about your staff.' My boss's tone was brusque. 'I've just asked Josh if you were in and he told me that there was a note stuck to the 'phone that said 'If Will 'phone's, tell him I'm out.'

I cringed. I hadn't realised my nine year old could be quite so stupid.

'It's the Easter holidays, Will. The kids are at home and I'm rather busy!' It sounded pathetic!

Surprisingly, he calmed down. 'Listen Kate, I've got a problem. The weather's fabulous and we should be out there filming. But half the team's on holiday this week. After a lousy winter, I can't afford to miss out on what could be the only sunshine we get all year. So, if you get any ideas, I'd be hugely grateful.'

I sighed. 'Okay. I'll do my best.' I said resignedly. But, surveying the chaos all around me, I wasn't feeling too hopeful.

As anyone who's tried it knows, there are 'pros' and 'cons' to working from home. On the plus side you don't waste time travelling to and from work, you're far more available for your children during the holidays or whenever they're sick, the surroundings are generally much cosier, refreshments are permanently 'on tap' in the kitchen (no, on second thoughts, that's a disadvantage) and, in theory, you have the ability to structure a day around the household's permanently hectic schedule.

Disadvantages include no definite hours of employment and, despite huge efforts on my part, an inability to curb my children's appalling telephone skills.

'Did Mr Harris call earlier?' I'd already had reason to give Josh a reprimand earlier that day.

His face said it all.

'I think he may have done,' he replied hesitantly.

'And did you think to take a message?'

His face brightened. 'Yes, I wrote it down.'

'Where?'

Blank face again.

Later, and not long after I'd spoken to Will, it was Lizzie's turn to cause maximum embarrassment. Unlike her siblings, she was often keen to offer more information than the caller needed.

'Mummy's on the loo,' I heard her giggle delightedly as she managed to beat the older children to the 'phone.

I got to the receiver as she was about to hang up. The lady on the other end clearly wasn't amused.

'I understand you are a researcher for a countryside programme,' she sounded very crisp.

I acknowledged this was true.

'Good. I have an issue I should like to draw to your attention.'

She launched forth.

To begin with, I couldn't quite make out what point she was trying to make. Then, suddenly, it became crystal clear.

'.....so you see our organisation is trying to stop the Church of England selling off its vicarages. And we'd like the public to understand the seriousness of the situation.'

Oh dear. To be honest, I could see her point. At least, I could see some of it. But she wasn't going to be very pleased with me when she knew where I lived. Or did she know already and was waiting to drop her bombshell.

And, she was very efficient. She obviously had a string of facts and statistics in front of her and she wasn't going to stop talking until she had told me all of them. Dutifully, I wrote it all down.

It wasn't difficult to work out exactly where this was heading.

Will would love the idea of exposing the church's dilemma. We weren't a controversial programme, but this fairly gentle tale of indignation was just 'up his street'. And I knew precisely who he would approach to talk about living in a 'vicarage' when you weren't the vicar...........me!

'So,' she finished, 'If I could just have your address, I'll post all our literature off to you, first class, today.'

I thought about it and then gave......my mother's address instead!

And as for telling Will about this one? It would have to wait until after the holidays had finished.

But as it turned out, the lady in question might not have been so thrilled about living in our house if she'd known the whole story....

## THE FLOODS

It was Dorothy who noticed it first.

'The river's high,' she commented as she looked up from the washing up one morning during the last week of the Easter holidays. 'With all that rain we've had overnight, I reckon it could 'go' later today.'

'What do you mean 'go'?' I asked nervously.

'You know, burst its banks. Surely they warned you when you moved here that this river generally floods once or twice a year.'

'No, I don't recall anyone mentioning anything so startling. Should I be ordering in some sandbags?'

'No. There are about eight steps up to your patio. It never goes that high. But you want to watch your cellar though. My friend Betty lives up the road from you. She's got one and it's always flooding.'

It had been raining heavily for most of the night and as I followed Dorothy's gaze I could see that the river had swollen to a raging torrent. As I watched, a couple of ducklings shot by backwards on the current, followed by an old tyre and a bale of hay.

'So how far does the water spread?' I wondered.

'You need to watch the ditches by the side of the road. Once they're full, they cover the road at either end of the village turning it into a small island. You can be trapped for several hours. But don't try and drive through the water until you've seen someone else do it. It can be quite deep in places. Insurance companies don't look kindly on flooded engines. There are several people in this village who have had bitter experience of that one!'

'It's Fred and Eddie's party at lunchtime. We're all due at the new play centre in town at midday. It would be more than my life's worth to miss it.'

'Well, you'd better get a move on then. If you get out now, the chances are that the water will have gone down again by the time you come back. At least that's what usually happens,' she finished optimistically.

So we did. But as we drove out of the village an hour later, we were blissfully unaware that the rain pouring down on us with such force was about to cause the worst floods to hit the region for a hundred and fifty years.

*   *   *   *

Nearly five hours later, with four exhausted children in the back of the car, I began to realise the full scale of the disaster.

'Let her through,' the fireman shouted. He meant me.

'Oh help!' He wanted to use my 'higher' vehicle as a guide to how deep the water was. Did he realise he had chosen the worst driver in the world to experiment on? What was it? Low gear, high revs? Or was it the other way round???

It was four thirty and it had taken us the best part of two hours to cover a relatively short distance. Rain, the likes of which I had never seen before, was now pouring in torrents off the fields and onto the already heavily flooded roads. But we couldn't turn round, (with all main roads grid-locked, the police were not encouraging that one). We had to go on.

However, despite my best efforts, we did not make it back to The Vicarage that day. As we approached the turning that led to Lower Hadbury, the flooding was so bad that road blocks had been set up to turn us away. Reluctantly, and with some difficulty, we turned round. Knowing that only a very close friend would be willing to take on five house guests at a moment's notice, I rang Judy and, after another hour and a half of fraught driving, we were back at her house again. But, whilst this impromptu sleepover had revived the kids spirits considerably, it had to be said that, as much as I was grateful to Judy, I was rather less excited by the prospect of setting up camp for the night.

Back in the village, Dorothy was preparing for a sleepover too. Her optimism that the floods would subside by mid-afternoon had been badly misplaced. The village was cut off at both ends and, next door, she was being deafened by the heartrending bleats of sheep who were about to perish in the rapidly rising water, despite frantic efforts by the villagers to save them.

As four feet of water poured into our cellars, Dorothy prepared to batten down the hatches.

Only the mad or very brave who were prepared to wade, waist deep, through the freezing water got into the village that night, and many who had come into the village to do various jobs had to stay in the village hall on mattresses on the floor

Apart from the water in the cellar, The Vicarage survived intact. But others were not so lucky. Several homes were flooded and many more suffered damage to cars and farm machinery. It was a day none of us will ever forget.

\*   \*   \*   \*

It is only the very stupid who learn nothing from that kind of experience. So, when, a few weeks later, I set out to collect Lizzie from Judy's and the older two from school and turned right into the lane to discover it was flooded, I should have turned back. But I didn't.

Being the calm, clear thinking mother that I am, I panicked. With vivid memories of the catastrophe the month before, I made my plan. Priority number one: must get to my children. So, without any other sensible thought, I drove straight into the flood.

But not for long. A few seconds later, there was a resounding thump at the back of the car and I slammed on the brakes.

'Stop! You'll not get through. The water's too high,' someone was yelling and banging their fist on the back window. I turned round to see Bert Moggins, the elderly, former rogue of the village, peering at me through the glass. He had a despairing look in his eye.

'Look in front of you. You're driving a car, not a ruddy boat. You'll sink if you go much further!'

'But I've got to collect my children. I've got to get out.'

'Well you won't get out this way for hours…and the road at the other end of the village is even worse. You're going to have to go home and make alternative arrangements. Come on, if you reverse slowly, you should make it. Your exhaust is still above the water level….but only just. If you're careful, you should be alright.'

Nervously, I did as I was told. Bert stuck close to the side of the car directing me every inch of the way. My reputation as a driver had obviously gone before me.

'You'd best be getting home,' he ordered once I was finally clear. 'You won't get out of the village tonight. The water table's still high from last time. It looks like debris from the last flood has blocked some of the ditches on the side of the road. This bit of rain has brought it up in no time.'

Thanking him for his trouble, I set about turning the car round in the nearest gateway. My window was still wound down and as I eased past him for the final time, I heard him say to his mate, 'That's Kate Arnold from the Vicarage. Women like her are all the same….. big house, small brain!'

A minute later I was home and trapped. A rapid call to Judy's mobile ensured that Lizzie would be safe until I could get to her. But my heart ached for my little daughter. Much as she loved Fred and Eddie, she hated dealing with the unexpected without her mummy by her side. But, as the water continued to rise higher and higher, I knew I had no hope of getting her until the floods subsided. Next, a quick telephone call to organise the older two. No problem there. The prospect of an unexpected sleepover would, I knew, be greeted with wild enthusiasm.

It was a tearful four year old who spoke to me later that evening.

'I promise I shall come and get you as soon as I can,' was all I could say.

'What the hell's going on?' Mac's voice boomed down the telephone when I called him later. 'Good God, not again. I thought we'd bought a vicarage, not a house-boat.'

'Looks like you're going to have to spend another night at The Coach and Horses,' I sighed. I could hear Mac's tone brighten considerably at the prospect.

'Oh well, I guess these things can't be helped,' he reflected. 'Ring me if there's anything I can do to help.'

\*     \*     \*     \*

That night the view from the top floor of The Vicarage was spectacular. As far as the eye could see was water. Every field, every road, every path. It looked like the sea. No more rain now. The sky was clear and the moonlight glittered everywhere across the still water. If only I had had everyone with me, it would have been perfect.

\*     \*     \*     \*

'How exciting!' Judy was bouncing Lizzie up and down in her arms when I drove into her driveway early the following morning. 'Here's mummy and very soon two daddies should appear too.'

As I opened the car door, Lizzie hurled herself at me as if she hadn't seen me for a month. 'Oh mummy, I missed you so much, I cried nearly all night.'

'Oh God,' I muttered anxiously shooting Judy an apologetic glance. 'And, by the sound of it, poor Judy had no James to help her either. What happened to him?'

'The poor man had a disastrous evening! He got caught in a horrendous traffic jam on the motorway. So, at the first opportunity, he came off and tried to take a short-cut through the country lanes. That was when he came across the flood at the far end of your village. He was in it before he realised it was there. The car promptly stopped and he was stuck!'

'Oh no! But why didn't he try to ring us.'

'I'd told him earlier that you were home alone – no Mac, so he didn't like to bother you. Luckily, as he was pondering his next move, a tractor appeared from nowhere and pulled him clear. The kind man then towed him to the next village where he was able to stay the night at the pub. He's due back any time now.'

'And the car?'

'That's still at the pub. It's got to be relayed to the nearest garage sometime this morning. James is not optimistic. He thinks the engine's a 'gonner'!'

Just then Mac's car turned into the driveway. Lizzie shot out of my arms and into his.

'Daddy, why are you here? I thought you'd stayed the night in Birmingham.'

'I did. But I had to come home this morning to get a change of clothing. Mummy told me to come here first to collect you in case she still couldn't get out of the village.'

With an effort, Lizzie pulled herself away from him. Looking at him critically, she nodded sympathetically. Then she whispered.

'Oh Daddy, don't worry, I've got new clothes on too. I was so frightened in the night without mummy, I accidentally wet the bed. Is that what you did, too?'

## CELLARS AND A SECRET ROOM

After both floods it took almost a week for the water to subside in the cellar, prompting Mac and me to think seriously about any future plans for the space.

'Could we turn the rooms into an indoor swimming pool?' Josh suggested hopefully.

'I think we've managed that already,' Mac concluded ruefully surveying the gallons of filthy water swilling around below us.'

'We seem to be rather good at creating indoor floods,' I reflected. 'This will be the third one this year!'

Ignoring the jibe, Mac continued. 'Even when the rooms down there aren't flooded, they're permanently damp.'

'And they smell,' Claire added pulling a face.

'The frogs like it, though' Josh giggled. 'Do you remember when you found one in your boot?'

Claire turned pale at the memory. It hadn't been a good moment for any of us. Her screams had rent the air like a wailing banshee!

'At least we were wise enough not to store anything down here other than wine and 'Wellies',' Mac consoled himself. 'There's really only one thing for it. If the rooms are going to be of any use at all, they're going to have to be sorted.'

So, we took advice from a friendly builder and he offered a solution. The answer, it appeared, lay in a couple of pumps that clicked in every time the water level rose ….and decking, strategically placed several inches above the floor. But before the work could begin, we needed to remove the muck off the walls. A combination of dirt and fungus had flourished in the forgotten rooms for over three hundred years, creating a slimy effect on the walls and a dangerously slippery one on the broken, uneven stone steps that led down from the hall above.

'These stairs will be a priority,' the builder reflected as we clambered back up to the more civilized surroundings above. They're lethal. Until they're safe, my advice is to avoid coming down here unless it's absolutely necessary and to keep your younger children well away.'

'Oh don't worry on that score,' I assured him. 'We've kept the door firmly locked ever since we arrived. As far as Lizzie and Archie are concerned, this door is just a boring cupboard.'

But, as it turned out, misleading the children nearly ended in disaster.

One wet afternoon a couple of weeks later, a series of fights between Lizzie and Archie convinced me that a wet walk was a far better way to let off steam than trashing the lounge. So, I piled both children into the car and was about to set off to the nearest park when I remembered the 'wellies'. Darting back into the house, I pulled back the heavy bolt at the top of the cellar door and, without a second thought, stepped into the darkness onto what I believed was the first 'tread' of the stairs.

But, somehow, in my hurry, I missed it and fell…….top to bottom landing heavily on the dirty stone floor below.

For a moment, I lay there…stunned. But, after several minutes I was able to pick myself up slowly and stagger back upstairs and out to the car, bruised and considerably grazed, but otherwise unharmed.

'What's the matter mummy?' Lizzie looked concerned as I gently eased myself into the front seat a few moments later. 'You're filthy.'

I looked down and realised I was covered in a kind of mucky, grey dust.

'I've just fallen down the cellar steps,' I whispered still very shaken.

There was a moment's silence while she stared at me in amazement. Then she spoke.

'Wow, have we got a cellar?'

Good God, I could have lain there, undiscovered, for days!

Sorting the cellar was suddenly a major priority.

\*   \*   \*   \*

The builder had had some strange requests in his time, but mine had clearly beaten the lot of them.

'No, I'm afraid we didn't come across any secret passages when we shot blasted the walls of the cellar.' This was going to be a good story in the pub later.

I could tell he was not taking me seriously but I was not to be beaten. After all, it wasn't unheard of for vicarages to have tunnels linking them to the church. I even knew someone who had one. But he remained unconvinced.

'You can't just stare at the wall and hope to see a secret tunnel, you know,' I argued defensively. 'You have to prod the stones until one suddenly swings round before your eyes.' Clearly this man had not read any Enid Blyton stories.

'I think you'll find that a shot blaster fired at a wall is as good a prod as any,' was his quick retort.

Things were not going well with the builder that day. Normally we got on fine but, as he met me at the door when I returned from the school run, I could see he had something on his mind. There was something he had to say.

One look inside the hall and it was clear no explanation was going to be necessary. The advice to seal the doors above the cellar before they started to shot blast the various rooms below had been woefully inadequate. The entire house, and by that I mean every towel in the airing cupboard, every book, everything on all three floors, looked like it had been heavily dusted with icing sugar.

'Wicked,' was Josh's only comment as he rushed from room to room surveying the damage. As he looked up at the collection of hitherto unseen cobwebs in the corners of the ceiling, all now highlighted with white dust, he added in rapture, 'it's just like a scene from a horror movie!'

Claire burst into tears. I was tempted to join her.

'I'm afraid that's what happens when you shot blast three hundred years of muck off the walls of three cellar rooms in one day,' was his only defence.

Mac was going to be thrilled when he found out!

But I was resigned to my fate. However, when Dorothy turned up unexpectedly, her reaction was rather different. Taking the senior member of the team to one side, it was soon clear from her body language that she found the situation entirely unacceptable!

It was a subdued team who turned up the following morning along with their boss and a huge industrial cleaner. By the end of the day, under Dorothy's close supervision, the house was back to its former state.

'Your housekeeper's quite a lady!' Sid the youngest member of the team, remarked as he shoved the kit back into the van. I've never seen the 'Guv' work that hard before. She's wasted as a cleaner, she should be running a boot camp!'

\*     \*     \*     \*

I am very romantic about cellars and attics. They conjure up a better picture of former times than any of the smarter rooms in most old houses. Those rooms have usually been redecorated many times as each new owner makes his or her own mark on their home. Cellars and attics, for the most part, remain unchanged.

One of the great appeals of our house when we first moved in was the top floor. As every new visitor arrived to have a look round our new home, either Josh or Lizzie would stand excitedly outside one of the doors on the first floor landing and say:

'I expect you think there's a bedroom in there.' And then, flinging the door wide, would exclaim: 'No it's not, it's a secret staircase! And, at the top there's the 'secret room'!'

There were, in fact, three rooms at the top. Two had been converted into a bedroom and bathroom. The third had been the attic room ...until we arrived. We called it the 'secret room'. The room that wasn't a proper room at all until we made it into one.

We hadn't needed attic space when we arrived. With our previous house being so much smaller, we struggled to fill the main rooms with the furniture we had. There was certainly none left over for storage.

The walls of the attic room were last decorated in the 1930s. The colours had faded, and, in places had been torn by suitcases, crates and old school trunks that had once had a home there. The carpet looked even older. Grey and covered with many bald patches, strange stains and holes, you could see areas where underneath old newspaper had been used as underlay. There were no curtains at either of the windows but, when you're three floors up, who is likely to stare in!

'Apart from us, only 'The Adams Family' would inhabit a room like this' Mac would lament from time to time. But I knew really that he loved it that way.

And I loved it too. So we cleaned it up as best we could and it became the playroom. It was perfect. I never minded what happened up there. After all, the condition of the carpet couldn't be much worse. And it was, as I pointed out, cleaner than it looked. Some of the mothers who came up to collect their children were slightly 'sniffy' about the state of the place, but most, like me, fell in love with it too.

'Do you think we'll ever do it up and make it look like the other rooms in the house?' Claire asked me one day.

I thought for a moment. 'Only when Aunt Lucy gets too frail to look after herself. She'd probably want to come and live with us if she couldn't manage alone. Mind you, if we offered her this room in its current state, I'm sure she'd never cross the threshold.'

'Well that's the best reason ever for leaving it as it is,' was Mac's only comment.

\* \* \* \*

It was while Mac was enjoying his second glass of wine that I decided to break the news of the day.

'Aunt Lucy called earlier today,' I tried to sound casual, mostly without success.

He bristled at the mention of the name. 'What did she want?'

'She wants to come to the family service in the morning.'

Mac looked appalled. 'And what did you say?'

I hesitated. It wasn't going to be the answer he wanted. 'Well, what could I say? I'm hardly in a position to stop her coming to a service. She's going to go straight to the church and then pop in here afterwards for a bit of lunch. I've told her it'll be a really simple meal as I've got to do the play.'

Mac shrugged his shoulders. 'I knew there'd be several downsides to your new responsibilities. What's the theme tomorrow?'

'The Ascension,' I replied. 'As soon as I can fathom out a way of getting a child to waft up to heaven in a cloud surrounded by angels, I'll have cracked it!'

'Not a problem that's ever going to befall my dear aunt,' Mac muttered under his breath. 'I think her journey, when the time comes, will definitely be in the other direction!'

## HE ASCENDED INTO HEAVEN

'The trouble with your 'plays',' Claire commented the following morning, 'Is that they lack 'edge'.' At eleven years old, she no doubt felt well placed to offer me her opinion.

'Lack edge!' I was quick to retaliate. 'I hardly think that's fair. I'll have you know we've had our moments! Take our interpretation of the Resurrection. That would have been very 'edgy' if that giant beanbag we used as the stone in front of the cave where the body of Jesus had been lain, hadn't been accidentally knocked by Josh, flattening one of the angels. Or how about Simeon's warning to Mary. That would have had buckets of 'edge' if it hadn't been for that late substitution.'

That day the child due to play the part of Simeon got 'cold feet' at the eleventh hour and the only available replacement (with five minutes to go) was his brother, aged barely two. Despite my help with the narration, we seemed to lose a certain amount of impact in the final performance.

Looking back, it could have been far worse. Having told my narrator how to pronounce the various names, she managed to call Simeon, 'Semen', during the rehearsal. My hope that the other children were too young to understand what she'd said, was dashed as I watched Josh dissolve into helpless giggles against the altar. Breathing a sigh of relief that we had, at least, sorted out that mistake in advance, I looked ahead and was only just in time to tell her that the next big word was…. 'Gentiles'!

And it wasn't just pronunciation that was a problem. Getting the children to say the words in the first place could also be a challenge.

And the theme for this week was The Ascension, the moment when Jesus, who had already risen from the dead, says a final farewell to his disciples and then rises up to meet his father in heaven….powerful stuff.

Except, I'd got a problem.

Jeanette Digby-Simons, the organiser of several village events and general 'bossy boots', had sent her son, Cosmo, along to take part. Although I had an array of much younger girls in front of me desperate to be angels, I wasn't spoilt for choice when it came to casting the male characters. So, with Josh still reluctant to play a leading role, Cosmo, once again, took the part of the Son of God.

All was going well until we came to the part where Jesus said his final goodbyes. I took Cosmo to one side to have a quiet word.

'The next line is very important so you must say it boldly. I want you to turn to Josh, who's playing Peter, look him straight in the eye and say 'Do you love me?'

There was a moment's silence. Then Cosmo spoke quietly.

'What did you say the line was?'

'Do you love me?'

'I'm not saying that.'

'No, look, it's not what you think. Jesus is just checking that Peter, his closest friend, is ready to take on the job of running the Christian church after he's gone. He needs to be sure that he's fully on his side. He let him down quite badly just before the Crucifixion you know.'

'I'm still not saying it.'

'But the scene doesn't work nearly so well without it.'

'I don't care, I'm not saying it.'

I looked round at the assembled company. I only had one other child in my cast that day old enough to play the part, and it wasn't difficult to tell from Josh's expression that he wasn't going to volunteer to do a last minute swap.

'Okay, okay,' I gave in. 'Say 'Do you like me' then. It's not as good, but I suppose it will have to do.'

Having sorted him out, I turned my attention to little Olivia. Barely four years old, she had only joined the team that morning. As she was so young, I'd given her lots of running around to do, in this, her debut performance, but only one line, in fact only one word. Surely that wasn't going to be too difficult. Someone was going to ask her what she thought and all she had to do was say 'Brilliant'. We rehearsed it a couple of times and she was faultless. But when her moment came, things didn't quite go according to plan.

With her proud parents looking on, she looked confident as she ran up the aisle at the start of the play. She turned to face the audience but, when her moment came, there was only silence.

'Brilliant,' I whispered from my seat in the front pew.

She looked at me, smiled but didn't speak.

'Brilliant,' I repeated with slightly more urgency in my voice.

By now her fellow thespians were beginning to look anxious. But still she grinned.

'Say brilliant,' by now my voice was insistent.

A look of recognition flashed across her face.

'Brilliant.' She'd got it and the show continued.

It wasn't until afterwards that I worked it out.

2. March, April, May, June

'I know that look,' her mother laughed afterwards. 'She didn't realise you were prompting her. She thought you were commenting on her performance!'

'Well done!' Vicar Vic was the first to clap me on the back. She was always enthusiastic, even if our interpretation sometimes left her bewildered. 'Loved the sleeping bag.'

'Yes, it's Mac's from his student days. It came in very handy. Blue on one side so ideal for the Sea of Galilee and then the white lining made a perfect cloud for Jesus to disappear into. Shame the angels looked as though they were strangling him inside it. I'd forgotten that Tess loathes Cosmo, but you can't have everything, can you?'

'How are the fete preparations going?' Jeanette bounced up enthusiastically. 'Only a couple of weeks to go, you realise.'

Mac gave her one of his withering looks, Jeanette Digby-Simons was not one of his favourite people. 'It would be a bit difficult not to realise the day was imminent with a dining room and a hall already piled high with half the village's junk,' he complained. 'Having looked through it, it's quite hard to imagine that anyone would want to buy any of it!'

'That's hardly fair,' I cautioned diplomatically for fear that any of the locals might overhear his damning indictment on their donations. 'We might well get quite a good price for some of it...once we've sorted it out.'

'What's all this about a fair?' Aunt Lucy's antennae had picked up the scent of a bargain. 'You never told me about this Mac,' she added reproachfully.

'It's just the village fete,' he explained as patiently as he could. 'And, no, before you get any ideas you will not be allowed to sift through the boxes until they are properly priced up and sorted. I don't want to find you've taken all the decent stuff and left us with nothing to sell!'

'Mac dear, you do me an injustice,' she replied in her most patient and dangerous voice. 'I was just going to offer my services on the day. As you know, my experiences of both buying and selling are legendary.'

'That's one way of putting it,' Mac replied darkly, Then, under his breath he added, 'though criminal might be a more apt description!'

'Sorry we were a bit late for the service,' Judy apologised. 'James had to pop into town after he'd dropped the boys off and was a bit late picking me up. With only one car, things are a bit difficult at the moment.'

'So whatever you'd had scheduled didn't happen this morning,' I said with a wry grin. 'I thought you two were always careful to keep that time free!'

'What? Oh...no. Sadly, that will have to wait until later. Won't be the same though! I've decided I'm definitely a morning person!' And with that she gathered up the two boys and left.

'What was all that about?' Mac queried.

'I'll tell you later!' I replied mysteriously.

'What happened about that chap's car?' Jim, a farmer from the far end of the village, asked me as he watched Judy and James leave the church.'

'Not good, I gather the engine's ruined.'

'Thought as much. I've never seen anyone look so desperate as he did that night.'

'Well, I think it all happened at the end of a bad day. He'd had a business meeting in Birmingham that went on later than he'd expected and he was in a bit of a hurry to get home. Judy had warned him about the floods round here, but he obviously had other things on his mind.' *

'I should think he did!'

'What do you mean by that?' I didn't like Jim's tone.

His meeting wasn't in town, it was at the far end of the village. He drove in, just before the river burst its banks sometime during the afternoon. As he turned into the gateway of Upbank Farm, a young girl was standing by some bushes. She'd been there a while and was obviously waiting for him. She jumped into the car and they drove up to the barns by the side of the farmhouse. I was gathering in my sheep in the next field and the girl noticed me staring and smiled. She was lovely. When I found him in the water at midnight, he'd obviously just left the farm.'

'Don't jump to conclusions,' Mac warned when I told him later. 'There could be a perfectly simple explanation.'

'Did the girl have long blonde hair?' I asked, suddenly remembering something.

'Yes. She did. Have you met her?'

'Yes. I think I have.'

'Well, I haven't seen her since. So, either she's moved or she's very private. But she's certainly a cracker,' he added mischievously and winked at Mac.

As Jim left the church, I turned to Mac.

'What do you think we should do?'

Mac look horrified. 'Absolutely nothing. Whatever James chooses to do in his spare time, which, knowing him, is probably perfectly innocent, has absolutely nothing to do with us.'

## THE FETE

'Okay. Item 9 on the agenda....The Fete. Anyone got any new ideas of how best to get the money off the punters?' Victoria was in a crisp mood in the church hall the following Wednesday evening. We'd spent the last forty minutes debating what colour to paint the village hall doors and I knew she was determined to end the meeting and get to the pub before closing.

For a moment there was a stunned silence. Under the supervision of the previous vicar, the fete had run to a strict format for years. The prospect of changing the way it was organised was a revolutionary idea that many of the people sitting round the table were less than ready for.

'What sort of changes do you have in mind?' Mabel Turner, who had run the book stall for thirty years, asked nervously.

'Oh I don't know,' she replied. 'How about having me balancing on a narrow plank and then getting people to throw bean bags at me until I fall off? You could call it 'Victoria Falls'. There are loads of people in the parish wanting to knock me into shape a bit.' Ignoring the guilty looks around the table, she continued. 'It could be a great way of getting them to vent their feelings.'

Mrs Carter, who always took the entrance money, was clearly shocked. 'How terribly undignified,' she muttered. 'When the Reverend Thomas was in charge, he only came along at the end to thank everyone and draw the raffle.'

'I don't think we're in any position to criticise people's dignity while we still have Madam Belise and her crystal ball,' Barry Bright, raffle ticket supremo, muttered from a corner of the room.

'Madam who?' Victoria asked intrigued.

Sarah Stanley, who had lived next door to her for years, was quick to explain.

'Madam Belise, better known as Mabel Belise, is in her early seventies. She moved into the village several years ago to convalesce with her sister after the driver of a large industrial vacuum cleaner mistook her for a pile of rags and nearly sucked her up on Platform 10 of Waterloo station. Rumour had it that she'd taken to 'living rough' after her mad French husband had become bored of her drinking problem and thrown her out. Poor Ethel took her in and, for a while, managed to keep her off the booze. But when Ethel died unexpectedly, Mabel began to drink again.

As a way of getting her involved in village life, several years ago Ethel persuaded the fete committee to allow Mabel to use her questionable psychic skills to raise some cash at the village fete. To begin with, it worked well. But, since Ethel's untimely death, she's required some supervision, mainly to ensure that she doesn't pitch her tent too close to the bottle stall.'

'I vote we tell her she's not needed this year,' Mrs Carter was adamant.

'How much money does she normally raise?' Victoria was curious.

'Oh at least £100.00. Some of the villagers hang on her every word.'

'Then I think she should come,' Victoria decided. 'I know I've never met her, but I feel we've already bonded!'

'Will Jeanette Digby-Simons be bringing her group of girls again?' Martin Shields from the farm opposite the church looked suitably unimpressed.

There was a groan from around the table.

Mrs Bridges, the chief bell ringer, was quick to explain.

'Jeanette organises the entertainment every year. She runs the ballet school in town and she's terribly bossy. Everyone's scared to death of her. For years now she's brought along a handful of children who tap dance on tables on the lawn. Last year there was a disaster when she didn't notice how wet the ground was. As the girls danced, one end of the table started to sink into the soft earth and, one by one, the entire troupe slipped to the floor. Actually, it was frightfully funny but someone could have been seriously hurt.'

'So, is anyone brave enough to tell her that we may try something different this year?' Victoria looked round the table, but no one volunteered.

'Moving on, what's 'Wellie Wanging'?'

'Jim does that one.' It was Matthew, the verger's turn to have his say. 'He runs the 'Young Farmers' round these parts and knows everyone. The idea is simply to see how far you can throw a Wellington boot. It's a bit like tossing the caber. We've only had one wellie go through a window. Normally they're quite a good shot.'

I looked anxious but no one seemed to notice.

'And will Bert Moggins be bringing that ancient nag of his for pony rides?' Mrs Bridges was on her high horse again. 'He made such a mess of the lawn last time and he never made any attempt to clear it up.'

I wondered if this would be a good moment to tell the assembled company that I'd just remembered we would be away that weekend.

'And do we have plenty of bunting to decorate everywhere?' Victoria wondered.

'Oh, Mrs Baker always organises that,' Mrs Carter explained. 'She's got the most amazing collection of stuff in her attic. You should see it. She's had it since the war. But I don't think she'll be able to give it to us this year.'

'Why not? Have you had a fall out or something?' Victoria was beginning to look very vexed. There was now only half an hour to go until last orders.

Mrs Carter paused. She suddenly looked rather upset. 'No, I can't ask her.'

'Shall I give her a ring, then?' Victoria volunteered.

'No you can't do that. Well, it's a bit difficult really. You see she died at the end of last year.'

There was a moment's silence. For a few seconds Victoria actually looked lost for words. Then she gathered her thoughts.

'So, what's your point, Doris? Were you expecting me to resurrect her for the day or were you hoping that Madame Belise might have a word with her from the other side?'

Mrs Carter's eyes widened in horror but she remained silent.

'Well if that's it then, shall we call it a day?'

'I've just got one small question.' I spoke rather nervously. 'What exactly am I supposed to do for all this?'

'Absolutely nothing,' Moira the church warden was quick to assure me. 'You just lend us your garden for the morning and leave the rest to us.'

\* \* \* \*

'It's actually quite a small affair compared to some of the other fetes in these parts.' Moira had called round a couple of days later to fill me in with a few details. 'There's really nothing to worry about. We just have a few stalls, a raffle and serve tea and coffee. Normally around two hundred people turn up. And don't worry. Although we borrow the garden and the kitchen for the morning, you really don't have to do anything!'

And, in theory, she was right. That is, providing that you happen to live in a house that is always tidy with a well manicured garden. Unfortunately, we didn't!

With four children including a four year old and a toddler in the house, we had a reasonable excuse for not keeping an immaculate home. But we, more than any other family I knew, could reduce a house to a 'tip' at a moment's notice.

'Why do we have to tidy the house?' Claire queried. 'They don't come inside, do they?'

'No, but they'll peer through the windows.'

'Well they won't see much if they do,' reflected Josh. 'They're filthy!'

'But they won't be by the time I've finished. So, stop moaning and get on with it.'

So, in the run-up to the fete, when certain villagers imagined us calmly filling vases with fresh flowers and laying out the odd napkin, we were frantic. The church committee was going to use my kitchen to wash up coffee cups etc. What if they looked behind the cooker? Help! I'd have to clean the inside of all the downstairs windows and deal with all the spiders' webs and dust in corners I'd never bothered to notice. I'd probably have to wash the kitchen curtains – another first! Or what, heaven forbid, if they opened a drawer in search of a tea-towel? Mind you, with so much rubbish crammed into most of my drawers, they'd be lucky to open one at all. And if they did find a tea-towel……help!

For the first time in thirteen years, I looked at my selection of cloths in a new light. Half had a pattern that was so faded you couldn't recognise it, some had holes and the rest …...well the less said about them, the better!

Having 'binned' half a dozen which had probably reached their 'sell by' date ten years ago, I set about ironing the remainder (first time for everything). I then tidied the rest of the drawer, removing in the process, six crumpled 'Happy birthday three year old' paper napkins, the broken ornament I'm too scared to tell Mac about, one pink sock (clean) that must have got caught up with the tea-towels when I last washed them and, whoopee, my missing watch. I then replaced the ironed tea-towels, colour coded and in neat piles. They had better want a tea-towel now or there'd be trouble.

In the garden I found Mac potting plants. He was not looking happy. So I offered to help. He looked doubtful. I am not at my best when it comes to anything that's green and grows!

'I could do a few cleaning jobs?' I suggested, hoping he'd tell me not to bother. Instead, he handed me a scouring pad.

'Okay. You can sort out these wooden chairs and tables if you like.'

I looked at them. They were filthy. I stared down at the little scouring pad in my hand. 'You're not serious?'

But he was. 'The bloody jet-blaster Tom lent us had packed up. So, unless you've got any better ideas……?'

So I grabbed a scouring pad and got scrubbing. But Mac hadn't finished.

'Once you've done the seats, we need to do something about the patio paving stones. Several of them are very slippery. We also need to patch up one of the stone steps down to the garden. It's badly cracked and, if anyone trips on it, we could be sued for millions!'

'Oh God!'

'Next, the wire fence around the garden needs to be checked to avoid the chance of an unsupervised toddler squeezing through and falling into the river. Oh, and while you're doing that,' Mac was in serious organising mode now, 'could you please check that all gates to the river and the footbridge are securely padlocked.'

'Hold on,' I complained. 'I've still got this set of filthy chairs to sort out.'

But he wasn't listening.

'We need to get Claire and Josh to sort out the mess in the Wendy House so that villagers won't think our children are total hooligans.'

I didn't like to tell him that it was probably too late for that.

'Then, all that's left to do is to tidy the 'bin' area round the back as the church committee are going to dump all the rubbish there. Oh, and by the way, we've still got about eight pots to fill with those plants I bought from the garden centre this morning.'

'Good thing we weren't planning to have any sleep this week?'

'So, shall I do the plants once I've done the chairs?'

'No,' said Mac, 'that's not a good plan,' reminding me once more of my shortcomings in that department. Putting on his official voice he added, 'First, we must get the jobs done that involve safety. Plants are decorative and can wait.'

'Ay Ay captain!'

Okay. But before I started I thought I'd just move that big pot, the very big one, the one that's half an old beer barrel.

'No,' he shouted as he watched me bend down beside it. 'Leave that one to me.'

'Don't panic, I'm not going to fill it,' I assured him. 'But, if I just move it a fraction, the ladies running the cake stall will have enough space to lay out their wares. It won't take me a second......'

Disaster!!!!

Somehow I managed to lift one side just far enough to get my fingers underneath the jagged metal rim at the bottom. But now, oh no, I couldn't get them out and the heavy earth-filled pot was gently crushing them to pulp.

'Mac, help, quick!!!!'

Too late! Two crushed torn, swollen fingers emerged from the base. This was a hospital job.

\*   \*   \*   \*

Two hours later I was discharged from casualty with my fingers strapped together and my arm in a high sling to reduce the swelling. Mac was not sympathetic.

'I told you to leave the pots. Why are you always so impatient? Now you're no help at all!'

'I'm okay to check fences,' I suggested feebly. But I could see he wasn't impressed.

We were gratified to hear that some people had offered sympathy and support when they heard about my predicament. But other members of the church committee, although concerned about my fingers, were less worried about where it left us.

'Moira was amazed when she heard that some people had offered to help you,' my neighbour informed me later that evening. 'According to her, as far as the fete's concerned, you only need to mow the lawn!!!'

\* \* \* \*

'Look at all those people Mum,' Josh was pointing at the queue by the garden gate. 'Isn't it odd to think that they have to pay to come into our garden.'

It was the day of the fete and we still had ten minutes to go before the doors opened. Peering out of our top window, down below I could see Judy and the twins towards the front of the queue. She'd come to help. Why on earth hadn't she come in through the back door? I looked further along the queue and a feeling of panic rose up inside me.

'Where's James? I can't see any sign of him.'

'Calm down, Kate. Calm down.' Mac replied irritably. 'He's gone to fetch his mother. Apparently she loves this kind of thing, though God knows why? And don't, for goodness sake, start searching for everyone's partners this morning. Village fetes are not, generally, a 'man' thing.' Then, lowering his voice he added, 'And please stop speculating. Judy and James seem fine to me. I think all this flood business is just a storm in a teacup.'

'Dad, you see that sweet old lady at the front of the queue,' Josh interrupted.

'Yes.'

'Well she's been there for almost an hour. Why on earth would she do that?'

'That's Betty Collins and there is absolutely nothing sweet about her,' I replied bitterly. 'She goes to every single fete or jumble sale with the sole intention of getting in first and beating everyone to the bargains. She steals stuff too when she thinks nobody's looking. She once bought a bike for £2.00 from a National Childbirth Trust jumble sale and then made my friend deliver it to her home. She lives miles away.'

'I didn't know we had a jumble stall?'

'We don't. But she won't mind. She'll just be first to the White Elephant stall instead. You should watch her. She's got a real eye for a bargain.'

'I'll be keeping a very close eye on her,' Mac stared at her critically. 'If she's capable of nicking stuff off the jumble stall, she's probably planning to nip in here for the odd bargain too.'

'Actually I doubt that. I think she sticks to jumble because she thinks that she'd never get done for taking it. Normally the organisers are just glad to get rid of it.'

Later, when the fete was in full swing, I caught up with Lizzie. She was carrying a large carrier bag full ….of her own toys!

'Mummy, you got rid of some of my baby toys. I found them on the stall and had to spend all of my money buying them back.'

'But you haven't played with them for years. I found them in a box that hadn't been unpacked since we moved.'

The argument was interrupted by a tap of the shoulder from Lady Henrietta. She was in charge of the cake stall and was looking slightly agitated.

'I'm so sorry to bother you but I have someone who wants to buy the fruit pies you made. She's just wondering what kind of fruit's in them?'

I looked at her, horrified. But there was nothing for it. I'd have to come clean. 'I've no idea.' I answered honestly.

'But you must. You did make them, after all.'

'No, I didn't. I bought them from the farm shop yesterday afternoon.'

'Oh my goodness!' She was clearly appalled by my confession. She turned to go, but then stopped. 'But if you bought them, didn't they have a label on the back listing the ingredients?'

This was getting desperate.

'Yes they did. But I wanted them to look home made so I threw their packaging away and put them in my own. I was far too busy getting ready for today to have time to make pies. Besides, I've got two fingers in bandages,' I ended, hoping to appeal to her kinder nature.

It didn't work. She simply shook her head sadly and went back to explain my heinous crime to her customer.

Feeling suitably chastened, I went into the kitchen where I found Dorothy at the sink washing coffee cups. When I told her what had happened, she was indignant.

'That's rich coming from that woman,' she exclaimed. 'She couldn't make a fruit tart to save her life. I had the misfortune to sample one of her efforts at one of her charity evenings at the village hall. Her pastry's like cardboard. Next time, get me to make one for you. I'm quite well known for my pies. It would certainly knock hers into a cocked hat any day.'

Only slightly reassured, I went outside again to join the queue for coffee. It wasn't a good idea. In front of me were a couple of ladies I hadn't met before and they were staring at our house rather critically.

'Have you met the new owners yet?' I heard one of them say.

'No. But I gather the husband's a lawyer. Very pleasant I've been told.'

'And his wife?'

'Oh, I understand she's quite a bit younger than him, though I've heard she doesn't look it. She comes from London and works in television,' she finished with a grimace.

'Oh dear!'

'I know. It's a bit of a worry really. The Campbells looked after this place so beautifully. It would be so sad to see all their hard work fall apart.'

'We'll just have to keep a close eye on them and hope and pray that they've got what it takes.'

*Chapter Three*

# JULY, AUGUST, SEPTEMBER, OCTOBER

### HAY FEVER

The village was in a high state of excitement. That afternoon we were expecting several special visitors.

'What exactly is a Green Man?' Claire wondered.

'He's a pagan figure,' Mac said knowingly. 'A god of all things that grow.'

'So is he like Jesus?' Lizzie asked innocently.

'No. Certainly not. Pagan means someone who's not religious.'

'And why is he here?' Josh was now interested. 'I heard someone say he's getting married.'

'He's not really getting married. He's just pretending. It's Midsummer's Day today. Very special for certain people. Lots of magical things are supposed to happen. If you read Midsummer Night's Dream, it's when all the trouble starts.'

'Can we watch the wedding?' Lizzie, who hung around the church every time there was a marriage in the hope of seeing a beautiful bride, was now fascinated.

'We can. But don't expect to see a traditional bride and groom. They'll look most peculiar. They dress up in leaves and other greenery. Some green men go the whole way and paint their bodies green too.'

'Wicked,' said Lizzie. 'I'm shall wear my fairy outfit when I watch.'

'I know your game,' said Josh. 'You'll be hoping they need a last minute bridesmaid and you will just happen to have an appropriate outfit. I've seen you do it before. Whenever there's a wedding at the church, you hover around the garden covered in your fairy togs…. looking ridiculous in the vain hope that one of the team will fail to turn up and you can step into the breach.'

'I do not!'

'You do, so! Everyone in the village talks about it. They think it's cute. But they don't know what you're really like.'

'Enough!' I glared at Josh. 'The best bit about this wedding is that when it's over, there's a walk around the village and then a big tea in the village hall. Everywhere's in full bloom. It'll be lovely.'

*    *    *    *

'Aren't you usually suffering by this time of year?' Mac remarked as I was leaving the house for the wedding ceremony. 'You haven't been sneezing nearly as much as usual and the pollen count's quite high today.'

'I know. I'm wondering if I was only allergic to something specific that grew near the cottage? Or maybe it's being by a river. So far, I've been fine.'

'Do you think it's a good idea to go on the walk? So many things are in full flower at the moment, you'll be immersed in pollen before you realise.'

'I'll be alright,' I assured him. 'Look, if you're worried, I'll take an antihistamine just in case.'

But I spoke too soon.

The wedding was extraordinary. Both bride and groom were covered in greenery from head to foot. Afterwards, dozens of villagers cheered them on their way. We then followed the crowd through the village and out into open countryside. For the first quarter of a mile, all was fine. It wasn't until I had battled my way through a field of towering cow parsley, that I began to feel my eyes itch. By the time we had got to the halfway point, my eyes and nose were streaming and I was beginning to wheeze.

'Are you alright?' Kind Mr Budbrook who lived in one of the tiny terraced cottages on the main road, looked concerned.

'I'll be fine,' I assured him. 'Just a bit of a pollen problem.'

I never made it to the tea. Dumping the children with a friend, I slowly made my way home and was soon steaming my swollen face under a large towel.

'I told you it was a stupid idea to go,' Mac was not sympathetic. 'Why are you always so stubborn?'

'The children wanted to go. They had a lovely time. This sort of thing is what living in the countryside is all about.'

'What is? Hay fever? If you carry on like this, we'll have to move back to the city.'

That evening I sat up in bed with a large packet of tissues by my side. My eyes were still badly swollen and my face was a blotchy red. Far more serious, I was now struggling to breathe. I scoured the medicine cabinet and took a fairly dangerous combination of decongestants and more antihistamines and somehow, by remaining propped up, managed a few hours sleep.

By the morning things had not improved.

'You are presumably not planning to accompany Lizzie to her trial day at 'big' school.' But Mac had made the wrong assumption.

Despite my efforts over breakfast to persuade Lizzie that it would be fun and very grown up to go with just Judy and the twins, she wasn't convinced.

'You promised, Mummy, you promised.'

Even though I couldn't see her very clearly through my puffy eyes, I recognised the tone in her voice. If I didn't make the effort, I'd have a major tantrum on my hands.

'I'd take her for you, but I've got to be in London by lunchtime,' Mac was beginning to feel guilty.

'Don't panic. I'll wear Claire's dark glasses. I'll be fine. They'll never suspect a thing.'

'Well, for God's sake don't drive. You're bad enough when you can see.' And with those words of comfort, he went to work.

Luckily, I didn't have to drive. As Judy was going too, I got a lift. She looked at me suspiciously as I got into the car.

'Are you sure this is a good idea? You look dreadful. The school will think you've had some kind of major trauma. You look as though you've been crying for weeks.'

'Loads of people suffer like me at this time of year. I'm sure her teacher will understand.'

But she still looked doubtful.

Luckily, I didn't notice the strange look Lizzie's new teacher gave me when we shook hands. The combination of Claire's dark glasses and streaming eyes made seeing rather difficult.

'I've organised a nature trail for the children,' the teacher informed us brightly. 'It's such a lovely day, it seems a pity to be indoors.'

What could be worse? At this rate I'd be dead within the hour.

'Why don't you go and sit in the car?' Judy suggested. 'Lizzie won't mind. She's so thrilled by everything, I'm sure she won't be bothered if you disappear for a bit.'

'I'll be fine,' I said stubbornly. 'I promised her I'd come and I have.' And clutching Lizzie in one hand and a very large handkerchief in the other, I allowed her to lead me down the path to the glade at the far side of the playground. By the time we returned to the classroom, my eyes were so swollen I couldn't see at all. I missed the door and crashed into the wall. Then I missed the step. Thank goodness Lizzie was so excited she didn't notice. But unfortunately the teacher had.

I didn't see her approach me and ask me if I needed help. Looking vaguely up at her, I assured her that I was just suffering from a bit of hay fever and I'd be fine by the morning. She wasn't convinced.

\*     \*     \*     \*

'How did it go?' Mac asked as he walked through the door that evening. 'Did you survive? I spoke to Lizzie in the garden and she sounded very happy about it all.'

I managed a smile. An afternoon indoors had improved my condition slightly and I was a little more cheerful. 'It went well, I think. The teacher seemed to have a soft spot for Lizzie.'

'Really?' Mac sounded surprised. 'What caused that?'

'I think she thinks I'm a drug addict or something similar. I got the feeling she's marked her down for lots of extra attention!'

## ANIMALS

For the next few weeks, I kept a fairly low profile. Despite trying nearly every antihistamine on the market, I failed to find one that cured my swollen eyes and runny nose. However hard I tried, I looked as if I'd been crying for months! I couldn't go anywhere without someone putting a consoling arm around my shoulder and offering their deepest condolences.

Surprisingly I got a fair amount of sympathy from my family. For, at times, their suffering was no less than mine. Sadly, the allergy genes had swept through the children leaving Josh allergic to horses and Claire to dogs and cats. As Lizzie loved all animals and had longed for a pony, puppy or kitten for as long as we could remember, she resented their afflictions hugely. So, predictably, the post card that arrived from her best friend one morning was not well received.

The screams on the landing could be heard all over the house.

'What on earth's the matter with Lizzie?' Mac came into the kitchen and banged his mug down on the table. He looked at his watch. 'Quite early for a tantrum. Even for her. Who's upset her this time?'

'Rebecca.'

'Rebecca? What's she doing here at this hour of the day?'

'She isn't here. But unfortunately she's been staying with her cousin and has sent Lizzie a postcard telling her about the new dog she's going to have for her birthday. Apparently her aunt's retriever has just had six puppies.'

'And Lizzie's clearly delighted for her.' Mac raised despairing eyes to the ceiling. 'How many times do we have to tell her that the only way she can have a puppy, is if she can persuade her big sister to move out.'

'She knows that. But suggesting this morning that Claire move in with granny didn't go down well with either Claire or me.....hence the hysterics! Leave her, she'll calm down in a moment.'

'Can't we get her something else.....like a rabbit or guinea pig?' Josh wondered. 'Anything to stop these awful scenes.'

'Apparently it's a dog or nothing! But if you like, I'll give it one more try.'

$$* \quad * \quad * \quad *$$

The man in the pet shop was clearly used to dealing with novices like us.

'Yes,' he explained with the utmost patience. 'I've got some hamsters in stock at the moment.'

'We'd like two please,' Lizzie was beside herself with excitement.

'Ah, now I can't do that I'm afraid.'

'Why not?'

'Because one would probably eat the other. They eat their young too. Not all of them of course. It's a form of natural culling. Too many mouths to feed, I guess.'

Lizzie looked horrified. Mac nodded sympathetically.

It didn't take long for Lizzie to choose the one she wanted. Eight weeks old and, as Lizzie was quick to point out, only £6.00, he was clearly a bargain. Another £50.00 later and we also had a cage, straw, exercise wheel, nest and bedding. Not quite the cheap present we'd had in mind.

'You need to keep the cage at ground level for a couple of weeks, the pet shop owner advised. 'Your daughter's going to need time to learn to handle him properly. At least if she drops him from floor height, she shouldn't do him too much damage.'

So we took his advice and 'Lucky' took up residence in a corner of the lounge where thick rugs could protect the tiny creature from even the clumsiest fingers.

Two days later disaster struck.

'What's the matter with Claire?' Mac wondered. 'She's on the sofa watching the television and she looks as if she's been crying for a week.'

'What?' I rushed into the lounge and stared in horror at Claire's face. It was red and swollen. I looked across at the hamster. I'd found the culprit.

So Claire was dosed up with antihistamines and Lucky was banished to the utility room. Lizzie was indignant.

'He won't like it out there,' she protested. 'There's nothing to look at.'

'On the contrary,' Mac pointed out. 'He can spend hours watching the washing machine go round. If what you watch on the television is anything to go by, he'll find that a lot more entertaining.'

But I had other concerns. The utility room was at the far end of the house and had no heating. It faced north so it was often chilly in there, even in summer. What if he caught a chill? Mac thought the idea was ridiculous. But I wasn't so sure.

So, after everyone had gone to bed that night, I covered the cage with a cosy blanket. Satisfied that he was warm enough, I retired.

Screams of horror woke us early the next morning. I rushed downstairs to find Lizzie holding up a handful of tattered bits of cloth. Lucky had clearly loved the blanket...every last mouthful.

'You've poisoned him,' Lizzie said accusingly. 'Look at his face. It's all swollen.'

'That's because he's pouched most of the wool,' I explained. I was nearly as distraught as Lizzie by the loss of my bed cover.

'He'll choke,' she wailed nearly choking herself.

'He won't,' I assured her.

'He might be poisoned by the red dye in the wool,' Claire pointed out unhelpfully. More tears from Lizzie who was now looking at me with murderous eyes.

'He will be absolutely fine!' I said irritably, snatching what remained of the blanket off the cage. The sawdust inside was covered by a thick layer of fluff. He wouldn't need any more bedding for weeks!

'Another thirty quid on top of the fifty odd pounds it's already cost us then,' Mac lamented as he stared at what remained of my beautiful blanket. 'At this rate, he's going to be the most expensive hamster in history!'

It was a week later when the second disaster struck. In Claire's temporary absence, Lizzie had been allowed to take Lucky into the lounge for a play. While I sat on the sofa, supposedly supervising the scene, I could only watch in horror as he suddenly slipped through her fingers onto the carpet.

Lizzie went white with horror and shot out of the room. I bent down, picked him up and stroked him gently. There didn't appear to be any damage. As I shouted up the stairs that he was absolutely fine, Josh's face appeared at the top.

'Mummy, mummy, you've got to come and see Lizzie. She's gone funny.'

I rushed upstairs. Lying under the bed and refusing to come out, an hysterical Lizzie was clearly hyperventilating.

'What on earth's the matter?' I cried trying, unsuccessfully to pull her out.

'I've killed him...I've killed him,' she gulped barely able to speak.

Grabbing a bag of sweets from the table, I quickly emptied the contents onto the floor and shoved the empty paper bag over her face. For a moment, Lizzie fought against my emergency treatment, but I was insistent.

'Come on now Lizzie, just a few big breaths into the bag and you'll be fine.'

Josh looked on in horror. The he shouted loudly down the stairs. 'Dad, come quickly. Mum's gone mad! She's trying to suffocate Lizzie.'

'Don't be ridiculous! She's breathed in too much oxygen and, believe me, breathing into a paper bag is the best way to sort her out. If you want to do something useful, hold this.'

I shoved the wriggling hamster into his hands. 'Look Lizzie, Lucky's fine, and so will you be, if you keep taking those deep breaths.'

'What the hell's going on?' Mac demanded breathlessly as he swept into the room.

'Nothing,' I replied brightly. 'Everything's fine now...at least it will be in a second. Josh, you can give Lizzie her hamster now.'

Now completely recovered, she took him and lovingly gave him a cuddle.

'There now, no harm done. Just a little misunderstanding.'

Mac shook his head. 'So, just another normal, hysterical moment in our mad household, then.' And with that he left the room.

\*     \*     \*     \*

For a while things calmed down and Lizzie wisely said nothing about her desire for other animal playmates. Then, quite unexpectedly, early one Saturday morning, the 'animal' issue came firmly back on the agenda.

'Mummy, Dad, come quickly,' Josh shouted excitedly. 'There's a bat hanging above my desk.'

Oh God. Please no.

But there was. A tiny little bat had come in through the open window and was obviously enjoying the warmer surroundings of Josh's room to the colder weather outside.

'Oh, he's been coming and going for days,' Lizzie commented as she walked into the room. 'He's called Dracula.'

'If you knew he was there, why on earth didn't you mention it?' Mac stared incredulously at his younger daughter. 'Have you any idea what sort of mess these things make? I dread to think what we'll find when we pull that desk away from the wall.'

'I didn't say anything because I knew you wouldn't let us keep him once you found out. You're horrid about us having pets. I was trying to get him to live in the airing cupboard where he'd be safe, but I couldn't wake him up.'

'Ugh!' I shuddered. 'Thank goodness we found him. He'd have buried himself inside all our clothes.'

'Or buried himself in the bedding,' Claire added turning pale. 'Can you imagine waking up to find that Dracula was sharing your bed?'

As Mac gently lifted the tiny creature out into the garden, Lizzie looked on wistfully, clearly hoping it wouldn't be long before another animal took a liking to our home. She didn't have long to wait.

A few weeks later another uninvited guest tipped up unexpectedly. But I didn't notice her until she'd gone.

'Mac, I'm just ringing up to warn you that the flowerbed outside the kitchen's a bit of a mess. It looks like we've had a cow in the garden.'

There was a pause at the other end of the 'phone. Then Mac laughed.

'A cow! Don't be ridiculous. It'll be a dog. I've seen it before. They wander in off the public footpath. Don't worry. I'll sort it when I come home.'

I looked out of the window at the mangled pile of plants and the large piles of dung on the lawn.

'Okay,' I replied sarcastically. 'I'll start again. I think a dog, the size of a cow, has been on our lawn this afternoon. You see what you think when you get home.'

It was around six o'clock that evening when I was startled by a strange sound on the patio. I looked up to see a large cow peering at me through the window.

'Mac,' I yelled up the stairs. 'I think you'd better come down. That 'dog' you were talking about earlier has come back. And she's taken a liking to your pot plants.'

The sight of Mac's enraged face at the window rocked the calm demeanour of young 'Daisy.' So she took flight. Had she retraced her steps, all would have been well, but unfortunately she took a wrong turning and the next thing we knew, she was trotting down the lane.

'Follow her,' I shouted. 'If there's a car in the road, there could be a terrible accident.'

'I hope you're joking!' For a moment, Mac looked at me as if I'd completely flipped. 'Dear God, Kate, why do you assume that every damn thing that happens in this village is our responsibility. That cow doesn't belong to us and is no longer on our land. Look at it, Kate. It's quite clearly on the public highway happily chewing next door's hedge. If I was to start chasing it now, it would only confirm what most of the village already think of us …that we are barking mad and, on this occasion, they'd be right!'

'But what if it ran onto the main road and killed a car load of people. Wouldn't you then feel a little bit guilty that you'd done nothing to help?'

'Chasing it won't help. 'Phoning the farmer to tell him that his mad cow is in the lane and letting him know at the same time that he owes me a fortune for the damage it's caused, might,' Mac added bitterly.

'Well, I don't care what you think. I'm going to sneak round her and go to the main road so that I can stop the traffic.'

'You do that. But don't blame me if everyone thinks you're certifiable. If it's all the same to you, I'll stay here and 'phone for more sensible help!'

Unfortunately, just as Mac had predicted, the moment the cow sensed me creeping up behind it, it took flight.

The spectacle of me chasing the cow through the lanes was one that the village would remember for years to come. Yelling 'It's not mine!' to everyone I saw, only seemed to add to the eccentricity of the scene. By the time the farmer had come out and persuaded it back into its field, both the cow and I were several pounds lighter.

\*     \*     \*     \*

'It's bound to be in the local paper,' Josh predicted later. 'Scarlet Broadwell's mum took a picture.'

'In that case, order me ten copies,' Mac's face was triumphant. 'They could prove to be very useful should I ever need to prove your mother's insanity!'

'The embarrassment of it all,' Claire shuddered later that evening. 'All my friends heard about it. I'll be a laughing stock at school.'

'Well, what was I supposed to do?' I complained. 'I didn't ask it to go running off.'

'You should have kept the gate shut,' Lizzie said knowingly.

'Quite right. Your mother's finally realised that she's not the country bumpkin she thought she was,' said Mac. 'Still I'm sure you'll know better next time, won't you dear,' he added unnecessarily as he patted me patronisingly on the hand.

But luckily there wasn't a next time and, on the whole, the local wildlife gave us few problems. The rabbits and squirrels that pranced around the garden every morning brought endless delight to Archie and Lizzie. They gave them all names and convinced themselves that some of them were tame. Then there was our neighbour's cat. Every morning, against my better judgement, Lizzie would put out a saucer of milk, ensuring its regular attendance. But the day she forgot, forcing Dibbles to go in search of other forms of nourishment, was one she'll never forget. The moment Lizzie pulled back the curtains and saw Dibbles eating the last mouthful of 'Snuffles the rabbit' was not a morning any of us would like to repeat.

\*    \*    \*    \*

'If you could have a nose transplant, would you still be allergic to pollen?' Josh wondered one evening as I sat at the tea-table nursing a large packet of tissues.

'Possibly? But I'm not sure it's that simple. Anyway, apart from this time of year, I quite like my nose.'

'Do you?' Josh sounded surprised. 'I'd have thought you'd have liked a new one.'

'Why?' I asked defensively. 'What's wrong with the one I've got?'

'If you had one like Rebecca's Mum,' Lizzie considered. 'I think you'd look younger.'

'Lizzie's right.' Josh reflected. 'Hers is less thin and bony than yours. I bet the extra padding would take out some of the wrinkles you've got round your nose and mouth too.'

'And your face wouldn't be so blotchy for months on end,' added Claire who'd just come in. 'I think you should try it.'

'Thanks,' I snapped. 'I'll bear it in mind.'

### LEAFLETS

'I presume the problems with your nose have got you out of any involvement with the flower festival,' Mac had seen the poster pinned to the church notice board. 'At this time of year, all that pollen in a confined space would probably finish you off once and for all.'

'Mmmm,' I nodded. It wasn't very convincing.

'Oh God, please don't tell me you've volunteered to help. That really would be so stupid.'

'No I haven't! Think about it. They were hardly likely to ask me to do anything in the church. My ability, or lack of it, in the flower department is legendary.'

'So what are you doing?'

'Technically nothing. They've asked the children to deliver some leaflets round the village. I swear that's all we've been asked to do.'

'Asked the children?' Mac gave a derisive laugh. 'We both know what that means, don't we?'

I stared at the pile of leaflets on the hall table and sighed. They had been there since Moira, our church warden, had handed them to me early that morning. At the time it had seemed a simple request.

'I don't suppose your older two would be able to pop these leaflets through everyone's door during the coming week?' she had wondered. 'It would be such a help.'

I had taken the leaflets and smiled. But as Mac knew, I wasn't holding my breath either.

When I suggested the idea to Claire and Josh later that evening, they hardly jumped at the idea.

'I couldn't possibly do it,' Claire protested. 'I've got exams next week and I shall be far too busy revising. I really want to get good grades.'

'That'll be a first then.' Mac glared at his eldest daughter. 'Your last report didn't exactly put 'determination to do well' as one of your priorities!'

I turned to Josh. He was looking indignant too. 'If she won't help, I don't see why I should do it all. That's not fair. Anyway, I can't possibly do them on my own,' he sighed. 'It would take me ages.'

'This village only has four roads,' I pointed out. 'If you got your skates on, you could do it in less than an hour.'

But by Wednesday they still hadn't moved from the table. If we didn't deliver them soon, we'd miss the deadline.

So, after lunch, I set off with both Lizzie and Archie in tow. It was a warm afternoon. Everywhere gardens were bursting with summer flowers. The village looked lovely.

A mix of black and white timber-framed buildings, Warwickshire red brick houses and a few cottages made of local stone lined the main road. Some were set back, their gardens a riot of colour, while others had front doors that opened almost straight onto the pavement. Several had old, gnarled pear trees crawling up the front, while others were covered in Virginia Creeper which, in autumn, would curtain any upstairs windows with its thick, red leaves.

Half way down the road was the wide entrance to a large farm. Here the parish council had thoughtfully placed a bench for anyone wanting to break their journey and enjoy the beautiful buildings in their glorious countryside setting. But there was no time to sit and reflect today. I had two enthusiastic 'tinies' with me who, unlike their elder siblings, found the idea of 'playing postman' overwhelmingly exciting.

It didn't take long for the novelty to wear off.

Two hours and several crushed fingers later, we had completed our task.

'I could never be a postman,' I complained to Mac that evening when the children were in bed. 'By the time we'd got to the end of this lane, Archie had narrowly avoided being bitten by a dog, Lizzie had got her fingers stuck in a letterbox with a vicious spring on it, and I'd been yelled at by that grumpy man on the corner who told me in no uncertain terms that he didn't take kindly to people he didn't know cluttering his doormat.'

'He's got a sign up on the gate saying 'No Hawkers or Circulars.'

'Well, if you think I was going to notice things like that when I had two little ones running amok and showering leaflets like confetti across the countryside, you are sadly mistaken. But it wasn't all bad. When you deliver things through people's doors, you do get a chance to have a closer look at their houses. You know that new couple who moved in a few weeks after us? Well, they're painting their hall a kind of psychedelic pink! And Mr Green was really strange. When we peered through the window, he was sitting in his lounge in his pyjamas and it was two o'clock in the afternoon.'

'That's because he came out of hospital yesterday afternoon having had an operation on his foot. Honestly, Kate, I'm surprised at you.'

'Oh, and that family down School Lane obviously got that planning permission they were after.'

'How did you discover that?'

'When Archie fell head first into their footings. It could have been very nasty. Then Lizzie nearly drowned herself in a pond I didn't see. I only just managed to grab her coat tails in time.'

'Did you manage to get as far as Upbank Farm? I wouldn't have thought you could have resisted the opportunity to have a closer look?'

'Certainly not! Who do you take me for? Actually, the truth is, I just might have wandered up there, if I'd had the chance. It would have been so easy to look legitimate, you know, with all those leaflets to deliver. But Lizzie and Archie had had more than enough by the time we had it in our sights. Pity though, I'd love to know what went on that night.'

'You can't leave it alone, can you?'

'I'm only wanting to find out the truth so that I can do something to help. Something's not right. Judy looked distinctly agitated when I saw her the other day.'

'Honestly Kate, you do say some daft things sometimes. She's got twin boys to deal with. That's enough to make most women agitated for a lifetime. If you want my opinion, I think Judy and James are fine. We've seen them together loads of times and they've behaved perfectly normally and seemed perfectly happy. Like I've said all along, there'll be a simple explanation to that 'flood' incident, and I think that time has proved me right. The whole episode has been a 'storm in a teacup' created by a couple of village busy-bodies who you've taken seriously. I'm not saying your motives weren't good, but all you've done is get yourself worked up over nothing! Let the matter drop before you do or say something you're bound to regret.'

'Yes, maybe you're right.'

'There's no maybe about it. I am right!'

'Mummy,' Lizzie interrupted. 'Tell Daddy about the pony man.'

'What? Oh yes. By far the best discovery of the day was the alleyway between Martin's house and the Village Hall. Did you realise that there's a small cluster of houses down there? We've lived here for months now and I never even knew they existed. That old man called Bert lives in the end one. You know, the man who rescued me from the flood. You met him briefly when he brought his horse to the fete.'

Mac nodded distastefully. It wasn't difficult to recall that disreputable man and his apology for a horse.

'Anyway, he invited us in for a cup of tea. He seemed sweet. However, all was not as it seemed. When I bumped into Moira on our way back, I told her about our meeting and she filled me in with a few details. Apparently he's lived in the village all his life. Was a bit of a wild child…Jack the Lad, you know. He was in trouble with the police a few times in his youth for a variety of minor offences. But, he's a reformed character now, though, according to Moira, still a bit of a mean 'so and so' at times. When I told her he'd let the children stroke his horse and then offered us all some sweets from the bowl on his dining room table, she looked appalled.'

'Why?'

'According to her, he's had them there for years. Every so often he takes one to suck. When he's had enough, he wraps it up again and puts it back in the bowl!'

## THE PAPER CHASE

By the beginning of August, my nose and eyes had recovered sufficiently for me to start believing I was a normal human being again. The surrounding countryside lost its 'off limits' sign and I was suddenly desperate to run across the neighbouring fields sniffing the hedgerows. There was only one problem. The places I most wanted to visit didn't offer me that option.

'The trouble with living in the countryside,' I moaned to Mac one evening, 'is that you may look out over glorious fields and woodland but unless there's a public footpath nearby, you aren't allowed to walk on them.'

'That's because they don't belong to you,' he replied, clearly surprised that I'd failed to grasp this simple concept.

'Precisely,' I was warming to my case. 'It's like taking you to a sweet shop and then not letting you eat the sweets!'

Mac gave me a look which made it clear he thought the analogy was highly flawed.

Mac grew up in the countryside. We lived on the edge of a village but he would have preferred to be in a remote farmhouse in the middle of nowhere. I maintained we had the perfect compromise. If I looked out of my study window I could see the church and the other houses in the lane and feel I was part of a community. If he looked out of the windows at the back of the house, he could only see open fields and imagine he was quite isolated......well, nearly!

We'd been in the Vicarage for almost six months and, in spite of my hay fever break, we'd done nearly all the footpaths within the parish boundary. I was now looking for something a bit different. I asked Moira if she had any bright ideas.

She thought for a moment. 'Well, you could try up by Marden Woods. But be careful in the shooting season. The farmer keeps his pheasants up there. Just watch you don't get 'peppered' with shot.'

Funnily enough, we didn't take her up on her suggestion.

But, of course, we were lucky. We had a big garden and, as many of our friends were farmers, our children were often invited to play and get thoroughly filthy on their land too.

So it was that one afternoon during the summer holidays we were invited to a birthday party at a nearby farm. The games were to be traditional and, weather permitting, would include a paper chase.

'What's a paper chase?' Lizzie was curious.

'People drop paper and you chase it,' Josh's voice was deliberately flat. 'If you live in the countryside Lizzie, that's sometimes about as exciting as it gets!'

'There's a little more to it than that,' I glared at Josh. 'As I remember it, one person is the fox and he's got a bag of shredded paper. He runs off and drops some of the paper at various points to mark his route. After a while the hounds follow (that's you). Your job is to follow the piles of paper until you find the fox. If you get to him first, you're the winner.'

'Is that it?' Claire asked equally flatly. 'I don't think I'll come.'

'Actually, you will miss out,' I said looking at the date. 'You're on guide camp that week. But the rest of us can go and there's going to be a huge picnic afterwards. It'll be great fun.'

'But, mind you watch where you're going,' Mac warned. 'The game doesn't give you carte blanche to run blindly through fields of crops. Listen carefully to the instructions, or you'll be in serious trouble.'

'What do we do when we find the fox?' Lizzie wanted to know. 'Do we pounce on him like a pack of hounds?'

'And tear him to shreds? No such luck,' Josh lamented. 'I agree with Claire. It all sounds rather dull.'

'Unless, of course, you're one of The Railway Children,' Claire remembered. 'In which case a paper chase means dark tunnels, broken limbs and blood.'

Suddenly Lizzie was more interested.

'I remember that one,' said Josh his face brightening too. 'One of the hounds falls on the track and the train comes along and nearly cuts his leg off.'

'Sorry to disappoint you, but there are no trains on the farm. So, no blood, at least I hope not!'

I spoke too soon.

\*     \*     \*     \*

As it turned out, everyone enjoyed it...eventually. The chief hound turned out to be Henry, my friend's eldest son, back from university for the holidays and hugely energetic.

'Come on everyone, get lively. The fox left ages ago. We'll crack this within the hour...if you've got your skates on. Four miles, I reckon, as long as none of you gets lost.'

Josh gave me a withering look. He'd never walked four miles in his life. But Henry was only just getting into his stride.

'Take a whistle each, just in case. And stay in your small groups. There's an adult heading up each one so stick by them or there'll be trouble. Watch out in the woods and by the river. Okay then?'

The slightly bemused gang set off. On the lawn next to the house, a handful of mums settled down to wait. Liberally supplied with coffee and cake, we looked on indulgently as the younger children, including Archie, enjoyed endless entertainment from a pile of sand and a paddling pool.

By the time the gang got back they were all covered in mud, some more than others. To my surprise.. and relief, Josh was beaming.

'Our team won. But the best bit was when Lizzie fell in the mud. She tripped over a log and ....whooosh, she got covered!'

I looked across at my younger daughter. She was grinning from ear to ear and........black.

I cleaned her up as best I could. Then it was tea time, served up on a big picnic rug on the lawn. In the midst of it all was Archie, covered in a delightful mix of crisps, chocolate and orange lolly.

At six o'clock, I was just thinking about leaving, and wondering how I could drag the children away without an embarrassing scene, when my mobile 'phone rang.

It was Aunt Lucy.

'Oh darling. So sorry to be a bother but I've cut my hand and it won't stop bleeding.'

'Oh no,' I exclaimed, 'How did you do that?'

'On a knife sharpener I bought at an antiques fair this afternoon. I tried it out as soon as I got home. It worked a treat. The only trouble was that my hand slipped and the newly sharpened knife went straight into my palm. It's made rather a mess! But don't panic. I've called the doctor and he's told me what to do: apply a firm bandage and go to the hospital immediately. Can you take me or shall I call an ambulance?'

I was on my way.

The thought of a mercy mission was strangely appealing to the children. The idea that the car was about to become a make-shift ambulance made the job of piling them in far easier than it might have been at the end of an exciting day.

Ignoring Lizzie's questions about the possibility of Aunt Lucy dying en route, and closing my ears to Archie's siren noises, we sped off down the road. As we drove along the by-pass I cast an eye over the back seat. Josh was bright eyed. Lizzie, despite the initial excitement, was now struggling to keep awake and Archie was still negotiating a strawberry ice cream in a cone that I had been unable to prise off him before he got into his car seat. As he was filthy from a day romping around the garden with his friends, a colourful spread of ice cream over his clothes, hair and face didn't really make much difference.

*    *    *    *

It was a predictably bizarre sight that met us as we drove into her driveway. Aunt Lucy was sitting outside and had somehow managed to attach her raised arm to a hat stand by some sort of knot.

'The doctor told me to keep my hand elevated,' she explained. 'This seemed the simplest solution.'

'I hope you haven't got any intention of taking that to the hospital,' I warned. 'One look at that and you'd be flung out onto the street.'

'Yes, I had thought of that,' she smiled. 'Probably best to leave it at home. Pity, I bet they won't have anything half as efficient in casualty.'

With some difficulty, I detached her arm from the stand and manoeuvred her into the front seat of the car. In the remote chance of an overnight stay, she had packed her carpet bag. I hardly dared think what was inside it.

'I've asked Mac to meet us at the hospital,' I explained. 'With three children in tow, I hardly think I'm in the best position to look after you properly. No, Aunt, please don't hang your arm out of the window. Other motorists will think I'm signalling or else giving them some kind of rude sign. Look, let me attach your sleeve to the coat hook beside you. There now, that's much better!'

On the way to the hospital I worked out my plan.

By now both Lizzie and Archie were asleep and, with luck, would remain so for a while. Josh would surely be able to keep an eye on them in the car for a few moments while I took her into Casualty. Mac said he would come immediately. That would mean I'd only have to hang around for about a quarter of an hour. The prospect of getting my filthy, sleepy children out of the car was not appealing. One look at them was bound to prompt concern that I was unfit to care for my children, let alone my aunt. Surely it would be better to leave them in the car. I wouldn't be long, would I?

In the end it took about fifteen minutes to get Aunt Lucy into Casualty and properly booked in. Mac arrived looking distinctly hassled having been delayed by the evening traffic.

'Aunt, what have you been up to now?' he demanded. Staring at the blood soaked bandage, he added. 'It looks as if you've been in some kind of fight!'

'She has,' I explained. 'First with a knife sharpener and then with a hat stand!'

Leaving a bemused Mac to make sense of it all, I shot out to the car. As I got close, I realised I could hear the children long before I could see them!

Archie was screaming hysterically. Josh was shouting at him to stop and Lizzie was sobbing in complete bewilderment. It was a scene of complete mayhem!

As I opened the door, the sound rose to a crescendo!

'What's going on?' Glaring at Josh, who I had charged with the task of caring for everyone during my short absence, I yelled, 'What on earth have you done to Archie?'

Full of indignation, Josh retaliated. 'I haven't done anything to him. He just woke up and started screaming.'

'So why is he clutching his arm?' I shouted above the din. 'You must have done something to him. He couldn't have done it himself. He hasn't left his seat. Look at him, he's beside himself.'

But Josh didn't need to look at him to see he had a problem. By now he could be heard half way across the county!

'Arm, arm!' wailed Archie. He was completely inconsolable.

Well, this was a fine state of affairs. My aunt in hospital with a severed hand, and my children left unattended in a car park, all filthy and one clutching a probable broken arm. At this rate I'd be arrested for child neglect!

Above the noise, Josh spoke. His expression had changed from indignation to triumph.

'Well isn't this lucky,' he reasoned. 'Archie's broken his arm and look where we are? In a car park right next to Casualty. It couldn't be more convenient, could it?

Not trusting myself to speak, I leaned over Archie and carefully eased him out of his seat. Suddenly he stopped crying. Looking at his arm, he waved it around and then smiled in relief.

It was only then that I realised what had happened. He must have been lying on his arm while he slept and it had 'gone to sleep' too. All he'd had was a very bad case of 'pins and needles'.

\* \* \* \*

It was about eight o'clock before I managed to tip my exhausted brood into bed. Sleepily Lizzie looked up at me.

'It was even better than the paper chase in 'The Railway Children',
wasn't it Mummy?'

'Yes, I think it probably was,' I agreed.

'We had more blood,' she sighed before drifting into a deep sleep.

I thought of Aunt Lucy and nodded. 'Yes, Lizzie, we did.'

*   *   *   *

It was late when Mac finally arrived home, accompanied by a rather pale-
faced Aunt. After settling her in her room, he appeared, equally pale-faced,
in the kitchen.

'I don't believe it!' Mac sat at the table and buried his head in his hands.
'We only got rid of her in April and now she's back again. Last time it was
her legs that didn't work properly. Now it's her hand. She was bad enough
when she was fairly immobile. God knows what she'll get up to when she's
free to roam about.'

'Oh, it wasn't so bad last time. I quite enjoyed having her. At least it was
never dull!'

'You can say that again. During her stay she managed to dabble in illegal
trading, nearly drown Lizzie, purloin personal property from our bathroom
and cause havoc when she thought we'd been victims of a terrorist attack!
Shall I go on?'

'It'll be easier this time. She knows more people in the village now. Last
time she was bored.'

'Ah, but if you remember, she only calmed down when she started to knit.
With one arm strung up in a sling, that activity will be off the agenda for weeks.'

'Then we'll just have to come up with another hobby. I'm sure, if we put
our minds to it, we'll think of something.'

'You know what our problem is?' Mac moaned. 'We don't see things
coming. Have you noticed that, over the last few years, most of my relatives
have either moved to far flung places or down-sized. We missed that trick.
They now all have excuses for not accommodating their mad aunt. But what
do we do? We do the opposite and buy a much bigger place, leaving us
completely vulnerable! Unless we take action now, she'll end up living here.
I've warned you about that once before.'

'Mac, calm down! It's summer now. She'll be able to get out and about
around the village. She'll enjoy that.'

'If I were you, I'd put the neighbours on red alert and tell them to lock
up their children.'

145

'You're being very unfair. Children love Aunt Lucy. Whenever she's about, they're drawn to her like a magnet.'

'Precisely. She's just like the Pied Piper. And look what happened to those poor kids!'

'Don't be ridiculous!'

'Well, all I can say is, watch out! If you want the reputation of this family to stay intact, I wouldn't let her out of your sight for a moment!'

## STARTING SCHOOL

'The next week promises to be complete chaos,' I announced to Mac one morning as he prepared to leave for work.

'So what's new?' Mac replied with irritating indifference.

'The new term! And a very special new term for the girls. Surely you haven't forgotten. In seven days time Claire will be off to secondary school and Hadbury Primary will be bracing itself for the arrival of Lizzie.'

'So why is that chaos? I thought you'd welcome the peace and quiet. You're always moaning that you can't get anything done when they're all at home.'

'I've got to get them there first. That means buying uniforms, satchels, shoes, pencil-cases etc. The list is endless.'

'You've had all holidays to do that. Why do you always leave everything to the last minute?'

'Partly because children grow so there's no point buying uniform until the last minute. Partly because your dear aunt descended on us with no notice and mainly because children, since time began, hate the idea of preparing for their return to school in the middle of their summer break.'

'So what do you want me to do? I'm in meetings all morning, but I could get a few things in town at lunchtime if that's any help.'

'I don't want you to do anything…except to brace yourself for a rather large hole in your bank account!'

\*   \*   \*   \*

'How is Lizzie coping with 'big' school?' Victoria asked. It was a warm Sunday afternoon in late September and she and I were enjoying coffee and cake on the patio. 'I've been thinking about my little soul mate all week.'

'Surprisingly well, really. We were expecting a big scene. But, so far, she's actually taken to it like a duck to water. Apart from the slight hiccup on Thursday, that is.'

'Go on,'

'All my darling husband's fault, of course. Archie had been unwell overnight so I asked Mac if he could get Lizzie ready for school while I tried to persuade Archie to have something to eat. All he had to do was dress her in the clothes I'd laid out on the bed, give her a bowl of cereal which was already on the table, clean her teeth and remember her satchel which was packed and ready by the back door. Not too onerous really.

At half past eight, we were all in the driveway. While I strapped Archie into his car seat, he put Lizzie in the car next to Josh and Claire and went off to work. We then set off. When we were more than half way there and had just picked up two other children, Lizzie turned to me and asked me, quite calmly, if it was okay to go to school without knickers?'

'You're joking!'

'Sadly not. Tweaking her skirt as discretely as I could, I realised she was indeed knickerless. With five other children in the car, there was no time to go back. So, as soon as we arrived at school I persuaded her to slip her gym shorts on under her skirt and then to try and get to 'break time' without anyone noticing, so that I'd have time to nip home and get the necessary kit.'

'Why didn't you just explain to the teacher? They normally keep spare supplies in case of the odd accident.'

'Ah well, you obviously haven't heard about my first meeting with her in the summer. Thanks to a severe bout of hay fever on Lizzie's trial day, which left my eyes so swollen I kept bumping into things, she already thinks I'm a drug addict or something similar. I didn't really want to add 'kinky' to her list of concerns about me in the first week.'

'And did you get away with it?'

'Miraculously, we did. Mind you, Mac didn't get off so lightly. I gave him a huge mouthful when I eventually got through to him at lunchtime.'

'And what did he say?'

'He thought the whole thing was funny. His excuse was that the kilt was rather fiddly to sort out and, by the time he'd got it on securely, he'd forgotten about her knickers! Hopeless!'

'Actually, I think you're being a little unfair. Considering Mac's a man, I think he did quite well. Most members of the male species struggle to cope with more than a couple of instructions at the same time. I hate to say it, but on that occasion you may have been better off asking Aunt Lucy. After all, she's a bit of a fashion expert. She'd have never forgotten something as important as Lucy's underwear.'

'True. And, being so good with her hands, I bet she wouldn't have had any problems with the kilt either .....even with one arm in a sling!'

'How is she? She must have been with you nearly a month now.'

'Yes. Unfortunately, she damaged a nerve when she cut her hand. So, it's taken longer than we thought to recover. I tell you, having had four weeks of her, Mac's nerves are pretty shattered too. After the last session, he never thought she'd be back so soon.'

'I must say you seem to be holding up very well. Last time she stayed you were on your knees by the end of it all.'

'Last time she didn't know anyone round here. We'd only been here a few weeks, so it was all rather chaotic. This time round she's much more familiar with the locals. She's formed quite an alliance with Bert Moggins. You've met him. He's the one that brought that old pony to the fete. He's also the long-standing owner of some very dubious boiled sweets.'

'Oh yes. He offered some to me the other day but luckily I remembered your awful story!'

'Well, they're as thick as thieves. She's out with him most evenings. I dread to think what they get up to, but I'm not complaining.'

'I don't expect that Bert's a very good influence. I've heard he got himself into quite a bit of trouble when he was younger. Ended up in prison at some stage, I believe.'

'Given Aunt Lucy's track record, I don't think we're in any position to challenge the suitability of any of her friends. As far as I'm concerned, as long as she's happy, I'm happy. Anyway, he's old now. I doubt he's got the energy to do much harm. They're off to the cinema together tonight followed by a meal at the pub. I think it's rather sweet.'

\*　　\*　　\*　　\*

'What time did you say Aunt Lucy would be back?' Mac asked as he made his way up to bed later that evening. 'I must say I didn't expect to be worrying about my aunt's late nights when I got to my age. I thought I was saving that for when my children became teenagers.'

'She didn't say, and I didn't like to ask. So I gave her a key and told her to be sure to lock up.'

\*　　\*　　\*　　\*

The church clock had just struck one o'clock when the doorbell rang.

'Oh God. That'll be Aunt Lucy. I thought you said you'd given her a key?'

'I did. But it wouldn't be beyond her to lose it.'

Tweaking the curtains slightly, Mac looked down on the driveway below. I watched as his expression changed from irritation to horror.

'Kate, it's not Aunt Lucy at the door. It's a policeman.'

## HARVEST

'What on earth were you thinking of? I nearly died of fright when I saw that constable on my doorstep,' Mac was pacing up and down the hall carpet pushing his fingers agitatedly through his hair. 'One assumes the worst you know. With an enormous effort, I brace myself for news of a death in the family, only to discover that the reason for the unexpected visit is you, Aunt....drunk in the back of his patrol car! Have you no shame?'

'There was no need for him to pick me up,' Aunt Lucy sounded defensive. 'I was doing perfectly well on my own. It wasn't as if I'd collapsed on the ground or anything. I was just singing a little song as I went along and the next thing I know I'm being escorted into a car.'

'Singing! This gets worse by the minute! Did it not occur to you that people are generally trying to sleep at that time of the morning? We'll be a laughing stock!'

'I told the policeman that he should be pleased that I wasn't attempting to drive my car home. I would have taken it if my arm hadn't been in this wretched sling.'

'Do you think anyone saw you?' I asked, fearing the reply.

With an effort, Aunt Lucy screwed up her face and tried to think. 'I seem to remember Audrey Broadwell's curtains flickering slightly as I went past…….. but, there again, I couldn't be sure.'

'I could,' Mac sighed deeply. 'That woman never misses a trick. That's it then. The story will be all round the village by the morning.'

'Maybe she won't say anything.'

'Kate, there is an expression in this village which says, if you've told Audrey, you've told everyone. Aunt, you have disgraced the family name.'

I looked at Aunt Lucy. She giggled and then hiccupped. She certainly didn't look remotely chastened.

'I seem to remember several occasions in the past when you've been slightly the worse for wear,' she commented wryly. 'Clearly it runs in the family.'

'I have not been drunk for years. And I certainly don't intend to do so when I'm your age.'

'Frankly, I think you might have been a better person if you had.' Aunt Lucy reflected. 'It would do you good to lighten up occasionally. Besides, I am very young for my years. That policeman said that he was amazed I was still driving at eighty. Mind you, I don't do that so often these days.'

'Don't do what so often?' Mac looked momentarily puzzled.

'Drive at eighty! My old car just doesn't seem to be up to it any more!'

And with that she grabbed the banister and, slowly and a little unsteadily, made her way upstairs to bed.

\*    \*    \*    \*

'Kate, you know I'm not one for gossip, but I bumped into Audrey Broadwell this morning and she told me that Aunt Lucy was picked up by the police last night. She seemed to think she was drunk. I explained that your aunt has recently suffered a serious hand injury and that her unsteady gait may well have been due to the strong painkillers she's taking. I don't think she was very convinced.'

'Thanks for your charitable thoughts, Judy, but I'm afraid the slurred speech, ungainly walk and loud singing that no doubt woke half the village at one o'clock this morning, was purely due to an excess of alcohol.'

Judy stirred her coffee cup slowly. 'Audrey went on to say that Mabel Belise, of questionable psychic fame, was also seen tottering back home about an hour later. You've certainly got some spirited old folks in your village.'

'Well, that's not how Mac sees it. He's furious. Aunt Lucy wisely waited until he'd gone to work this morning before coming downstairs. She's been very subdued every since.'

'She's probably got a hangover.'

'I must say she's even surprised me this time. It's not the sort of behaviour you expect from an eighty year old.'

'I didn't think there was anything about Aunt Lucy that would surprise you. Actually, I think we should all be quite encouraged by her. I'd like to think I could still enjoy a good 'bender' at her age!'

'What am I going to do with her? I naively thought that Bert would help to keep her out of trouble, but, as you can see, it hasn't quite worked out like that. She can't use her right hand at the moment so she can't drive and worse, she can't knit.'

'Oh God, I hadn't thought of that?'

'I tell you, it's a serious problem. If she can't knit, she's got nothing to keep her occupied while she's here. And that means no bed-jackets, hats and socks to sell at car boot sales. They were, by far, her best lines. In short, she's bored. And when she's bored she's mischievous. The same thing happened when she was here earlier this year. And that nearly ended in disaster too!'

'There must be something she can do that doesn't involve her hands.'

'I did have one idea this morning. I've decided that as it's Harvest Festival in the church this weekend, the play on Sunday will centre around a fruit and vegetable market. And, who better than Aunt Lucy to help convey the noise and general chaos of buying and selling. She'll have to be well supervised though. I don't think the mums will be too happy if I leave an elderly woman, with a record of being drunk and disorderly, in sole charge of their offspring.'

'I'd love to see Audrey Broadwell's face when she realises. She'll probably withdraw Scarlet from the play the moment she sees her.'

'If that's the case, I'll make doubly sure that Aunt Lucy plays a major part in the proceedings.'

*   *   *   *

It was around five o'clock that evening when there was a knock on the door. I opened it to find a rather exhausted looking Victoria on the doorstep.

'I know this is a busy time of day for you, but I don't suppose there's any chance I could scrounge a cup of strong coffee?' she asked almost desperately. 'Bit of a cheek really but I've had one of those days. So, as I was passing your door. I thought I'd beg a favour and, at the same time, check the details for the family service. I heard on the grapevine that you've organised an extra helper for Sunday's performance. Is that mad or brave? I couldn't decide.'

'Funny you should say that. That's exactly what Mac said. At the moment, my plan is to create a huge market all over the church, each child with his own stall trying to shout louder than the next that his produce is the best. But the loudest of them all will be the one selling seeds and plants. It could be bedlam. And that's why I thought of asking Aunt Lucy to help. It's her speciality.'

'Markets or bedlam?'

'Both.'

'Excellent! That should get the congregation going.' She paused for a moment. 'But why is the seed seller the loudest?'

'Because he's the one who's trying to get everyone to believe that his seeds will produce the best fruit and vegetables. Except, as the wise customer points out, you can buy the best seeds in the world but if you don't plant them in the right soil and then give them the best conditions to grow, they won't come to anything.....just like a good Christian. See?'

'Just about. But how on earth are you going to make the stalls?'

'That's the easy bit. I've found out that, on Saturday, the church committee will sweep in and cover every available surface with a mass of produce. There'll be apples up the aisles, marrows in the pews, carrots on the font and pears round the pulpit. Judging by the donations they've amassed, there's bound to be loads left over when they've finished the displays, so I'm planning to borrow some of it.'

'And what happens to all the stuff at the end of the service?'

'I've absolutely no idea. Remember, I'm new to all this too. I only found out about it because I overheard Deirdre talking to Abigail in the playground yesterday afternoon. They always organise it.'

'I bet you it'll be sent to some old people's home or shelter for the homeless somewhere. The problem is that the elderly haven't the teeth for apples, unless they're stewed, and the young homeless struggle to get excited by a vegetable casserole. It's just the same with the harvest festivals at schools. Mothers spend hours putting together elaborate boxes of fruit and then the people who need the most help don't know what to do with them when they get them.'

'So what are you suggesting?'

Just then our thoughts were interrupted by Mac. Hurling open the back door with his shoulder, he heaved a large box onto the floor.

'Another load of apples,' he was smiling brightly. From the day we'd moved in, he was never happier than when he was in his beloved garden. 'I've left the pears and damsons in buckets outside on the patio. Just going to pick the last of the plums and that should be it for today.'

I looked at the box in deep dismay. I had been dreading this moment for some time. But Victoria was beaming.

'What perfect timing,' Victoria was almost gleeful. 'That's the answer. Mac is presuming that you are now going to do something with this lot. And now's your chance to put it to good use. You make all this into jams, pies and pickles or whatever you usually do, then you can sell what you don't need to raise money for those who do need it. Look at it all. One family could never get though all this lot. I'll spread the word and then we can have a big produce sale in the village hall after the service using all the donated goodies. I'm sure loads of people will pitch in. We'll send the proceeds to the homes for the elderly and the shelters and they'll make far better use of the money than they ever would with a few pounds of Bramleys!'

I opened my mouth to protest. 'Hey, not so fast, please. You're making one or two wild assumptions here. Firstly, I don't make jam, I've never made jam. I wouldn't have the faintest idea how to start. And secondly, my pastry's rubbish. Nobody would ever want to pay money to eat it. And thirdly, I don't remember your name coming up just now. What's your contribution to all this?'

'Oh I can't make anything. But then if I lived in a lovely vicarage with a huge garden dripping with fruit, and an Aga in the corner of my kitchen, I'd be gagging to do my bit. But, sadly, I don't. So, I'm afraid I'll be the one who has to organise it. You won't have time for that because you'll be too busy cooking!'

I threw a tea-towel in her direction. She was lucky it wasn't one of the apples!

So, the next day, fearing huge recriminations if I didn't do my bit (not from Vicar Vic but rather from the rest of the more talented cooks in the village), I dusted down an old recipe book and looked up 'jam' and 'pickles'.

Dorothy, who had both seen and sampled some of my cooking, was highly amused by the whole idea.

'You give me the fruit and I'll whistle up some jams and pickles for you in no time. Neither Mac, or anyone else, need ever know it wasn't you!'

But much as the offer was tempting, I felt obliged to turn it down. 'Mac will only believe I've done the cooking if he returns to a kitchen that shows signs of a massacre. He knows that all my culinary efforts go hand in hand with a mess. An immaculate kitchen with no smell of burnt jam or charred onion will immediately rouse his suspicions!'

So, an hour later I arrived at the local ironmongers to buy fancy jars, lids, labels and muslin. Next stop the supermarket for special sugar and vinegar. Total cost ... around £30! Then back home to start the challenge. By now, one thing had become glaringly obvious. I was going to have to make an awful of a lot of jam and pickle if the exercise was to be worthwhile!

*     *     *     *

Pickles first. By eight o'clock that evening the kitchen looked like a bomb site and the whole house smelt like a fish and chip shop. Far worse, of the dozens of jars I'd laid out, at least half remained empty. Nobody had told me the full meaning of 'reducing'. What had started out as a brimming bowl of plums, onions, apples and raisins etc, had ended up less than half the original amount. The book had said clearly that when the vinegar had disappeared the pickle was ready. What it didn't say was that you then needed at least another hour to clean the pot and all the other paraphernalia that went with it.

The next evening I bravely tackled the jam. My helpful neighbour had suggested I count the damsons before I started so that I could check that I had retrieved all the stones at the end. Not such a clever idea when you start out with nearly 40lbs of fruit. Luckily I was told to boil them before attempting the extractions. But then I encountered the second problem. If you're long-sighted like me, you can't see the stones, even if they're floating on the surface and, if you wear your glasses, they steam up so you're much worse off than if you'd attempted the exercise without them!

By the time I'd burned my fingers on the hot jars in the oven and got frost bite from the frozen plate in the freezer (apparently the best way to test jam has set!), I'd had more than enough of Victoria's mad plan. But, by the end of the evening, when I'd lined up countless lines of neatly labelled bottles on the work surface, I felt justifiably proud of my achievement. Mac was impressed too. Claiming that it was all down to the quality of the fruit, he gave me an unexpected hug.

'I'll plant some more trees next year. If you carry on at this rate, we could start our own label.'

I was just about to bite into a piece of toast spread thickly with damson jam. He only narrowly missed getting it plastered all over his shirt.

\*　　\*　　\*　　\*

The produce stalls proved to be an enormous success. By the time the last customer had left the village hall, the total cash raised was more than £150.00. Victoria was delighted.

'Well your pickles and jam certainly sold like hot cakes. Are you glad, now that you made the effort?'

'Yes. If today's play is anything to go by, I might have to give up writing in favour of cooking. With a bit of luck, my damson jam may have clawed back some of the self respect I lost during the family service.'

Victoria looked surprised. 'Why are you so glum? I thought it was great.'

'Yes, but you knew what I was trying to say. I'm not sure the congregation were any the wiser by the end of it all.'

'Rubbish. They loved it. Everyone knows the story so it was good to put a different slant on it.'

'And you certainly managed that,' Mac interrupted. 'There was only one thing that puzzled me. Why was Lizzie talking to a pepper?'

'She was nurturing it. The bible says that if you want your seeds to grow into plants that are big and strong, you need to look after them carefully. Just as a Christian needs to listen to the word of God…'

'Hold on a minute. Are you trying to tell me that a pepper that listens to what Lizzie has to say is like a Christian listening to God? I think that's rather stretching the point.'

'She didn't only talk to it, she planted its seeds in good soil and fed and watered it. Anyway, these days, lots of people talk to their plants to encourage their development. Prince Charles did it, if you remember.'

'And whose idea was it for Cosmo to stroke that cucumber?'

'Ah, I was afraid you'd mention that. I rather think Aunt Lucy had a hand in that one. Was it me, or did it look rude?'

'Judging by the dirty laughs from the congregation, I rather think the latter. Luckily none of the children seemed to have a clue why everyone thought it was funny. But unless you want to give your productions an '18' certificate, I suggest you refrain from asking my aunt's advice in the future. I did warn you.'

'Oh, why do I never learn? I was only trying to be helpful.'

Just then Judy walked past looking slightly distracted.

'Are you alright?'

'What? Oh yes I'm fine. James had to go into work early this morning and it rather threw me a little. You know how I enjoy my hour without the children every time there's a service. Anyway, with a bit of luck he'll be home by the time we get back. And he's promised to take us all out to lunch to make up for it. So that's a real treat, isn't it?'

And with that, she scooped up her two and disappeared. I shot Mac an anxious glance.

'Do you really think she's alright?'

Mac sighed. 'Oh God! Not that again.'

'Well, has it occurred to you that it seems that the only time James and Judy spend time together is when the children are here? And that's only once a month. You're the one that tells me that once a night is the bare minimum for a married couple. If that's the case, at the moment, they appear to be a bit behind the game!'

'So are you suggesting he's gone off elsewhere this morning? Seems a bit odd when today, of all days, he could have got what he wanted in his own home.'

'Oh I don't know. It's just that things aren't quite right in that family at the moment. I'm just concerned. That's all.'

'Once again, I think you're overreacting.'
'I'm worried about her Mac. Something's not right. I'm sure of it.'

## FLOWERS

As it turned out, my new role as self-styled domestic goddess was to be short lived. The truth hit me about a week later in the early hours of the morning.

It was one o'clock and Mac and I were trying to sort out the mess in the kitchen at the end of a dinner party.

Having mindlessly tipped the remaining parsnips in with the potatoes and filled a ramekin with a portion of beans nobody was ever going to eat, I came to profound conclusion.

'I think we need to look at the way we organise these evenings. If we had any sense, we'd wave goodbye to our guests and then jump straight into bed.'

Mac's eyes lit up. 'Sounds good to me.'

'No, no, I don't mean that! Seriously though, why do we always clear up at the end of the evening rather than leave it 'til the morning? I'm going to be up at six o'clock with Archie. I'll have at least an hour then to sort this lot out before anyone else even thinks about staggering downstairs.'

Mac didn't need telling twice. 'Right, I'm off. We'll finish this in the morning.'

I thought for a moment.

'No, on second thoughts, come back. It won't work. If we leave things as they are in this old house, the mice will invade. I can almost hear them scrabbling about under the floorboards waiting for the lights to go out.'

'Well at least if they scoff the lot we won't have to worry about it hanging around in the fridge all week gathering mould. I don't mind you saving the leftovers of the main dish for another time, but re-heated parsnips and beans have never quite done it for me.'

'And there's something else,' I continued. Mac sighed. He wasn't much good at serious discussions after several glasses of wine.

'Go on,' he said resignedly.

'I wish I was a better cook,' I lamented, hoping for a bit of sympathy. 'I always feel that I'm so much worse than everyone else.'

Mac thought for a moment before replying. It wasn't quite the reassurance I was hoping for.

'Well, our wines and cheeses are usually quite good,' he said reflectively. 'So, if I were you, I wouldn't worry too much!'

\*    \*    \*    \*

'Did he really say that?' It was the following morning and Judy was looking suitably aghast.

'Well, to be honest, he had a point. His answer really went to the core of the problem.'

'Which is?'

'That I haven't quite caught up with all the developments over the last year.'

'What do you mean?'

I cast my eyes round the room and sighed. 'It's this place. Lots of things have changed for ever just because we live here. For instance, before Mac and I were married, we'd often have people round for supper and I didn't think anything of it. It was always very informal – it had to be. His home was a tiny house in the centre of Birmingham and we neither had a proper dining room table or any suitable chairs. So our guests had to 'muck in'. It was usually good fun but it was always very simple. Often we'd get a 'take-away', or, sometimes, I'd cook a basic meal and people would bring us a cheap bottle of 'plonk'.

Later on, we moved to the cottage where we had a dining room big enough to entertain in……just. Standards were raised, but only slightly. At least now people had something to sit on. With a huge amount of effort I could produce, sometimes, a reasonable meal and guests tended to arrive with a slightly better bottle of wine.

The Vicarage, of course, is made for entertaining. Not long after we moved in, we invested in a proper dining room table and chairs. And, for the first time in our married life, Mac's started inviting clients here for supper. The problem is that my cooking hadn't improved to match the surroundings and, even more frighteningly, these people now tend to arrive with better gifts than before, clearly in the expectation of getting very well fed!'

'But I thought you loved entertaining. This place is always teeming with people. Charity coffee mornings, evening meetings, Easter workshops, not to mention the endless stream of children that pass through your doors. Whenever I come to visit, your driveway is nearly always full of cars.'

'Oh, I love all that,' I admitted. 'Maybe it was just last night's party that got to me. Two of the guests were Mac's main client and his wife. They turned up with the most magnificent bouquet of flowers you've ever seen! I took one look at it and felt this huge wave of panic sweep over me. God knows what the lady thought when she saw my expression. All I could think was, what kind of meal are you expecting if you bring a present like that?'

'I'm sure she wasn't thinking anything on the sort.'

'Well the next half an hour passed in a flurry of activity…you know the sort of thing. While Mac got the drinks, I was sorting out the odd tiresome query from children who should have been in bed, and checking that everything wasn't burning to a cinder in the kitchen. Finding the time to arrange the flowers so that my guests could see them displayed in their full splendour proved to be the straw that broke the camel's back! After several false starts, I finally managed to find a vase large enough to take them, shoved them in as best I could, and then managed to drop the whole lot as I rushed into the dining room to place them in prime position on the table!'

'Oh my God!'

'Exactly! Mind you the only good thing about the whole ghastly business was that it helped to break the ice. After all, it's rather hard for anyone to stand on ceremony when they're all on their hands and knees picking bits of glass and petals out of the carpet.'

'And did the rest of the evening go off without incident?'

'Yes, apart from the rather average meal. The most irritating thing was that, having rescued some the flowers from the floor, Angelica managed to produce the most magnificent arrangement using a rather tatty vase she found in the corner of my utility room.'

'Okay. So you're hopeless at flower arranging. Is that really such a big deal?'

'As it happens, it is. Because, as I fell into bed in the early hours of this morning, I suddenly realised that another floral challenge is looming large and dangerous! The week after next, it's my turn to do the church flowers!'

\*    \*    \*    \*

To be fair, I'd known about my fate for months. But it wasn't until the dreaded piece of paper telling me the dates that were my responsibility fell on my doormat that I started to take it seriously. Should I tell them that, as flower monitor in the top form at junior school, I lasted all of two days before I was replaced. Or that years later when I lived in a small flat in London, my mother used to long for me to go away so that she could sweep in and rescue the half-dead greenery. It wasn't just that I ignored the plants, it was more that I never seemed to learn how to look after them properly.

I confided in Mac, but again his thoughts were unhelpful, if not entirely inaccurate.

'It's your attitude that's all wrong,' he said confidently. 'Until you learn to take life at a slower pace, you'll never be any good with flowers!'

And that's why our house is full of flowers ....but the *dried* variety.

So, as my turn loomed, I got twitchy. With several professional florists on the rota, and many more who were 'naturals' at it, it wasn't just that I was bad at flower arranging, next to them I was utterly hopeless. Then I had a brainwave. I would get some of the village children to help me. After all, it was their service.

So the day before my stint, after a huge amount of false starts, I managed to produce what I considered to be a reasonable arrangement. Having twisted the arms of several mothers, a few agreed to turn up on the day with various size vases containing their own efforts. But I was determined that mine would be the biggest. After all, as I was hardly destined to be the next Paula Pike, it would have to be quantity rather than quality. I decided to give mine pride of place by the main door and then place the children's efforts in more remote corners of the church. But I hadn't banked on the family's reaction.

'Good God, what's that? Mac feigned horror as I approached the door with my effort. 'Is this some kind of bizarre re-enactment from Macbeth, that fateful journey from Birnam Wood to Dunsinane?'

'It really wasn't necessary to make up in size what you lacked in ability,' Aunt Lucy advised unnecessarily. 'If you didn't feel you were up to the job, you should have created something more.......discreet. You should have sought my advice. I'd have been delighted to offer some suggestions.'

'Since when have you ever been discreet Aunt, dear?' Mac looked suitably aghast. 'I didn't think you knew the meaning of the word. It is precisely because of your lack of discretion with a certain cucumber last month that your advice was not sought in this instance!'

Aunt Lucy opened her mouth to protest but then, after a moment, thought better of it.

'Help! What's that?' Josh exclaimed as he came down the stairs. 'Is it some form of human shield?'

'It's for the church. I made a large flower arrangement because the church is a very large space.'

'You'd better make sure people don't think it's some kind of barrier,' Claire advised. 'You'll end up turning them away.'

'I think it's great.' But Josh's words of comfort were short-lived. 'Can we use it in the garden after the service is over. It'll make a great camouflage for our war games.'

Defiant, I ignored their criticism and strode over to the church. Getting it through the door was harder than I'd imagined. But somehow I managed it and, with as much dignity as I could muster I placed it on the large table by the entrance. I then retreated to a dark corner to await the critical eyes of the flower committee.

I didn't have long to wait. As Joyce Brown, chief flower organiser, came through the door I watched as she gasped at my effort. Then, lowering her voice, I saw her whisper to Sandra Bridges, the chief bell-ringer and her noble assistant. 'What is it? Is it some form of modern art?'

'Actually, I think some of the youngsters may have done it.' Sandra advised. 'I did hear Kate say she wanted to involve them in some way.'

'Well it's certainly very child-like. What on earth did she ask them to do? By the looks of it, it seems she sent them out into the garden with a load of twigs and asked them to create a fence!'

'I think it's rather sweet,' Sandra said tactfully, clearly fearful that some of the mothers may overhear their conversation. 'And very different.'

'I wonder what age the children were who created it?' Moira, the church warden, had come to have her say.

'Pre-school.......judging by the look of it. We'll have to move it onto the floor. It's far too big for that table,' Joyce Brown was beginning to sound distinctly irritated.

'Oh I don't think either the children or their parents will like that. They'll want to be able to see their effort from their pews,' Moira, who was always keen to encourage the children, looked round anxiously.

'Well, in that case, you'd better make sure no one uses the pews at the back. They won't be able to see a thing!' Joyce advised, and with that she moved off to find a pew that would ensure her an uninterrupted view of the proceedings. The others followed leaving me speechless and fervently hoping that my family didn't give my secret away.

But if I hoped my nightmare had ended at that point, I was wrong.

'Has someone told you where to find all the watering cans, oasis, plant food etc?' Joyce Brown's voice boomed across the aisle at me at the end of the service. 'It would be a shame to allow some of the arrangements to die before everyone's had a chance to appreciate them.'

I looked at her blankly and then suddenly the light dawned. Horror of horrors, this woman was expecting me to maintain all the flowers until the next person took over. Some chance! But with Joyce in full flight, it was hardly the moment to express reservations.

So, accepting my fate, I allowed her to escort me to the cupboard at the back of the church where a range of flower equipment was arranged neatly on the shelves.

'I know Moira spent ages on that beauty next to the pulpit,' Joyce was quick to point out. 'Hers usually last for ages. She takes such care with her arrangements,' she added unnecessarily. 'It would be a shame to let them die before we'd all had the chance to enjoy them to the full.'

I nodded, noting that she clearly wasn't so worried about the fate of my effort.

'I'll leave it with you then,' she muttered and moved away leaving me to survey the contents of the cupboard with abject horror. Did she realise that the flowers would probably do a lot better if left to fend for themselves. Under my misguided ministrations, they were bound to be dead before the week was up.

However, fearing divine retribution if I didn't make an effort, I bravely entered the church the following afternoon. It didn't take me long to learn that pulling out the dead flowers and watering the others that still clung to life could be a dangerous business.

Having risked my life clambering up to the ledge behind the altar, I discovered that the magnificent arrangement balanced precariously on a high shelf was a dried one! Shame I didn't notice that there was also no life in the one by the coffee table at the back of the church before I watered it. That dose so narrowly missed the electric cable underneath that I spent the next night having nightmares that I'd wake to find the church a pile of smouldering rubble.

\*   \*   \*   \*

It was Mac who saw it first. He'd arrived early for the next family service and quickly spotted the amendment on the notice board.

'Hey Kate. Someone's crossed your name off the flower rota. Blooming cheek!'

But, far from being upset, I was hugely grateful. As far as I was concerned, they were doing me an immense favour.

They probably thought they were saving the village from a fate worse than death!

**FILMS**

Although my shortcomings in the plant department were well known, Mac's horticultural skills failed to give him total control of the garden. From the moment we moved in, I'd had a plan too and, although I said so myself, it was proving to be reasonably successful.

'Has it ever occurred to you to charge Will for the use of this facility?' There was a serious note of sarcasm in Mac's voice. For the third time since we'd moved, I was sitting at my desk planning a film that could be shot entirely within the grounds of our house.

'It's convenient,' I argued. 'So many of the stories I come across involve people round here, it makes sense to use this place as a base. Besides, if I use my own garden, I cut down on all the time I usually spend getting permission to film somewhere else. It saves loads of travelling time too.'

'And how does Will feel about it?'

'Well, he got a bit 'uppity' the other day.'

'What did he say?'

I screwed up my face trying to remember. 'Oh yes, he said: 'May I remind you that our programme is supposed to reflect issues across the Midlands and not just places within a three mile radius of your establishment.' But I think he was just having a bad day. When I pointed out the money it saved him and that we'd done countless pieces from his place over the years, he shut up. To be honest, as long as the story stands up, I don't think he minds.'

But there were disadvantages......

\*     \*     \*     \*

'I'm not doing this again,' I moaned at Mac. 'There's too much tidying involved.'

'You said you weren't house-proud.'

'I'm not. It's just that I don't want people I hardly know to see how we really live!'

'So when exactly are they all arriving?'

'Ten o'clock this morning. And, with a bit of luck, it should be over by mid-afternoon.'

'Well count your blessings that we don't have Aunt Lucy with us any more. I can't tell you the relief I felt when I delivered her home last night.'

'You are awful! Although I agree that she's a bit of a liability, I do miss her in a funny sort of way. And she would have loved today with all the excitement.'

Mac shuddered. 'The thought of my aunt getting stuck into all this is too awful to contemplate. So far, mercifully, most of her misdemeanours have been confined to the village or a few miles beyond. Can you imagine the possible implications of the crew capturing her antics on camera! Emigration would probably be our only option!'

\*   \*   \*   \*

The film was all about a local girl who sold children's clothes from home with enormous success. We were planning to stage one of her sales in our house with a percentage of the 'takings' going to a charity, as that was how she usually operated. The idea was that some of the pre-school children, who were bound to arrive with their mothers (the customers), would model the outfits in the garden if the weather allowed.

'The last thing you need is hundreds of screaming toddlers everywhere.' Will had been very specific when I spoke to him on the 'phone. 'Filming children can take ages, and the days are getting shorter at this time of year. The last thing I'd want you to do is run out of time.'

'So how many children did you have in mind?'

'Half a dozen, maximum. Oh, and by the way, I won't be around. I'm filming in London that day. Your director will be Daniel Stubbs. He's new to our show but he knows his stuff. I'll brief him this afternoon. And, don't worry. He's excellent.'

'Is he used to working with children? I'll know all the mothers, remember. I don't want anyone to be upset.'

'Daniel's got four children of his own. There isn't anything he doesn't know about them.'

'And you'll tell him you only want a maximum of six children?'

'For the last time, yes!'

'Okay, I'll get a group of mums and toddlers round and he can choose the ones he wants. But please tell him to be tactful. Years ago, I worked on a short film for one of the cable channels. With the mothers standing by, the director lined all the children up on the stage. Staring critically at a freckle-faced boy with black hair and glasses, he said to his assistant: 'He's got a weird face, let's use him!' I thought the mother was going to sue us for damages.'

'For goodness sake, Kate, calm down. I assure you, I've got it all under control. Daniel will be very sensitive. You don't need to worry about a thing.'

So I took a deep breath and rang my friends with under fives. They all got the same message.

'If your children would normally be with you, bring them,' I had said clearly. 'If they would usually be at nursery school, I suggest you leave them there. There's invariably loads of hanging around which can be very boring. And,' I added, 'as my boss has made it very clear that he will only use six at the very most, please don't bring them if you think they'll mind if they're not chosen.'

When Will 'phoned back I told him I'd sorted it. There would be no problem. After all, my friends were very sensible. Not one star-struck, 'pushy' mother amongst them!

The day dawned bright and sunny. The crew arrived early and went out to check the garden. With the autumn leaves glistening all shades of red and orange in the sunlight, it was clear that they wanted to 'milk' the weather while it held out. Before I could stop him, Daniel had swept into the lounge where my guests had assembled and started issuing instructions.

'Right, dress all your children in an outfit and bring them outside. I want lots of shots of them playing in the leaves.'

'Hey, not so fast,' I protested. 'Will said he'd tell you we only needed six children.'

'Yes. That's right, he did. But I had a great idea as I was driving here. And it will only work if I have loads of children running around the garden. Trust me Kate, it'll be fine.'

But it wasn't. The sense of indignation amongst my child-free friends was palpable. In the corner, Cordelia, who ran Lizzie's musical movement group, was fuming.

'You told me not to bring Amelia?' She gave me a look that implied I had excluded her on the basis of her looks.

'I didn't say that! I just said don't bring her especially.'

But she wasn't convinced.

'Hugo will be furious when he finds out he's missed out,' Angie from Tumble Tots lamented.

'Well, don't tell him then,' I suggested, 'He's only three!'

'Jessica wants to be a model when she grows up. She'll be so sad to have missed out on all these pretty clothes.' I could see my neighbour was most put out.

'You said it would be boring.' Joanne, my cousin had now decided to join the dissenters. 'Look at them all, they're having the time of their lives.'

I went into the kitchen for a cup of coffee laced with gin! Judy was there filling a kettle. She looked up as I came in.

'I can't understand what all the fuss is about. The idea of bringing my two to a smart clothes sale is too awful to contemplate. I'm relishing every child-free second!'

As the sun shone down, the children rushed about looking adorable in the beautiful clothes. At least the girl who was selling them was pleased. The only consolation I could give to the mothers who had not brought their children, was that Archie, who hadn't started at the nursery yet, would have nothing to do with the proceedings. To that end, I had asked Mac, who was working from home that day, to look after him for the hour that the outside filming was taking place. Under normal circumstances, he would have had his nap during that time so would be no trouble. Mac had heard that one before!

'What's he doing down here?' I demanded when I suddenly spied Archie with a biscuit in his hand. 'For God's sake don't let him near the clothes with that, he'll ruin them.'

'Don't panic! I've got it all under control.' Why was it that whenever Mac said that, alarm bells rang in my head? Casting his eyes round the room his gaze fell on the boys outfits. 'And don't worry,' he continued as he looked down at Archie who was busy rubbing a Jammy Dodger into an already filthy T-shirt, 'we won't be contaminating any of these little designer jobs. When Sarah created this lot, somehow I don't think she had our scruffy son in mind. Good God, look at him!'

Archie was now trying to pick crumbs out of his hair. 'Where did we get him from?' He moved slightly so that one of my smarter friends, whose child was kitted out in velvet knickerbockers and a quilted jacket, could give Archie a wide berth without risk of contamination.

Scooping Archie up into his arms, Mac went into the kitchen to grab a coffee. I took a deep breath and went to see how Sarah was faring.

But neither of us had seen the sou'wester and cape. If we had, we might have averted the forthcoming catastrophe.

It was a few moments later when Mac came up to me and, looking slightly distracted, whispered. 'Have you seen Archie?'

'No,' I said irritated. 'You're the one in charge of him right now. But he can't have gone far. With all these children around, I've bolted every door except the one into the garden and Ann's guarding that.'

A quick search of the house revealed nothing. He couldn't have gone outside, surely?

'Oh God, look,' I called as I peered through the window. 'Disaster!'

Tearing round the garden, followed closely by the cameraman and Daniel, was our son. With a red sou'wester pulled right down over his head and a long red cape flying out behind him, he was clearly in his element. Fireman Sam meets Superman! And in hot pursuit we had Lex Luther and his gang, at least that was how Archie saw it. Round the bushes, through the mud, across the flowerbed and up a tree. When he finally came the rest, the sou'wester was over his left ear and the cape was covered in mud.

'Where did he get that outfit from?' I was completely confused.

'It was on the table in the hall,' Sarah explained. 'I went out there to get my bag and he was trying it on. He looked so cute I decided to take him outside. Look at him, he thinks he's flying!'

I looked again. Archie was jumping off a tree trunk, his arms waving frantically. I didn't see anything cute about it!

Daniel was beaming when he came up to me a moment later.

'That was wonderful,' he panted. 'We'll get the Superman theme music and run it under the pictures. It'll look great. Your timing was perfect. We were just looking for something to liven things up a bit. Quite the star of the show!' He looked down as a somewhat dishevelled Archie came up beside him.

The two girls standing within earshot of me, whose children were currently at nursery school a mile down the road, gave me a stony stare.

'I never thought he had it in him,' Mac was obviously feeling proud of his youngest child.

'He only ran round the garden,' I pointed out, 'managing to ruin all my plans in one fell swoop. By the time he blazes across the screen looking like some kind of demented superhero, I'll have lost all the friends I've ever had!'

Later that evening, when I told Claire and Josh what had happened, they were equally unimpressed.

'We'll be the laughing stock of the neighbourhood,' Josh reflected, 'I shall probably have to move schools to escape the embarrassment.'

'It was all your father's fault,' I said bitterly.

'When he's earning millions on the big screen, you'll eat your words,' was Mac's only comment.

## ALL EYES

When Mac had first seen the Vicarage, he'd imagined a haven of tranquillity, a place where he could have complete privacy from the prying eyes of the outside world. Admittedly, my idea of having film crews in the garden had put paid to some of that, but it soon became clear that there were some who found gawping at us a mesmerising experience.

For a start, few people had a better excuse to stare for hours into our garden than the fishermen who had rights on the river that ran alongside our land.

'I find their blank expressions quite disconcerting,' I confided to Mac one afternoon. 'For all we know they could be spying on us, monitoring our every move.'

'I caught Lizzie pulling faces at them earlier. I think she was trying to see if they were real. They don't seem to move a muscle for hours on end.'

Then there were the tourists who, throughout the year, came to admire the church which claimed, with some justification, to have many 'Shakespeare' connections. Once they'd seen all there was to see inside the church, many would gaze up and down our lane peering through the windows as if in hope of finding one of the Bard's relatives.

'I think some of them think that Lower Hadbury is some kind of theme park,' Mac concluded as he gazed out of the study window at a group of American tourists who'd been gawping at our house for the best part of ten minutes. 'With all the black and white timbered buildings and the ancient church, they probably think half the village is paid to act out the lives of ordinary people from another time.'

'Hardly ordinary in our case.'

'True.'

As if to prove this point, one morning, I discovered Claire at her bedroom window acting out what appeared to be a selection of Lady Macbeth's more dramatic moments, while half a dozen Chinese students looked on in bewilderment.

When I later questioned her eccentric behaviour, she was defiant. 'They'd been staring at me doing nothing for quite a while, so I thought I'd give them something more interesting to look at.'

So, on the whole we shrugged our shoulders and, like most of the other villagers, put up with the extraordinary interest our part of the world seemed to generate.

But it was Aunt Lucy who put it more succinctly.

A screech of brakes heralded the arrival of Mac's elderly relative one Sunday in late Autumn. Two minutes later, raised voices could be heard in the driveway. Mac was outside in a second.

Aunt Lucy had leapt from her car and was yelling at Josh who was half way up one of the oldest yew trees in the churchyard trying, unsuccessfully, to shake his ball down by hurling his racket repeatedly at the higher branches.

'Stop that at once,' she shouted. 'That tree is probably several hundred years old. If you damage it, you'll be destroying a piece of history.'

Mac's reaction was rather more blunt.

'What the hell do you think you're playing at?' he yelled. 'Get down at once before you do any more damage!' Ignoring the surprised look from the gathering of Christening guests who were in the churchyard, he continued: 'I never thought I'd hear myself saying this but, for once, your aunt is quite right. Those trees have been there for centuries. What do you think gives you the right to hack them to bits? I hadn't realised I'd fathered one of the village hooligans.'

'I wasn't trying to hack it to bits,' Josh protested. 'I just wanted my ball back.'

Seeing a couple of guests he half recognised, Mac strode back into the house, bristling. Aunt Lucy followed, leaving Josh at the mercy of the Christening party as he planned his descent.

*   *   *   *

Unusually, Aunt Lucy had come to baby-sit while Mac and I nipped down the road to a drinks party. Mac had been unhappy about the arrangement, but I had insisted.

'She'll burn the house down,' he muttered darkly. 'They'd be far safer left to their own devices.'

'Don't be silly,' I argued in her defence. 'Besides, I couldn't get anyone else to come on a Sunday lunchtime. And we're only down the road. We shouldn't be gone for more than a couple of hours. We can't possibly leave Claire in charge. Archie is only two years old. Aunt Lucy won't have to do much. Lunch is all ready. I've made a big salad and it's all in the fridge. It'll be fine. Archie will be asleep for most of the time. She won't have time to do anything wrong.'

But when we returned around three o'clock, we were greeted by a group of slightly indignant looking children.

'She's been going on and on about custard,' a slightly bemused looking Lizzie told us as soon as we came through the door. Claire was more forthcoming.

'It would have been a lot more interesting if it had been a talk about custard,' she moaned. 'But for about an hour after you left, she went on and on about our responsibilities as 'custodians' in this village. Thanks to Josh's antics up a tree, we were reminded again and again that we had to look after our beautiful surroundings for future generations. Then, to make it worse, Vicar Vic arrived asking if we had any books on the history of the village as, following the success of the reminiscence afternoon, she wants to write a series of light-hearted articles for the parish magazine. Aunt Lucy invited her in and they talked for ages. Lizzie was convinced that 'custodians' was another word for custard and got the idea the vicar was writing a cookery article. That's when it all got a bit confusing.

'Where's Aunt Lucy now?' I asked looking around.

'She's asleep. I think all that talking must have exhausted her. She sat down in the lounge about half an hour ago and we haven't heard a peep out of her since!'

Mac gave me one of his 'I told you so' looks.

'Not much point putting a responsible adult in charge if the moment we turn our backs, she's out for the count.'

'Oh, but we do have responsible adults here,' Claire was quick to point out. 'They're upstairs.'

'Who's upstairs?' I asked nervously.

'Just before Aunt Lucy took her nap, a couple knocked on the door and the lady explained that she was evacuated here during the war. She lives in Australia now. She's come to England with her husband to learn more about Shakespeare and to retrace her roots. Aunt Lucy invited them in and now they're upstairs so that the lady can show her husband the room that was once her bedroom.'

Mac was up the stairs in a flash. As he shot into the front bedroom, a slightly bemused looking couple turned to greet him.

After a short cross examination, Mac conceded that the visitors might possibly be genuine. Reluctantly, he decided to give them the benefit of the doubt. They, in turn, had been highly embarrassed to discover that Aunt Lucy was not the owner of the Vicarage. 'She gave us the impression that this was all hers,' they explained. 'She actually said that she saw her role as custodian and that it was her duty to share this lovely home with anyone who expressed an interest in it. We will always be so grateful that she made us so welcome.' A slightly strained looking Mac assured them that it was no problem. But no sooner had he seen them off the premises, than a rather sleepy Aunt Lucy was shaken awake.

'While you were sleeping peacefully, that couple could have been upstairs stealing the family silver!' he fumed.

'Aunt dear, you really can't go about letting total strangers wander around the house at will. It isn't safe.' I added.

'I knew they were genuine,' Aunt Lucy defended herself. 'I could tell the moment I set eyes on them.'

'Aunt, for your information, prospective burglars do not always arrive in balaclavas carrying crowbars. Before you got the Dobermans, I seem to remember that you played host to several people who had distinctly unworthy plans for your property. As I recall, you even invited one of them to tea before he took himself upstairs to nick your stuff. For all we know, those two could have been 'casing the joint' this afternoon. If you want to claim you're a custodian looking after the surroundings for future generations, you're going to have to do better than that. It won't go down too well with me if, over the next few weeks, we discover that half the contents of the Vicarage had been shipped out to Australia..... with your help.'

But Aunt Lucy was quick to retaliate. 'Last time I was here, I seem to remember a wedding party appearing out of the blue just as we were having drinks on the lawn. You didn't know them from Adam, but you seemed perfectly happy to allow their photographer to take shots of them by the river. How do you justify that?'

Mac could see just where this was heading.

'That's different. They were in the garden,' he argued defensively. 'Besides, it's always been a custom in this village to allow that to happen. It's gone on for generations! Lizzie loves it. Whenever she's here she puts on her fairy dress and hands out sweets to the waiting guests. It makes her feel part of the proceedings. You could say that she is now the 'custodian' of that particular tradition.'

Suddenly Lizzie burst into the room. She was clutching a small furry kangaroo. 'Look what that nice Australian lady gave me,' she exclaimed.

Mac snorted. Aunt Lucy looked wistful.

'In a small way, that will add to the history of the house,' she commented. 'A charming reminder of one of its former occupants.'

*     *     *     *

'Quite an eventful day,' I whispered to Lizzie as we trudged across the hills later that afternoon. 'That kangaroo is beautiful.'

'Was Aunt Lucy always that dizzy?' Josh wondered. 'Or is it just old age that makes people go funny?'

'She can be quite serious sometimes,' Claire reflected 'She was really interested in Vicar Vic's history project on the ups and downs of village life. I think she's going to help her write it.'

'Well, she did run an antiques business with her husband for many years,' I explained. 'On that basis, she's bound to be interested in the past.'

'The less said about Aunt Lucy's past, the better,' Mac sounded anxious. 'Heaven help us all if any of that gets into Vicar Vic's booklet!'

'She's certainly very keen on preserving old things,' Josh added bitterly, recalling his encounter with his aunt in the churchyard earlier that day. 'All that business about custodians sounded quite scary.'

'Lizzie thought that 'custodian' was some sort of winter pudding,' Claire mocked unable to resist the jibe.

Suddenly Josh's face brightened. 'If they do ever get round to writing the history of this village, I bet they'll call it something boring like 'The History of Lower Hadbury'.' But after what Lizzie said, I've got a much better title which is guaranteed to sell heaps more copies.'

'Go on?' Mac asked, bracing himself.

'Given that most of our village events seem to involve the mums preparing home-made food at some point, and not everybody's very good at it,' he added unnecessarily,' 'I think they should call their book 'Lumpy Custard!''

We carried on for a few more minutes until we reached the top of the hill. As we reached the summit, we were rewarded with a wonderful view across the valley. Suddenly Claire clutched my arm. 'Mummy, look, down there. That's Fred and Eddie's dad, isn't it?'

I followed her gaze. Strolling calmly along the path below was James..... with his arm around the shoulders of a beautiful young girl.

'Damn,' I looked at Mac and sighed. 'I knew I was right but I so hoped I wasn't.'

## BOXES

For the next twenty four hours, I worried about the implications of James' behaviour. And, despite being fairly dismissive about it all to Claire, I was very anxious about what she'd made of it. To that end, I needn't have been so concerned.

The following evening, she suddenly appeared in the kitchen, bursting with excitement.

'Mummy, I've had the most brilliant idea. I thought about it all last night. You don't need to worry any more. I've worked everything out for you.'

'Oh darling, how sweet of you to worry so much. What do you think we should do?'

'I think we should have a Halloween party.'

'A Halloween party? How on earth would that help Judy?'

'Judy? Why should I want to help Judy? You asked me the other day to think about Lizzie's birthday. And I think that a Halloween party would be perfect.'

'Hold on a minute. Last night she said that she didn't want to have a party this year. She'd like to take some friends to the cinema instead.'

*171*

'Well, she's changed her mind. Josh and I have just spoken to her and she thinks that a party where everyone can dress up and play lots of spooky games and have lots of spooky food would be much more fun.'

'And was she instantly keen or was she subjected to some heavy persuasion, I wonder?' Mac interrupted. 'Sounds to me like you and Josh would be quite keen to muscle in on the action too. Are you sure it's really what *she* wants?'

'No. Honestly, she's really keen. She just hadn't thought of it before.'

'And what suddenly gave you the idea?'

'It was the house that made us think of it,' Josh reasoned. 'Now that the cellar's finished, we've got the perfect room for it. Think about it…..a basement full of spooky corners right next to a graveyard. It would be perfect.'

But I had reservations. 'Hold on a minute, not everyone approves of Halloween. When Josh had a 'pumpkin' party a few years ago, I seem to remember that a couple of mothers from our old church refused to let their children come. Now that we live in a Vicarage, there's even more chance that we'll upset some of the locals.'

'Well that's even better then,' Josh was quick to reason. 'If half the people we invite don't come, it'll be far less work for you. And, as we still have the stuff from the last party somewhere, you'll save heaps of money on decorations too.'

'Well I'm not sure,' I protested. 'I'll have to think about it. I don't really want to start upsetting people so soon after we've moved in.'

But, across the table, Mac's view was different. 'I think it's a good idea. Having almost reached the end of October, I've just started to realise what it's going to cost me to heat this place over the winter. So, I'm keen to make a few cutbacks. A party for which we already have the 'kit', that confines most of the mess to the cellar, and where half the people are unlikely to turn up, sounds like a cheap form of entertainment to me. Far more sensible than a trip to the cinema which would doubtless have to include feeding a gang of starving kids at some fast food outlet too.'

As Josh and Claire gave me a triumphant look across the table, I could see that I was beaten.

'Okay,' I said, still with great reservations. 'If it's really what Lizzie wants, we'll see.'

*   *   *   *

To: Kate Arnold
From: Judy Barton

Apologies for e-mailing rather than 'phoning, but due to lack of voice at the moment, this was only alternative.

Arrived in the Lake District for mid-term break with my parents and have been confined to barracks ever since. Clearly am now being punished for being so smug about my natural immunity to all bugs brought into the house since the boys started school. It now appears that, far from dodging them, they have been lying dormant in my body and have chosen this week to join forces and ravage me. For three days now I have barely been able to lift my head off the pillow. Ironically, my mother is telling everyone that she's delighted to see me getting so much enforced rest. Frankly, some sun-drenched beach in the south of France just might have been a better way of doing it! And, to add insult to injury, James had to leave today as he's been called to an urgent meeting in Birmingham. Despite his protestations, it wasn't too difficult to work out that he was rather pleased to go. No doubt the thrill of being on his own with me, whilst granny whisked the kids off somewhere, has been somewhat dampened by the sight of my snotty nose, swollen eyes and hacking cough! He's left me his lap-top as that's the only way he has any chance of communicating any vital information!'

To: Judy Barton
From: Kate Arnold

So sorry to hear about your sad predicament. Hope you feel heaps better soon. Mac, however, although concerned about your health, is delighted by our new method of communication. Recent 'phone bill was almost as much of a shock as our heating bill.

By the way, did you, by any chance, find Lizzie's invitation for her Halloween party in the boys' school bags last Friday? Would have told you about it, but everything has been, as usual, very 'last-minute' here. And, as you were dashing off on holiday straight from school that day, I didn't get a chance to talk to you.

To: Kate Arnold
From: Judy Barton

Thanks for reminder. They'd love to come. Usually only find out about parties when an irritated mother rings to ask if we ever received the invite!

Must make more effort to brave the often unspeakable contents of my kids' satchels. Surprised you are celebrating Halloween. Thought Claire was pathologically afraid of anything spooky!

To: Judy Barton
From: Kate Arnold

Halloween party's fine as she knows it's all make believe. And, as it's aimed at five year olds, she's worked out that there won't be too many scary surprises. No 'Murder in the Dark' or spooky 'Sardines'. Instead, plenty of apple bobbing and dressing up!

To: Kate Arnold
From: Judy Barton

Yuk! Last year we tried 'apple bobbing'. However, did not realise ghastly consequences until I'd blown whistle to start. Then watched in horror as six snotty noses dived into the water. In less than a minute, apples had taken on a slimy hue as water turned into 'snot soup'. No better form of cross infection in the world! My hitherto healthy children 'streamed' for a week!

To: Judy Barton
From: Kate Arnold

Good advice. Will attach apples to string and hang them from the washing line instead. More hygienic but rather more tricky. Given their tiny milk teeth, they should take about a week to eat them! With a bit of luck, that would also save me the bother of providing other forms of nourishment, though Lizzie has made that easier than usual. She's requested party food with a 'black' theme......has always been my speciality anyway! Also, black costumes are the order of the day. Aunt Lucy has just found some black-out curtains at one of her sales and has promised to make them for me. Lizzie wants to be a bat. Having missed out on adopting the one that temporarily took up residence in Josh's room earlier this year, she's become obsessed with the creatures. I think it's the wings. She's already got about four pairs of glittery ones to go with her various fairy outfits. I think she believes that a pair of bat wings will add serious status to her collection.

To: Kate Arnold
From: Judy Barton

And does this mean that Aunt Lucy will also be a guest at the party?

To: Judy Barton
From: Kate Arnold

Oh yes. Despite Mac's insistence that she resists the temptation to dress up, to avoid embarrassing us or our children, she's determined to come as the Wicked Witch of the North.

To: Kate Arnold
From: Judy Barton

And how did Mac react to that?

To: Judy Barton
From: Kate Arnold

Surprisingly, he thought it was perfect….doesn't think anyone will notice the difference!

\*   \*   \*   \*

'Look at these. I spotted them in one of those cheap shops in town yesterday. They'll be perfect for the party bags.' It was the following Sunday and a somewhat pale looking Judy was sitting at our kitchen table cautiously sipping a cup of coffee. On the floor next to us, Fred, Eddie and Lizzie were whooping with delight as they explored the contents of our Halloween box.

Astonished, Judy looked on as I wound up a little plastic box. A second later, the lid opened and a skeletal hand snatched the penny I'd placed on the top. 'What do you think of that? Does that bring back any memories? I'm sure I remember having something similar when I was their age.'

For a moment Judy stared at me, a strange look in her eyes.

'What's the matter? Oh help! I haven't offended you, have I? Don't you approve of Halloween either?'

'No. It's not that. When I was a kid I liked nothing better than to dress up as a witch and frighten my friends. But I'm amazed that you, of all people, should send out coffins as party presents given that it's not just Lizzie's birthday.........it's also Sarah's!'

I paused for a moment and stared down at the minute coffin in my hand.

'But a tiny toy like this, doesn't, for me, have any connection with the horror of losing my beautiful baby.'

'No, I suppose it wouldn't. But all your friends think about you at this time of year, and some will make that connection and might think you're being a little flippant!'

'I would never be flippant about Sarah. You, of all people, should know that.'

'Of course I do. It was just that seeing you with a joke coffin shook me a little! I suppose I thought that anything like that would trigger your memory.'

'I don't ever need my memory triggered! Mac and I changed forever on the day she died. But silly things like this don't touch me. Hearing about other babies who have died or been seriously ill, now that does affect me, as does seeing pictures of children starving in Africa. But Halloween and all that goes with it, is entirely different. Having a birthday at the end of October means that Halloween will always be associated with Lizzie and Sarah's birthday and there's nothing anyone can do to change that. The last thing I want is for her to become fixated about all the spooky things on sale in the shops at this time of year. If I allow her to do that, I'll have done her far more harm than any silly box can do!'

'Yes, I can see that now. Actually, now that we're on the subject, I often wonder how you feel about my two...you know, seeing them grow up together, especially as they're almost exactly the same age as Lizzie and Sarah. You see, although I didn't know you then, your ordeal often haunts me, particularly as I feel sure that I'd have never been brave enough to befriend someone with twins born at a similar time. I just don't think I'd have been able to cope.

'Well, we never really felt we had those choices. Sarah was born with a serious heart condition which, within three weeks, killed her. We had to keep going because of Claire, Josh and baby Lizzie. It was very hard work when we both felt so terrible but we were so lucky to have them to comfort us. I simply can't imagine what it must be like to lose your only child. Sarah's death was too awful to imagine but at least we had other children to cuddle during our darkest moments. Without them, I've no doubt that we would have both fallen apart.

And as for your twins, well, just look at Lizzie now. She's been a different child since she's had Fred and Eddie to play with. I would never have wanted to deny her that.'

'Yes, I can see that now. Sorry Kate, I shouldn't have mentioned it.'

'No. You're wrong. You should mention it. If you must know, I quite like to talk about it. Most people avoid the subject, partly because they find it awkward and partly because, being so little when she died, only our close family have any memories of her. She never came home from hospital, you see.'

'Do you still spend a lot of time thinking about her?'

'Yes. but in a different way. The pain I get now is more for Lizzie. Although her friendship with your two has helped her enormously, she's still the loner in our family. Josh and Claire are close in age and, most of the time, get along reasonably well. So, when she muddles things in her head, as she frequently does, and throws the odd tantrum, I yearn for Sarah to be here to defend her. Archie isn't old enough yet to be a proper playmate for her.'

'I'm not sure that my two are always that quick to defend each other. Sometimes I think they're glad when the other one gets into trouble.'

'Yes. I know and I've seen your two fight like cat and dog on several occasions. All siblings do that but basically, they're inseparable, and, I think, much closer than they would be if they were different ages. I notice that and I think Lizzie does too. She knows she's a twin so she's probably begun to work out what she's missing. Who knows?'

Judy paused for a moment. 'What can I do to help?'

'Nothing. It's fine. Honestly it is. To begin with, I was too sensitive. Lots of things upset me. But I've sorted it in my head now. It's as if I've put all my worries about her in a box. From time to time I get the box out and go through it. Then I tuck it away again. Just occasionally it bursts open and, along with other boxes that I keep in my head, the contents fall on top of me. That usually happens in the night. But, by and large, I've learned to move on. It's the only way to survive.'

'So, if my twins don't upset you, what sort of things do?'

'Oh, to begin with, the slightest thing would set me off. I'd be going along fine, then something minor would happen like burning the toast or breaking a mug and I'd howl for an hour. Also, any awful news reports involving children would 'floor' me. Sad plays, books or films were another trigger. I guess that's because we all feel we intimately know the characters by the end. And that's probably why other people were not as traumatised by Sarah's death as they might have been had she died at home. They never knew her so they couldn't identify with her, whereas a film, a book or TV drama, done well, makes you do precisely that.....even though you know that none of it is real!

And I tell you what else upset me. You'd be amazed how many people hugged me and assured me I'd be able to have another child very soon, as if the simple answer to everything would be to have a replacement! I tell you, had they seen Mac and me in our darkest moments..... or our beautiful baby, they could never have been so tactless. But, also, what a weird thing to say to someone who's just had a baby. I mean, Judy, nobody in their right mind wants to think about giving birth again when they've only just done it. Then I go and have a baby that causes monumental panic in the delivery room and subsequently dies.... and people immediately suggest I repeat the exercise. How insane is that?'

'So what did you say?'

'Oh, I was completely pathetic! I just said meekly, 'Yes that would be lovely, thank you.' To be honest, I was too broken to say anything else.' I paused. 'I'm sorry. I'm sounding like some whinging old bag!'

'You certainly aren't. Besides, I'm the one that started the conversation. Do keep talking, if you want to. It's helping me to understand.'

'Okay. Well, another thing that upset me, were the people who told me that Sarah's death was for the best. I knew they were only trying to be helpful, but she was my child and I wanted her to live. I couldn't see how any child's death could be good.....especially my own. Had she made it, I was convinced I would have found ways of making her life have real meaning. But I never got that chance.'

'Did Mac feel the same way?'

'No. I don't think he did. If there was one thing I learned from the experience, it was that we all react in different ways to tragedy. There's no right or wrong way to feel. Mac was devastated by it all. It was a terrible shock. Whereas most women tend to worry about all the things that can go wrong in a pregnancy, men tend to dismiss all the possible complications. When we lost her, he cut himself off for a bit. When the letters of condolence started to arrive from our friends, I found them quite comforting, but he couldn't even bear to lift them off the mat.'

'So didn't he show any emotion?'

'Oh yes. When she died and we finally left the hospital, he suddenly clutched me. I could see that he had tears in his eyes. Stupidly, I asked him why he was crying. Holding me tight he said simply that he was crying for the little girl who would never know her mummy.'

'Oh God.'

'Oh sorry, I didn't mean to depress you. Actually, there were lighter moments, despite the tragedy of it all.'

'Lighter moments?'

'Yes. About a week after the funeral, a dear friend of mine turned up with her four year old boy. She'd hardly had time to get through the door before he'd marched up to me and, bold and brass, said: 'Mummy says you've got a dead baby in a box. Can I see her please?''

'A dead baby in a box! What a stupid thing for the mother to tell him!'

'Well, I don't suppose for one minute that she put it quite like that. But that was clearly how he saw it. But he wasn't upset – he was fascinated.'

'So what did you tell him?'

'Well, I told him that might be a bit difficult to arrange, but I'd got a 'live' one in a carry cot if that would do instead. You could tell from his face that it was a poor compromise, but it made me smile. Then I looked at my friend and she was looking so horrified, that I simply laughed! Then we hugged, shed a few tears, and felt much better than we'd have ever done had her child not said anything at all.

But enough of all this! I'm not the only person with awful memories. It's your turn now. Tell me what most bothers you? You've not been your normal self lately. Are you hiding any dark secrets in your boxes?'

'Boxes?'

'Yes. I just told you that I put all my worries, like Sarah, in boxes in my head to stop them getting muddled. Do you have any of those?'

'Oh goodness, hundreds probably. When you don't get married until you're forty, the chances are that you've had plenty of experiences you'd rather forget! Mind you, once I'd had the twins, the list of worries probably filled dozens more. If you must know, my head's pretty full of a jumble of them, not to mention the skeletons I have in various cupboards. I try not to go anywhere near them if I can help it.'

'What about James?' I asked provocatively.

'Oh I expect he's got some too. Everybody has. But, now that you mention it, there's probably quite a lot we share. When I first knew him, he had another lady in his life and that was certainly complicated for a while. We don't tend to talk about that 'box' too much, though we probably should,' she added reflectively.

Just then Lizzie came across, ruining my master plan with a stroke. 'Mummy, can I use that dead frog Josh found in the garden yesterday to make a witches brew? Fred's just tried to 'magic' Eddie into a bat with the wand we found in the box, but it won't work. He's crying now and we can't get him to stop.'

'Oh, not again,' Judy sighed. 'What were you saying about soul mates? Eddie, listen. None of the stuff in that box is real. Nobody's going to get turned into a bat or anything else for that matter. If you can't all be sensible, we're going to have to take that stuff away.'

Lizzie was indignant. 'That's not fair. All those things are mine. I like witches and mummy likes them too. She sometimes talks to them on the telephone.'

'Really?' Judy was intrigued. 'You've never mentioned that before. Is this another of your boxes, Kate?'

'No. Don't be silly. And I haven't spoken to a witch. I've only spoken to Will about a possible story we may be doing about a coven. Lizzie's got in to a very bad habit of listening on the other 'phone, haven't you?' I glared at her. 'And she generally gets the story completely wrong. For your information, Lizzie, Judy is completely right. Witches and wizards who turn children into frogs are only in fairy tales. They're not real. Mind you, if they were, you might be a bit more careful before you answered back so rudely.'

Suitably chastened, Lizzie went back to join the others.

'Well, go on then,' Judy pressed. 'What's with the coven story?'

I sighed deeply. 'If you must know, I wish I'd never started it.'

'So, you don't believe in witches then?' Judy sounded disappointed.

'No. Certainly not!'

## WITCHES

'Whose stupid idea was it to do this story…as if I didn't know?' George muttered to me darkly as we clambered up to the top of the hill. 'Not only is my arm nearly breaking from the weight of this camera, our guides are clearly doing their best to scare us witless.'

We had been brought to Meon Hill in the Cotswolds by Terry and Bill, two brothers who had had lived in the area all their lives. On this freezing October day, they'd kindly agreed to guide us to the summit. However, as they casually listed a string of unnerving events that had taken place on the slopes over the years, it soon became clear that, one by one, the crew were beginning to lose their nerve.

The wind was howling round and the rain was lashing in our faces. To our horror, as we reached the plateau, everywhere we looked, strange faces appeared to stare back at us through the mist. Some joker (or jokers) had had the idea of carving strange shapes and what looked like hideous effigies into the bark of the trees around us. The effect was seriously spooky!

And the brothers' tales weren't reassuring. Many people in the area were into 'black magic'. We knew that. That was why we'd come. Safe in a warm office, the idea had sounded good. Sixty years earlier, a farmhand had been murdered on this hill by his own pitchfork. Although the crime had never been solved, it was widely believed to be linked to witchcraft, a practice that had made the area famous for centuries.

'Shakespeare came up here one day and the experience he had here inspired him to write Macbeth,' Bill informed us darkly. 'Oh, and by the way, 'beware the black dog!'

'What for?' Will asked gruffly as he rejoined the party. He, too, wasn't looking for any additional anxiety. He'd unwisely chosen to go on ahead of us to the far side of the hill to identify possible shots for the film. It was clear from the expression on his face that it was a decision he now regretted.

'If you see a black dog, you're doomed!' Bill repeated. 'Everyone round here knows that.'

'Right, that's it. Everyone look down. Whatever you do, don't let your eyes wander,' Will ordered, 'or we're all in trouble.'

At my invitation, we'd also been joined on this mad mission by two policemen. Between them, they ran the Black Museum of the county police force. One of them was carrying the very pitchfork used in the murder. He could have left it in his car...or could he?

'You didn't need to bring that up here,' Will shouted when he saw it, clearly appalled that we had a weapon on hand that could be used to kill any one of us. 'George got all the shots we needed before we set off.'

'We had to bring it because we can't leave it in an unlocked car.'

'Why? Won't your car lock?' Will was puzzled. The policeman looked sheepish.

'Well...' he started hesitantly. 'according to the book we have on black magic, anyone who locks up the weapons of a witchcraft murder will suffer a terrible fate.'

This was too much for George. As he sat down on the damp grass to take a break, his camera balanced precariously on his lap, he 'tutted' under his breath. But looking to the rest of us for some kind of support, he caught Will's reproachful look and thought better of it. It didn't take a genius to work out from the expressions of the rest of the crew, that no one was brave enough to challenge the theory.

But, after a few moments, he seemed to get himself together again. Straightening up he continued. 'Right, do you want me to get some shots from the plateau? We won't get much of a view in this weather, but I'm assuming you'll want lots of pictures of the faces on the trees. They'll look great through the mist, that is if they don't spring to life the moment we turn the camera on.' He turned an accusing glare on our guides who hastily assured him he should be quite safe.

'We told you, you'll be alright as long as you don't see that dog.'

George gave the men a look of despair. I quickly shot an anxious glance at our hosts but, to my surprise, they did not appear to be offended.

'It's okay,' Terry, the taller of the two, assured me. 'We're quite used to cynics...even scared ones! But if you'd grown up here, you might feel differently about it all. More than one person has died here in unusual circumstances. My friend rides up here sometimes but, no matter how hard she tries, she can't get her horse to go along the plateau. It's as if he senses something... ....something that no one can explain.'

'He's right, you know.' This time it was the turn of our other guide, Bill, to have his say. 'When I was little, I had an aunt who lived at the far end of the village. Yet, although her cottage was only a few hundred yards from here, she never came up on the hill. But I do remember her telling me some frightening tales. One was about a black dog and another was about a snake. She'd been told that, if you ever found either of them up here, the crops would fail and then some terrible tragedy would follow.'

He scratched his head as if trying to remember some more details. Next to him George had turned a whiter shade of pale!

'Thanks for that one,' Will replied through tight lips. 'Just the kind of reassurance we were looking for! I woke up this morning with no belief whatsoever in the supernatural. Now I'm beginning to think we'll be lucky to get off this hill in one piece!'

For a moment we all walked on in silence. Then, suddenly Will stopped dead in his tracks. Curious, Terry moved across to join him.

'What's up?'

With an unsteady finger, he pointed to the ground about ten yards from him. Deep in the undergrowth, he'd spotted something long, dark and thin.

'It's a stick,' he reassured him. 'I doubt if you'll see many snakes up here on a freezing day in late October!'

Just as Will was about to reply, from somewhere not too far from us, we heard a dog bark. As the wind carried the sound across the hill, everyone looked at each other anxiously.

'Right. That's it,' said Will. 'We'll get our shots and then we're going down. I've had quite enough of this place. What I need now is a stiff drink.'

\*   \*   \*   \*

The story was full of strange coincidences and weird happenings. Back in the mid 1940s, it had demanded the attention of one of the foremost detectives of the time, 'Fabian of the Yard.' He'd travelled up from London and then spent weeks scouring the area for clues and suspects. It had been a nightmare to get about. Wartime meant that there were few, if any, road signs and, in the winter, as darkness fell, travelling was almost impossible due to the blackout. That was probably why the 'black dog' became a symbol of death. Thousands died on the roads during the war. In the blackout, nobody saw them before it was too late.

By the time I got home that evening, I was thoroughly spooked. It was great to be back in a warm kitchen, preparing tea for the kids. Lizzie had a friend over and Josh and Claire were doing their homework. Archie was playing happily by my feet in the playpen.

I'd only nipped outside for a couple of minutes to sort out the dustbins ready for the bin men the next day. But, when I came back, the back door was open and a strong wind was blowing through. Strange! As I went across to close the door, my eye caught the small blackboard on the wall. Normally, we used it to remind us that we were running out of things like 'milk' or 'bread'. But not now. Daubed across the entire space was a picture of…a witch.

I froze. Oh my God. I'd tampered with black magic and now I was going to pay for it. Was there someone in the house already, upstairs, murdering my children?

In a strangled voice I called out to everyone to come downstairs at once. Surprised by my tone, they obliged, including Josh who had nipped outside to retrieve his skateboard.

'What's up?' asked Josh.

'Does anybody know anything about this witch picture?' I asked accusingly.

'That's not a witch,' Lizzie's friend Jemima looked horrified. 'That's my mummy. Lizzie said I could draw a picture and you wouldn't mind.'

I stared at the picture more closely. Oh help, she was right. It looked like every four year olds picture of a mummy. Straight hair at right angles to her head, triangular dress and triangular hat! How embarrassing!

Get a grip, Kate, get a grip!

My children, suitably appalled at their mother's insulting attitude to a guest, made exaggerated attempts to console her.

'Take no notice. It's a great picture. Our mum's just a bit weird sometimes.' Josh said, while glaring at me.

'You should hear what she says about our drawings. I drew her a beautiful picture of a cat once and she said it looked like the Loch Ness monster!' Lizzie's lie was almost convincing.

Determined to top everyone's insults, Claire was quick to pitch in with her contribution.

'She hallucinates, you know. Sometimes she looks at us and thinks we're all rabbits!'

Sheepishly, I went back to preparing tea.

'I'm sorry, 'I muttered apologetically. 'It was the witchcraft story today. It spooked me. I'll explain it all to her mother when she comes to collect her.'

'You will not,' Josh sounded appalled. 'If you start mentioning witches and wizards to her, she'll only think you're even battier than you are. Once she's heard what you've done, I bet Jemima won't be allowed to come here ever again.'

## GHOSTS

Despite Josh's misgivings, Jemima's mum thought the whole thing was funny. Spookily, she too had had a bad experience in the same place. Many years earlier, and newly married, they had lived in a village close to Meon Hill. Knowing nothing of the rumours, not long after they arrived she and her husband had walked to the summit. They had seen the eerie faces carved into the trees and listened to the wind howling through them. Saying little to each other, both were glad when they were back in the car. Arriving home and still feeling 'spooked', they were surprised to hear a crash upstairs. When they rushed up to their bedroom, they were horrified to see that a mirror had fallen off the wall and shattered into a thousand pieces all over their bed. Had they been in it, they would have stood no chance at all.

After that, nothing more was said about witches for a while, partly because the subject alarmed Claire and partly because Mac thought the whole thing was quite ridiculous. As the days passed, my experience on the hill became a distant memory and gradually I came round to Mac's way of thinking. He was right. It was all in the mind. I would have to learn not to be so silly!

But then, just as I'd got my head round it all, my cousin Anita came to stay. The guest room was in the oldest part of the house. The next morning she came down to breakfast convinced that the house was haunted.

'I heard footsteps, slow deliberate footsteps,' she said mysteriously over her second slice of toast.

'Oh, not you as well,' Mac was once more in dismissive mood. 'That was me you heard going downstairs for a cup of tea when I couldn't sleep last night.'

'They weren't your footsteps,' she continued mysteriously, 'they were heavy strides, as if someone was walking on the floor above me in heavy boots.'

Mac's eyes rolled. 'He'd have had to have worn the boots on his knees then. The roof space above your room is only about four feet high!'

But Anita wouldn't let the subject go.

'This house is bound to be haunted. Parts of it are more than three hundred years old. Think of all the people who must have died here.'

Mac remained unimpressed.

She continued: 'It's not just crazy people who believe in the supernatural. There has been much written on the subject by some very sensible experts. I, myself, once wrote to a newspaper after I'd had a strange experience in a hotel in Weymouth.'

I could see the corners of Mac's mouth twitch slightly, but he remained silent.

'To be honest, there's a part of me that wants to believe in ghosts as long as they're friendly,' I admitted. 'Many years ago, when I worked in a London hospital, we all feared 'The Grey Lady'.'

Now it was Anita's turn to sit up and listen.

Mac gave me a warning glare.

'Don't start winding everyone up again. I can't cope with any more sleepless nights.'

'We're not talking witchcraft here. We're talking ghosts. The one I'm talking about was very helpful and friendly!'

'Go on,' said Anita clearly agog. Mac left the room.

'Rumour had it that she visited very sick patients just before they died. Rather eerily, she was said to float a few inches above the ground because the floor had been lowered since she trained there. I think she'd once been a nurse who had suffered a terrible death, but I was never quite sure whether the doctor who told me the gruesome story in the middle of my night-shift was telling the truth or just trying to scare me to death. Either way, he did a very good job.

Anyway, in the cold light of day I dismissed the various stories I'd heard until, one night, my flat-mate told me that she had been very busy when a sick patient asked her for a bedpan. She'd asked him if he could wait a few minutes. When she'd finally got back to him, he had smiled up at her and said he no longer needed it. 'The nice lady in the grey dress helped me,' he said. By the morning, he was dead. Had he heard the story or dreamed it? Either way, my flat-mate didn't sleep for days and I was left wondering!!!'

Anita nodded knowingly. By now Mac had left to catch his train.

Nothing more was said about ghosts until a week later.

It was about eight o'clock one evening. Mac was still at work and I had just got Lizzie and Archie out of the bath when there was a knock at the door. I don't quite know who I was expecting at that time of night, but it certainly wasn't a strange looking man, aged about 25, with long hair and wearing a coat down to his ankles.

'Is John Stevens in?' he enquired.

Laughing I said: 'I doubt it. As far I know he died about eighty year ago!' I'd heard about John Stevens from my neighbour who ran the village history society. The Rev. John Stevens had been the vicar in the village at the turn of the century.

'Oh,' he looked disappointed. 'Sorry to have troubled you.'

He turned to go and I shut the door. How strange! No, not strange.....spooky!!! Really spooky! I threw the door open again. But he'd gone!

Our driveway was long and I didn't think he'd had time to get to the end of it. Was he lurking in the bushes preparing to murder me or was he a........... ghost?

When I told Mac he laughed. 'Someone was having you on. They'd obviously heard how gullible you are and fancied a joke. Either that or, more likely, there's a John Stevens junior who lives round here somewhere and the man was trying to locate him. As a relative of his used to live here, our house was a fairly sensible place to start looking. He must have thought you were bonkers!'

I had to admit that this was a very logical observation. I didn't know whether I was relieved or disappointed.

We never found out any more. But try as I could, I couldn't get the strange man out of my mind. From then on I registered every unusual creak, rattle or unexpected draught.

Mac thought it was a load of rubbish. Well he would!

*    *    *    *

But it was Aunt Lucy that finally brought our ghost problem to a head. A car boot sale on the outskirts of our village had attracted her attention. So she invited herself for the night to ensure she got an early start.

*    *    *    *

'Aaaaaaaaaaah!' A yell from the dining room just before dawn had everyone awake in a second. Mac was first down the stairs. He entered the dining room to find Aunt Lucy clutching a mug of tea in one hand and pointing an accusing finger in the direction of the fire place with the other. She was as white as a sheet.

'It's my Edmund,' she groaned dramatically. 'I would recognise those eyes anywhere. Help me someone. My husband's come back to haunt me.'

'What?'

Mac followed her gaze and was momentarily shocked to see two eyes blazing through the smoky glass door of the wood-burning stove. But his fear was short lived.

'It's not Edmund. It's a jackdaw.'

'Pardon?'

'You are staring at a very angry jackdaw who's just fallen down the chimney and is now desperate to be released. And if there is an afterlife Aunt dear, I just hope that Uncle Edmund didn't hear your rather unflattering comparison!'

'It startled me!'

'May I assure you that you startled us. Dramatic screams are not the best way to start the day. You seem to have forgotten, again, that we have impressionable children living in this house who, like me, struggle to understand your wild fantasies. When you claim that your deceased husband is trapped in our chimney or that tormented spirits are hovering above the graveyard, you terrify some of them. Aunt, this is your final warning. One more mention of the supernatural and I shall be booking you into the nearest asylum!'

*    *    *    *

'How's Mac?' Judy queried on the 'phone later that night. He sounded pretty fed up when I spoke to him earlier. I gather your 'witches' film has

187

unleashed a string of 'spooky incidents at the Vicarage. It doesn't take a genius to see that it's winding him up.'

I sighed. 'You're right, though I never thought that a crime that was committed sixty years ago would cause so much upset. We've all ended up being 'spooked' in various ways.'

Judy snorted. 'So what's your next project....other than getting Aunt Lucy locked up? Mac told me you're filming again on Friday.'

'Yes, the story of the evergreens. Lots of holly, ivy and mistletoe.'

'How festive!'

'Yes, though I'm worried that it's yet more mysticism. I don't think Mac's too impressed.'

'Well, just make sure you keep the children and him well out of it.'

'Easier said than done,' I replied wisely. And as it turned out, it was!

# Chapter Four

# NOVEMBER, DECEMBER

### REVELATIONS

'Christmas time, Mistletoe and Wine,' Claire sang tunelessly as she wandered into the kitchen. Mac looked up. Much to his annoyance, since starting secondary school, Claire's bedtime had become a more flexible event. If he could have had his way, he argued, they'd have all been tucked up in bed by eight o'clock. Sadly, his eldest child had steadfastly refused to take his advice.

'If you must sing, would it be asking too much of you to learn the words? You've been chanting the first line of that song for days and you clearly don't know any more. And may I remind you that it's only the middle of November. Christmas is still more than six weeks away.'

'But Mummy's doing a story about mistletoe. So, it's put me in the mood.'

'Well, go and take your 'mood' to your bedroom…before you drive us all completely mad!'

'Scarlet's mummy says it's never too early to plan for Christmas. She's already made the cake and done all her cards.' Claire knew exactly how to wind me up.

'Oh, for God's sake!' I sighed deeply. 'I haven't even bought mine yet.'

'There you go, Kate. You're doing it again. Stop comparing yourself with people whose circumstances are entirely different. The fact that she's telling everyone how far ahead she is, proves that she's very insecure.'

'I think I might like that sort of insecurity. Mine is based on the fact that I am usually about six months behind everyone else!'

'We've got four young children, Kate.'

'So you keep saying!'

'Can I help make the cake this year? You've never let me before,' Claire asked indignantly.

'That's because I've never made one.'

Claire looked puzzled. 'But we always have cake at Christmas.'

'Granny does it.'

'But Granny's not coming this year. So you'll have to do it yourself.'

'No I won't. I'll buy one. I haven't got time for that sort of thing.'

Claire gasped. 'Mummy, that's cheating!' And with that she grabbed a glass of water and took herself upstairs to bed.

Mac put down his paper and sighed. 'Look at us Kate, I mean look at us! Years ago, pre-children, you and I used to sit down late every evening and calmly reflect on the events of the day with the lights dimmed and romantic music playing in the background. Now, if we're lucky, once the children have finally gone to bed, we grab a few moments by the Aga surrounded by wet knickers and socks, a fluorescent light blinding us and the washing machine, tumble drier and dishwasher droning in the background.... and that's on a good day. More often than not at this point in the evening, you're flying around the house muttering darkly about missing games kit and school permission slips.'

'As you've just said, we've got four children.'

'Tell me about it! When will it ever end?'

'Well, seeing as Archie is only two, I wouldn't get too excited yet!'

The conversation was brought to a sudden stop by the doorbell.

'Who on earth can that be at this time of night?'

'Aunt Lucy's not on another drinking spree with Bert tonight, is she?' Mac wondered. 'They do say that once you've started, it's quite difficult to break the habit.'

'Don't be ridiculous!'

'Maybe it's your ghost friend...Mr Stevens?'

'Shut up! Maybe we could stop the speculation and answer the door before whoever it is goes away.'

In the hallway, I could just make out a solitary figure through the frosted glass. It was James.

\*     \*     \*     \*

'Hope you don't mind me popping in at this hour,' he asked sheepishly as I ushered him into the kitchen, 'but I was passing this way on my way back from work. I gather your village is rife with rumours about the new young lady in my life. Some guy, I vaguely recognized from your family service, made a sarcastic comment as I was leaving the farm yesterday afternoon and your church warden glowered at me as I turned out of the village. It wasn't too difficult to realize that they knew me as the dad of those 'twins at the church' and strongly disapproved of whatever they thought I was doing. Obviously I didn't want Judy to hear about it from another source before I'd had a chance to talk to her. So last night I told her everything. Having spoken to her, I'm here now because she felt that you had a right to know the facts too.'

'In your own time,' Mac said gently as he passed James a large glass of brandy. I looked on accusingly.

'I'm so sorry to be so dramatic,' he said apologetically. 'To be honest, I didn't think anyone in this village, apart from you, knew who I was. The only time I've ever met any locals is when I've been to see the children perform at the church, or to come to your house for some kind of event. When I worked out that the local gossips were full of the story, I was horrified.'

Mac shook his head sadly. 'I'm afraid it happens all too often in places like this. Quite a few of the locals are quick to jump to conclusions, I'm afraid. Believe me, I should know! A story like yours is probably the most exciting thing they've heard in ages.'

Avoiding Mac's reproachful look, I stared James in the eye. How dare this man 'do the dirty' on my best friend. 'So, go on,' I said accusingly. 'Who is she?'

Staring straight back at me, James said quite simply. 'Erica is my sister.'

For a moment there was silence. Then I spoke.

'I didn't know you had a sister. Judy has talked about your brothers but she never mentioned anyone else.'

'Oh, Judy knows all about Erica...at least she did until recently. She probably didn't mention her because.....well, because a few years ago there were several 'incidents' that made her want to push any thoughts of my sister right to the back of her mind!'

He paused to take a much needed sip of brandy.

'Erica was born when my mother was forty seven. She'd had her three sons in her twenties so, as you can imagine, the pregnancy came as a bit of a shock ...to all of us.

All was great until Erica was sixteen. By that stage my parents were comfortably off, so she had many of the luxuries we three brothers had been denied when we were growing up. She also had three siblings who were more like benevolent uncles. We all spoiled her rotten!

Then, one terrible night, my parents were killed in a car crash. They were coming back from a party and skidded on black ice. They died instantly. As you can imagine, we were all devastated. Erica was almost grown up, but not old enough to live on her own. So, as the eldest brother, she came to live with me. I was with Judy by then and, for a while, it worked reasonably well. We all missed my parents dreadfully but for Erica, being so young, it was an unbelievable blow. I don't think I quite realised how traumatic everything had been until it was too late.'

'What do you mean...too late.?'

'Sixteen is not an easy age.....even if you have parents. I don't think I understood the terrible pain Erica was suffering. She became quiet, to the extent of being withdrawn, but with a hectic job and a new relationship to deal with, I missed the signals she was giving us. I realise now that I never gave her the emotional support she so desperately needed. I let her down.

Judy did her best but there was no way a lady Erica hardly knew could be any kind of replacement for her mother. Soon she began spending more and more time with her friends. At first, she seemed happier and we, in turn, got more time to ourselves. We didn't know what was really happening until it was too late.'

James paused to sip his brandy.

'Gradually we realised that her 'friends' were not quite the great gang we thought they were. First it was alcohol and then drugs. It was bad enough picking her up from the police station when she was drunk. Dealing with someone who's abusing drugs was a very different issue. It was all a hideous nightmare and we couldn't see any way out.

Soon she began to steal to fuel her addiction. First it was from me, then from Judy. When Judy found her with her hands in one of our friends' coat pocket as it hung on a hook in the hall, things rapidly came to a head. By then Judy was pregnant with our long awaited twins. Erica's behaviour was affecting Judy's health. So I had to make the biggest decision of my life. I loved my sister but I couldn't risk losing my babies. Erica was making Judy ill. If anything had happened to those children, I knew she would never get over it.'

'So what did you do?'

'I asked my brother in Worcester to take over. The day I drove Erica across to him was one of the worst days of my life. I felt I'd let her down... and so did she. But I couldn't see any other alternative.

For the first year, after she'd left, things went from bad to worse. She wouldn't speak to me and she gave my brother and his family hell. She was in and out of rehab. but she always returned to her addiction. Then, just as everyone thought there was no hope, she met someone. Not a man, but a lady who she felt she could talk to. Rachel Jackson was my brother's new neighbour. She was an artist and Erica started spending time with her, watching her paint and create works of art from the wood and stones that she found in the woodland near my brother's home. Rachel took her under her wing and, with her help, she slowly managed to kick her drug habit once and for all and, for the first time in years, began to take a real interest in the world around her. With Rachel's encouragement, Erica went back to college to do an art course. Before long she was helping her in everything she did.

When the chance came to set up her own workshop making children's toys, Rachel asked Erica if she'd like to go into business with her. Erica had some money left in trust to her by my parents, but she couldn't touch it until she was twenty five. My brother rang me and suggested we lent her the money until she was old enough to fund herself. By amazing coincidence, they then found a suitable barn to rent on the edge of your village. It seemed an obvious time to rekindle our relationship. At first Erica rejected the idea. She still couldn't forgive me for, as she saw it, abandoning her when she most needed help.

But, slowly, under Rachel's guidance, she worked through her feelings. Last April she agreed to meet me and show me her new work place. That's when we got stuck in the floods. Over the last few months, I've been visiting her on a regular basis and we've slowly become close again. But I didn't want Judy to know until I was absolutely certain that Erica was back on track once and for all. I can't tell you the trauma she'd put us through. Judy's quite old to be a mother. The last four years have been difficult enough without the added burden of a wayward sister-in-law. As you know, thanks to you, she is only just beginning to see the light now. The last thing I wanted was to set Judy back when we were just beginning to get our lives in order again.'

'And is Judy happy about the situation now?'

'She was wonderful when I told her. And we're meeting up at the weekend. I'm sure she'll tell you all about it. She was desperate for you to know the full story. She never talked about it to you because she, too, felt guilty. But, believe me, trying to handle Erica when she was at her worst, was the hardest thing either of us had ever had to deal with. Far worse, even, than the sudden death of my parents.'

He sighed deeply. 'I hope everything will be fine from now on. But we both know that it may not be that simple. Kate, you know that Judy really values your friendship and she may need your support in the weeks and months to come.'

I nodded. We both knew there'd be no question about that.

\*   \*   \*   \*

It was late when James finally left us. As he got into his car, he turned to me.

'Oh, do tell those rumour mongers in your village that the lady concerned is my sister. And, if they want to keep poking their noses in, tell them that they can visit her barn anytime and buy a few Christmas presents off her. That could go some way to repairing the damage.'

As he drove out of the driveway, I turned to Mac.

'Oh God, do you think he's worked out that I was one of those gossips?' I waited for the rebuke, but surprisingly, it never came.

'No. At least, not unless you've said something to anyone other than me.'

'Claire saw him with Erica that day on the hill. But I told her not to say anything.'

'Don't worry about it, then. Once we saw him out with her, you had every right to be concerned. He's just tense at the moment. These past few months can't have been easy for him. The rumours brought the matter to a head. In time, I think he'll realise that it was probably for the best.'

\*   \*   \*   \*

'They're like pigs in the proverbial,' Judy's voice was full of excitement. 'Can you imagine it? They've just discovered they've got an auntie, young enough to be their big sister, who not only makes toys for a living…she has a share in a toy factory too! Erica gave them both puppets as a present when she met them. I think they believe she's Mrs Gepetto! Fred keeps looking at his puppet expecting it to lose its strings and turn into his big brother!'

'So, I can assume the meeting went well?'

'She was sweet. She adored the boys. We didn't talk about anything very deep, but I felt a real warmth come from her. I'm not quite sure what her relationship is with her business partner, Rachel, but whatever it is, James and I are both hugely grateful for what she's done for her. They've got quite a little business going there. You should go and have a look.'

'So, what next?'

'Erica's coming for Christmas. Just for the day. But it's a start.'

'You look different. I've been worried about you for ages. You were really tense at times recently.'

'It was James. He'd become quite remote over the past few months and I couldn't work out why. He was often late home and sometimes the excuses just didn't add up. But I clung to the belief it was work. He's under enormous pressure at times and, like many men, he doesn't always want to talk about it. So, I didn't push it because, God knows, I'd been bad enough while the twins were babies. He deserved the chance to be moody for a change. After all, he'd had to put up with my fragile emotions over the last few years. Now I know why he was behaving that way, I do understand why he decided not to tell me what he was up to. It could all have gone horribly wrong. And I'd have been very nervous about lending her money. For several years, the ups and downs of Erica's life took a real toll on our relationship. But it all seems to have worked out for the best and I'm delighted.'

'I'm dying to meet her. Though I'm not quite sure how I'd deal with a sister-in-law who's young and terribly attractive. It wouldn't do my self-esteem any good, that's for sure.'

'Kate, if you knew how low her self-esteem had been these past few years, you wouldn't say that. I'm just so grateful that she seems to be back on her feet. Anyway, talking of sister-in-laws, how's yours?'

'Ah, interesting you should ask that. She rang yesterday evening with a strange request. But, I can't tell you about it until I've spoken to Mac. He got back so late last night I was already asleep. But, once we've discussed it, you'll be the first to know!'

## UNINVITED GUESTS

'Daddy, did you know that it's about to be Advent. We talked about it at school today.' Lizzie was sitting at the kitchen table colouring a Christmas card.

'Go on,' Mac replied absently. He was reading his post and barely listening.

'My teacher says that in Advent we remember the time when the Angel Gabriel comes to Mary and tells her that she's going to have a baby. He says that Mary will be the mummy and God will be the daddy.'

She paused, clearly waiting for this devastating piece of news to sink in.

'Everyone knows that,' Claire sighed dismissively. 'I've done that story heaps of times at school. After the angel Gabriel's been to Mary, he goes to Joseph and tells him the same thing. When he hears that Mary is pregnant, he gets very worried.'

'You know what? I never understood that bit.' It was Josh's turn to have his say.

'Why not?' Mac asked. 'In those days, it was truly shocking to be pregnant when you weren't married.'

'Yes, I know that. But once he'd found out from the angel that God was the dad, he didn't need to worry about that anymore. Actually, I'd like that to happen to me.'

For a moment Mac stared critically at his son, 'What would you like to happen to you, exactly?'

'I'd like to be like Joseph and discover that my girlfriend was pregnant without me having to do that 'yukky' thing we learned about at school last week! After all, he was still allowed to be Jesus' 'earthly' daddy, so he didn't really miss out. I think Joseph was really lucky!'

'I think it was lucky that Mary only had to be pregnant for a few days,' Lizzie was keen to have her say again.

'What on earth are you talking about now?' Claire sighed.

'Well, Advent only lasts about four weeks, so she didn't have long to wait, did she?'

'Stupid, stupid, stupid!' Claire chanted.

'It's true isn't it Daddy?' Lizzie's lower lip was beginning to wobble. 'I know Advent only lasts that long because I've got an Advent calendar to prove it!'

'If that's the case, how come Easter comes a few months after Christmas and by then Jesus has grown up?' Claire sneered.

Lizzie's eyes widened in bewilderment.

'It must have been very odd to give birth in a stable,' I interrupted trying to move the conversation on. 'Mind you, I'm not sure I'd want all those uninvited guests turning up so soon afterwards.'

'I thought you liked uninvited guests at Christmas time. I heard you say that to Auntie Sue when she telephoned yesterday.'

'What's this?' Mac looked up sharply.

'She asked Mummy if she could come and stay for Christmas, didn't she?'

'How do you know this?' I demanded staring Lizzie straight in the eye.

'I heard you talking on the 'phone,' she replied gazing back at me in wide-eyed innocence.

'I bet she was listening on the upstairs 'phone. I caught her doing that the other day,' Josh interrupted.

'Never mind that for now,' Mac suddenly seemed very agitated. 'Just tell me. What did she say?'

'She asked if it would be possible for all of them to come and spend Christmas and New Year with us. Apparently their building project is not likely to be finished until the end of January and they're in chaos....even by my standards!'

'And Sue actually asked to come here?' Mac was clearly aghast at the news.

'Well, think about it Mac. You're her brother. At short notice, four beds for a week at Christmas is quite a big thing to ask of your friends.'

'Yes,' Mac smiled. 'I can't imagine any of her friends agreeing to that one. They're all far too house-proud. If Sue's anything to go by, they'd never agree to that level of disruption at short notice.'

'So, are you saying she only asked to come here because we're always in such chaos that an extra family wouldn't make any difference?'

'No, I'm not saying that. Or rather not in the way you think. If Sue had wanted an organised Christmas, she could have gone to a hotel. But clearly she didn't. Regardless of the state of our house, she asked to come here. If you want my opinion, I think you should take her request as a huge compliment. She wouldn't ask to come and stay if she didn't like you. I've always said she was your secret admirer. Now you know it's true.'

'Hardly. A reasonable hotel at Christmas would have cost her a fortune. No, if you need accommodation at a rather critical time of the year, you need a relative with a fairly big house. In her case, seeing as Terence's family are in South Africa, that rather narrowed it down a bit. If you must know, I'm not flattered by the offer, I rather think she was desperate.'

'Rubbish.'

'Well think about it. She never stayed at the cottage.'

'We didn't have the space.'

'Precisely. I think it's the house more than its occupants that swayed her. Although she would never say so, I think she's rather taken with it. Her home is modern, immaculate and completely lacking in character. Ours is, well, homely ....especially at this time of year.'

'What about her kids? Jolyon and Tobias are teenagers now. I must say, I'm surprised they agreed to all this. I'd have thought the prospect of spending the festive season with our four 'little ones' would have been awful for them. '

'Well, you're wrong. Sue says they're very keen on the idea.'

'Well she would, wouldn't she. If she's trying to scrounge an invitation off us, she's hardly likely to say that her kids don't want to come.'

'Apparently they jumped at the offer. But I don't think she's worked out why..... although I rather think I have.'

'Go on.'

'Think about it. Television and junk-food are forbidden in her house. Here, the rules are rather different…..especially at Christmas. While their mother's fiddling about in the kitchen ensuring they only eat food of the highest quality, they're going to be free to gawp at a screen in some remote corner of the house whilst consuming crisps and chocolate to their heart's content.'

'Hold on. What about our dust? Don't you remember the fuss she made the first time she visited!'

I bristled. 'It has obviously escaped your notice that we don't have that problem anymore. Now that we have Dorothy, we are a dust-free zone. Sue must have noticed the change when she popped in briefly last week. She was obviously checking up on us. The shiny, dust-free surfaces must have swayed her decision.'

'What about our mess?'

'Well, when she came last week, her visit was so short that I managed to confine her to downstairs. Luckily, Dorothy and I had 'blitzed' the kitchen that morning so all I had to do was bundle up all the mess and throw it into the airing cupboard. For the duration of her short stay, our house looked reasonably presentable.'

'But you can't start shoving things into airing cupboards if she's coming for a week.'

'Ah, well I've thought about that and I've decided to put all the stuff in the shed.'

'In the shed?'

'Yes, at lunchtime on Christmas Eve, I shall trawl the house with several bin-liners. Anything left lying around, whether it's on the floor, stairs or strewn across the furniture, will be temporarily 'binned' until after New Year.'

'If you're going to do that, you won't need bin-liners, you'll need a truck! So, are Sue and company the only relatives intending to dump themselves on us this festive season?' Mac had a resigned look on his face, fearing he already knew the answer.

'Oh, Aunt Lucy's coming. I told Sue about that.'

'And how did she react?'

'Fine. She would have been expecting it. Anyway, she's hardly in any position to object. I'm not quite sure what she'll think of Bert joining us for Christmas lunch, though.'

'Hold on a minute. I was never consulted about that. Why on earth is he coming?'

'He's a friend of Aunt Lucy's. She wouldn't want him to eat Christmas lunch alone.'

'But why can't she go there?'

'The children would hate that. Whatever you may think, they are terribly fond of their aunt.'

Mac sighed. 'I see. Once again, my feelings have been rejected in favour of my offspring. My role in this family seems to diminish by the day.'

'Come on, Mac. It won't be that bad. Okay, so she'll have Christmas lunch with us. But, with a bit of luck, now that Bert's on the scene, she'll be spending most of the time with him, along with several bottles of whisky, if previous experiences are anything to go by. She won't want him hanging around here with you around. You'd be bound to cramp her style.'

'Well I know what I'll be doing, if the going gets tough.'

'Putting on an entertainment? Organising exciting events for the children?' I queried sarcastically.

'No. I shall be taking a good book and a bottle of whisky outside and, surrounded by my dearest possessions, I shall enjoy the peace and quiet of the shed! And,' he added, 'be very clear about one thing. Unlike, the stable in Bethlehem, there will be no guiding light over the roof!'

## HOLLY, IVY AND MISTLETOE

Mr James, who had lived in the village all his life, claimed to know a lot about country matters. As he glanced up at our enormous holly bush bursting at the seams with berries, he sighed resignedly.

'It's going to be a harsh winter, that's for sure. Look at all them berries. Nature's way you see,' he nodded knowingly. 'Plenty of food for the birds on that tree. It'll help to keep them alive when there's three feet of snow on the ground.'

But if he thought his deadly warning would frighten me, he was wrong. The idea of being marooned in the house for days on end was hugely appealing. No need to get up for school or work. We could all huddle round the fire and read endless books. Quite perfect, as far as I was concerned.

But his musings had set me on another track too. I didn't really believe his story about the berries, especially as the holly bush at our other house had been equally laden and we'd then had the hottest winter on record. But the idea of telling the many legends associated with holly, ivy and mistletoe struck me as an excellent idea for an item for our winter series. I spoke to Will about it and he seemed keen.

'Obviously you've thought all this through. The days are short at this time of the year. It'll be dark by four o'clock. So make sure all the evergreens are close together. The last thing I want to be doing is trailing half way across England to get a decent shot of mistletoe. We did something about it years ago and the damn researcher hadn't realised how difficult it was to find mistletoe in certain parts of the country. Can you believe that?'

I laughed. Of course I knew where to find mistletoe. Why, I'd seen masses of it just the other day. Except, thinking about it, that was last Saturday when I was on the Herefordshire borders visiting a cousin. Surely the stuff grew in this part of the Midlands too.....or did it?

Obviously, finding holly and ivy would be no problem. The male tree was in our back garden and 'mummy', covered in red berries was in a corner of the driveway. Perfect! Ivy grows everywhere so that was okay. All I needed was the damn mistletoe.

'You'll be lucky to find much round these parts,' a local gardener informed me. It's abundant in Hereford and Worcestershire but I've hardly seen it hereabouts. My heart sank.

'There's a clump on that big tree on the corner of the High Street,' Josh was trying to be helpful. 'I see it every time we go shopping.'

But that was no good. Location not very 'country like' and far too noisy.

'I think my neighbour's got a bunch at the top of her tree,' Judy sounded uncertain as we waited at the school gates. Later I sneaked a look over her fence. It was mistletoe, but it was far too high up. We'd need a crane to get a camera close enough.

Someone else suggested what proved to be a pathetic sprig in a nearby village, but apart from that.....nothing.

Ignoring Mac's tuneless rendition of 'I saw Mummy kissing Santa Claus,' in desperation I got in the car and drove to the Worcestershire border. Around eight miles from my house, it wasn't exactly close, but it would do. Stopping at the first village on the map, I began my search. Ignoring the strange looks from passers-by, I set about peering into every garden.

For half an hour, I searched in vain. Then just as I was beginning to give up hope, I turned a corner at the end of a quiet lane and found exactly what I was looking for.

In a tiny garden on the outskirts of the village, the biggest crop I'd ever seen almost engulfed a poor apple tree. The charming gentleman who owned it was slightly bemused by my request. But we struck a deal and behold, I had unlimited access. It would look great on camera.

So, I had my ingredients. All I needed now was a fine winter's day.

The day dawned bright and sunny. By ten o'clock the abundance of fantastic mistletoe had put Will in a good mood. It was a great start.

The ivy bit was easy too. It was everywhere. Next we got some lovely shots of the holly in the church. The huge stained glass window above the altar, featuring Jesus on the cross wearing his crown of thorns, was a powerful image in the Autumn sunlight.

Over lunch Will went over my notes. We were about to hit the first 'snag' of the day.

'It says here that the infant Bacchus, God of wine, was lain naked inside a Holly wreath.' He looked about him. 'So, come on then, where's the baby?'

'I haven't got one,' I said emphatically. 'After that 'bun fight' with all those children in the garden, I decided I couldn't face another round of mothers and their offspring....certainly not naked offspring, in this weather. You'll have to use a painting instead. I've got just the thing.'

'Too expensive,' Will's mood was turning. 'It would cost a fortune to get the TV rights.' He paused for a moment. 'I know. We'll use Archie. Could you sew some leaves to a pair of swimming trunks to make it look authentic?'

'No! Definitely not! Anyway, Archie's too old!'

'It doesn't say baby, it says infant.'

'Same thing!'

'What if I haze the shot up a bit? No one will know who he is.'

'No, and that's my final answer!' Making a determined effort to look forceful, I finished my drink and went out to my car to check my notes.

\*      \*      \*      \*

It was half past three and a rather bemused Archie was shivering beside me.

'You can shoot him from the waist up.' We had reached a huge compromise. 'But he's not removing his trousers.'

'Fair enough,' Will conceded. 'Lay him down and arrange the holly around him. It won't take a minute.'

Looking slightly bemused, Archie obliged. He had fallen in love with the cameraman during the 'clothes' film and would have done anything for him. With his eyes shut and his hands across his chest, I thought he looked dead. But it was too late to go back now.

\*      \*      \*      \*

It was about a month later when the film went out. The older children's reaction was even worse than I feared. Despite the haze, they had no difficulty identifying their little brother.

'Oh my God, it's Archie…. and he's naked! Mum how could you?' Claire shrieked in horror.

'He's wearing trousers,' I said defensively. 'You just can't see them.'

'All this attention will be very bad for him,' Claire who fancied herself as a bit of an actress, but had never quite made it to the small screen, was clearly jealous.

But, looking across at Archie who had been busy scrunching Rice Krispies in a bowl and had missed the entire item, I felt reassured that the fame hadn't gone to his head…yet!

\*    \*    \*    \*

'Did your 'evergreen' story give you any sense of dread about the weeks ahead?' Judy wondered when we spoke later that evening.

'What do you mean?'

'Come on, holly, ivy, mistletoe. Christmas is a month away. The season of ill-will and mind-blowing panics…that is, if you're a mother. And with Sue and co. coming, not to mention dear Aunt Lucy, your reasons for panicking are probably greater than most.'

'I haven't had time to give it much thought,' I confessed. 'Far too many other things to worry about. All in all, it's been one hell of a year …if you remember.'

'But this year, of all years, you can't let it go by unnoticed.'

'What's so special about this year?'

'Your house, of course. You can't live where you do without making a big deal of Christmas. It's what living in an Old Vicarage is all about!'

## CHRISTMAS CAKE

For several days I managed to dismiss Judy's concerns as scaremongering. After all, I hadn't exactly done nothing towards the big day. I'd bought some Christmas cards and, somewhere about the house, I'd hidden a few stocking presents for the children and a shawl for my mother. Quite where I'd put any of them was another matter, but I was sure I'd remember if only I could give myself enough time to think about it.

When the 1st December came and went without me being any further forward, I decided to panic. A quick delve into my 'Countdown to Christmas' book that Sue had so thoughtfully given me some years earlier and, until today had never been opened, confirmed my worst fears. I was, at best, around six weeks behind schedule.

Staring out of the opening page, a young woman in a pristine apron was effortlessly stirring a Christmas cake. On the wall behind her, the calendar revealed the month….October.

'Right, you sad woman,' I spat angrily. 'Two can play at that game.'

The picture also revealed an immaculate kitchen. It didn't take a genius to work out that I had no chance of replicating that one. But, remembering Judy's words, I held onto my resolve. This, after all, was the new Kate in her new home. And, against the odds, I'd already mastered jams and pickles. After that, a cake would be simple…or would it?

\* \* \* \*

So, that afternoon, when Aunt Lucy had taken the older two into town after school to buy presents and Lizzie was with Judy, I put Archie in the car and drove to the supermarket. An hour later, we were back. Archie, refreshed from a short sleep, now seeking urgent entertainment and me, so tired, I hardly knew what to do with myself. But, with a huge effort, I knew I had to get over that one. With Christmas less than a month away, I wasn't in any position to indulge myself. No, I had a plan and I was determined to see it through. What better way to educate and amuse an energetic toddler than to make the Christmas cake together. With no older siblings around to offer unwanted and unhelpful advice, Archie was about to get a serious dose of quality time. But as darkness fell on that cold afternoon, it soon became clear that I hadn't quite thought it through.

At first all went well. As I extracted the multitude of ingredients from various bags, I congratulated myself on my brilliant idea. Ignoring the fact that I'd never made a Christmas cake before (that had always been my mum's job and this year she was spending Christmas with my brother), I laid out the utensils with boundless enthusiasm. This Christmas, in my new home, my task was to impress my dear sister-in-law. Hadn't managed that one yet. But maybe this was to be my moment!

As I undid all the dried fruit packets, vague memories from my childhood conjured up an image of a large bowl of mixed peel, cherries and raisins standing on our sideboard at home covered by a tea-towel. It would stay there for days, in preparation for the time when it would be part of the cake. But I never asked why it was there so long…or indeed, why it was there at all. Oh well, it was too late to worry about that now. With the school holidays looming, it was now or never.

When I was little, I used to love getting messy as I tasted all the raw ingredients in the mixing bowl. Well, we wouldn't be doing that today. Far too many newspaper articles had left me in no doubt that the merest sniff of a raw egg would result in my child suffering a lingering death from salmonella poisoning. No, Archie would have to remain clean and disciplined throughout the process. He could look but not lick. He would just have to understand.

But it only took a few minutes for the master plan to fall apart. Moments later Archie found the raisins and, before I could stop him, had accidentally opened the packet, showering the contents in every direction!

As I surveyed the mess across a less than clean floor, it was tempting to cut and run. Bending down to scoop them up whilst trying to extract the remains of the box from my stubborn son, the next obstacle rose up to greet me. Above his angry shrieks, I realised I could just make out the doorbell ringing. And, horror of horrors, as I peered through a corner of the kitchen window, I realised it was my intellectual and newly pregnant neighbour, Carol.

Hastily wiping my sticky fingers on my trousers, I opened the door. Casting a disparaging eye over Archie, who was still howling on the floor behind me, she handed me an environmentally friendly and extremely early Christmas card.

'Sorry about the chaos,' I mumbled. 'Archie and I have just fallen out over a packet of raisins.' I smiled, but she didn't smile back.

'Stewart and I are planning to avoid conflict,' she said smugly. 'I have just read a very good book on toddler training. I'll pop it through your door sometime.' Archie looked up from his tantrum and pulled a face. My sentiments entirely.

'Excellent,' I replied between gritted teeth whilst mentally removing her from my Christmas card list. 'You do that!'

Refusing my offer of coffee, she left us but not before casting her eye over my kitchen as if it were a potential health hazard. For a moment, I felt overcome with an intense feeling of failure. But it was too late to turn back. It was now or never.

So, giving myself a quick moment to compose myself, I turned back to the job in hand. Right. I was ready. First line of recipe: 'Weigh out dried fruit and mixed peel and soak overnight in brandy.' Hah!

Bad start. Never mind. Next line: 'Sift flour, salt and spices from great height for good airing.'

'No, Archie, no.' Oh help! Cannot sieve and control eager toddler at same time, as sieving from great height requires two hands and restraining a toddler at the same time requires three hands.

'Ahhh!' Archie had now grabbed the sieve and bore a passing resemblance to 'Frosty the Snowman'. The tussle continued for several seconds until I wrenched the object from his hands. He screamed and I looked at a table covered in flour and a half empty mixing bowl. Okay, deep breath, take time out.

As I yanked him off the table, the doorbell rang again. Not Carol again, please. But to my relief it was Victoria.

As I led her into the kitchen, initially she tactfully ignored the mess, preferring instead to focus on the mixing bowl. 'Yummy, cake mix!' she exclaimed. 'Can I lick the bowl?'

'Not quite there yet,' I admitted. 'Thanks to Archie's able assistance, we're running a little behind schedule.'

'I don't suppose you could run off a couple of dozen mince pies for me and a few chocolate logs, while you're in the mood?' she ventured as I poured her a cup of tea. 'I'm supposed to be organising a stall for The Children's Society this week and any sort of Christmas food sells like hot cakes, if you'll excuse the pun.'

It didn't take a genius to work out from my expression that her supposition was rather wide of the mark.

'If you only knew how far behind schedule I am with all this Christmas lark, you wouldn't dream of asking me questions like that! What with Christingle services, carol singing evenings and a nativity play to organise, not to mention a million and one other things I haven't quite got round to doing yet, I won't have a spare second for your project. Besides, having watched my battle with jams and pickles, you might be better advised to ask someone with a little more time, not to mention ability, in the cooking department! I take it, from your enthusiasm, that you have never sampled any of my pastry! I made it once at school and nearly broke my teeth on it!'

'Fair enough,' Victoria let my barbed tones wash over her. 'It's just that anything's worth an ask.' She stared down at the mixing bowl and the surrounding devastation and then ventured a second suggestion.

'If you want my advice, I suggest that next year you do what most of us do these days and buy your Christmas cake from the nearest supermarket. If you were brazen enough, you could always pass it off as homemade. Some of them are really quite good.'

'Hang on,' I was now feeling extremely indignant. 'You didn't say that when you persuaded me to make all that jam and pickle earlier this year.'

'That's because I didn't want to see all that fruit go to waste when Mac had taken such trouble to grow it. And, besides, there's nothing to beat home-made pickle!'

'And what's wrong with home-made Christmas cake?'

'To be honest, I don't like it much, at least not when it's cooked. As long as you let me lick the bowl, I'll be quite happy.'

'Bit difficult to do that with a bought one, though.'

'True, very true. Now, I'll finish my tea and let you and Archie get on with this mad project. If you are as behind as you say you are, you're not going to be ready until February, unless I leave you in peace.'

I looked at my flour-coated child and wondered if 'peace' would ever be on the agenda. But, as I surveyed the mess, I knew there was no going back now. So, up to the bathroom for a quick brush down, and on with the job.

Five minutes later....... I lie.....fifteen minutes later we were back at the table, calmed down and dusted down.

Continue. Next step: 'Whisk butter and sugar in basin. Then add the eggs keeping the whisk running as they are incorporated.' Tricky, but not impossible. Archie was now standing on the table looking fascinated. This was more like it. The noise of the whisk was obviously a great distraction and had stunned him into silence.

But not for long. As soon as I stopped the whisk, he took a big step forward right into the mixing bowl. Foot, leg and trousers were covered in a second.

That was it! With a yell of 'For God's sake, you stupid child!' (not a phrase recommended in any parenting book), I grabbed him and, screaming and kicking, took him to the bathroom for the second time. On the short journey the offending 'foot' caught me, the wallpaper and the carpet, doing nothing to improve my mood. Minutes later he was downstairs again, but this time in the playpen. Cooking with a toddler.....don't go there......ever!

\*     \*     \*     \*

'What on earth have you been doing?' Judy demanded when she arrived back with Lizzie a few minutes later. 'It looks like the remains of a chimpanzees' tea party.'

'If you must know, this is all your fault,' I fumed, pointing at the mixing bowl. 'You told me I had to do things properly now that I lived in the Vicarage. For your information, I've never made a Christmas cake before and I'm not doing it again.'

'I never told you to *make* a Christmas cake or anything else for that matter. When I suggested that Christmas would be extra special now that you lived in the Vicarage, I thought you'd be rather taken with the idea. I certainly didn't expect you to start making cakes, rearing turkeys or embroidering the children's stockings. I just meant that an old English Vicarage would be the perfect place to celebrate the festive season.' Sweeping her hand across the kitchen as if to make her final point, she added. 'Doing it this way is no fun at all. Christmas preparations are all about cheating when you've got a family. I've become rather good at some of the shortcuts over the last few years. I had to. Nobody was mad enough to invite my two to share Christmas with them, so I had no alternative but to do it all myself.'

Judy was right. The place looked like a bomb had hit it. Staring down at the table, I extracted 'Countdown to Christmas' from under a packet of flour. With an irrational feeling of satisfaction, I noted that the lady with the pristine apron now had cake mixture splattered across her face.

*     *     *     *

It was nine o'clock when, with the children safely in bed and Mac away for the night, I felt brave enough to complete the project. Alone, with only the radio for company, it was somewhat easier to concentrate. Forty minutes later, I had popped the cake in the oven and made a reasonable attempt at clearing up the mess. No need to rush. I remembered from my childhood that fruit cakes always took longer to cook than a traditional sponge. Now what did it say? Excellent!!!! 'Bake for four and a half hours' and, worse, don't look until at least four hours has passed. With a bit of luck, the cake would be perfect at……..ten past two in the morning!

### RUDOLPH!

The 'Cake' incident had not proved to be a great start to my Christmas preparations. Over the next few days I tried to get excited about present buying and Christmas cards, but it wasn't easy. I needed something to lift my spirits if I was to survive the rigours of December. It came when I least expected it.

It was a Friday and we had woken up to a hoarfrost. The trees looked as if someone had coated them in sparkling silver. The lawn was pure white.

'Claudette, my French friend at school, says Father Christmas is coming to her house tonight,' Lizzie said excitedly at breakfast time. 'French children get their presents earlier than us,' she added knowingly. 'They call today 'Papa Noel'.' Isn't it good that he's got such a frosty day for his sleigh ride.'

'It might be alright for Santa, but Mum will have to be extra careful when she drives you to school this morning. Some of the back routes could be very slippery.' Mac stared at me critically. He never thought my driving was up to much when the weather was good, let alone when it was icy.

'Do you think we'll see Santa and his reindeer when they fly across the sky tonight?' Lizzie wanted to know.

'I think you're going to have to be patient and wait a little longer,' I explained. 'As far as English children are concerned, the excitement doesn't start until Christmas Eve.'

Lizzie shrugged her shoulders but I could see that she was staring hopefully into the cloudless sky.

Despite Mac's misgivings, I successfully managed to negotiate the icy roads on the school run. By nine thirty I was back home and in urgent need of a cup of coffee. It was while I was waiting for the kettle to boil that I looked outside. I couldn't believe my eyes!

There, in the middle of the lawn, calmly munching an apple, was a full size deer.....with antlers. I appeared to have taken early delivery of......... Rudolph!

Grabbing a camera I took several shots as proof of the event. What a pity that the children were at school and not here to see him.

But they soon were.

At three o'clock, as I left to collect them, 'Rudolph' was sitting under the tree, still chewing thoughtfully.

By the time I'd collected everyone, it was dark. During the short journey home, despite my repeated warning that he may have gone by the time we got back, excitement levels on the back seat had reached fever pitch.

'Do you think Santa and the other reindeer are somewhere in the garden too?' Lizzie was bouncing up and down excitedly. 'Maybe there's something wrong with his sleigh and his animals are having a rest while he tries to sort it out.'

'How do you know he's Rudolph, Mum? Did you see his red nose?' Josh, who was almost a non-believer, needed serious proof that this was one of the team.

I considered my reply for a second. Josh, was after all, old enough to know the truth. On the other hand, Lizzie was sitting beside him, her eyes sparkling with anticipation. This was hardly the moment to burst her bubble too.

'I didn't really get close enough to check. But if it isn't him, it's bound to be one of the other eight.'

From the back seat, Lizzie gave a sigh of disappointment. Clearly the coup would lose some of its edge if we hadn't got the main man.

Anxious to keep the magic going as long as possible, I moved quickly to reassure her.

'Of course, it's quite possible that Rudolph's nose is only red when he's at the North Pole. It's probably only glows when it's freezing cold.'

In the back seat, Lizzie and Josh looked more hopeful. Next to me, Claire, a non-believer of some two years standing, raised her eyes to the ceiling.

'Santa, Santa,' Archie chanted, banging his hands excitedly on his lap. For the past few weeks he'd been caught up with the excitement of the festive season with only the vaguest notion of what it was all about.

As we pulled into the driveway, Lizzie flung the door open and was about to leap out when Josh grabbed her jumper.

'Slow down, you idiot. You'll frighten him away.'

'It's alright. If he's still there, he won't be able to see you from the driveway. Now, walk slowly to the gate,' I whispered. 'I'll just get Archie out of his car seat and then you can all go and have a look.'

As we entered the garden, much to my relief, 'Rudolph' was still ensconced under the apple tree. We must have looked an extraordinary sight as we all crept slowly towards him. But, although the deer must have 'clocked' us, he showed no signs of moving. I was beginning to think he simply didn't have it in him.

'Do you think Santa accidentally came to our house today?' Lizzie queried hopefully. 'I've got that poster of Paris on my wall. Maybe he thinks we're French too.'

'No, I don't think he'd be delivering presents here today,' I said gently. 'But he may have come early to check the chimneys. We've got quite a few. He wouldn't want to go down the wrong one. Imagine if he ended up in Aunt Lucy's room. The sight of her in her curlers would be enough to send him straight back to the North Pole.'

Josh and Lizzie nodded, conceding the point. Claire only just managed to turn her snigger into a cough.

As the deer sat there motionless, I dragged my reluctant gang into the house. Despite Lizzie's best efforts, I only just managed to quash her attempt to run outside again with her revised Christmas list.

By eight thirty the children were all asleep. Outside, Rudolph still hadn't moved an inch. When Mac 'phoned to say he'd be back by nine, I seized the opportunity to fill him in with the details.

'Do you think he's ours for as long as he's on our land?' But Mac knew me well enough to know where I was heading.

'No I don't. And don't, for God's sake, suggest that idea to the children. Besides, what on earth would we do with a deer, especially one that two of our kids think belongs to Santa? And just remember our track record with animals, Kate. We'd have the RSPCA out in no time.'

Half an hour later Mac arrived home and went outside to review the situation. But, as I watched him tramp across the lawn, the temptation to follow him was irresistible.

'Do you think we should call the vet?' I whispered. Less than five feet from us the deer was clearly fast asleep.

There was a pause while Mac considered my suggestion.

'No, I don't. He's a wild animal. We don't even know if there's anything wrong with him. Let's leave him overnight and see if he's still there in the morning.'

'But what are we going to say to the children in the morning when he's been savaged in the night and is lying in a pool of blood on the lawn? That's not quite the Christmas image I want.'

Mac gave me the look. 'And what kind of animal do you think will be roaming the garden in the middle of the night with an urge to attack a deer? We don't go in for lions and tigers in this part of Warwickshire.'

In the end, ignoring Mac's sarcasm I called the vet. The woman on the telephone knew exactly what the problem was.

'He's only been eating windfall apples,' I explained. 'There aren't any poisons about. I've got four children so we're very careful.'

'Then he's drunk,' she said quite simply. 'Your pile of windfalls will have fermented nicely by now and he'll be 'two sheets to the wind!' He'll sober up overnight and no doubt be gone by the morning ...with a terrible hangover!'

So, true to form, 'Rudolph' slept it off. And by the morning, he'd gone.

As soon as they were awake, I told Lizzie and Josh that Rudolph had returned to Santa. I told Claire the truth.

Over breakfast, Josh was reflective about the events of the previous day.

'You'd think Rudolph, of all animals, would know about the dangers of alcohol given what Santa must consume on Christmas Eve,' he said thoughtfully. 'After all, he always finishes our bottle of beer by the chimney and some people leave him sherry. How many millions of gallons is that?'

*     *     *     *

'You should have rung me,' Judy chastised me later that evening. 'Eddie and Fred would have been enchanted.'

'If I'd known he was going to hang around for so long, I would have done. I must say it was an enchanting sight to see Lizzie and Archie's faces when they caught a glimpse of him. Even the older two were secretly impressed.'

'It's a wonderful story,' Judy reflected. 'Just what I needed to take my mind off the realities of this ghastly season.'

'I've decided I'm going to make a list of all the things I have to do between now and Christmas,' I announced proudly. 'As soon as the children get home from school, I'm going to start by going through all of their school bags to check there are no vital bits of information lurking in the depths.'

'It could produce some shocking results,' Judy warned. 'When it comes to Josh's, I'd put on your rubber gloves before you delve too deeply. You never know what you might find!'

## CHRISTMAS CHAOS

The trawl of the school bags late the night before had confirmed my worst fears. Between now and the end of term I was due to attend four Christmas concerts, three carol services and two Christmas bazaars. On top of that I was required to make three costumes (Claire, mercifully, had come to the end of her nativity play days) and to attend two dress rehearsals to help with hair, make up etc. And that was only my school commitments. Looming large on the horizon were also the annual 'Christingle' service, the carol singing evening and the village nativity play not to mention the various relatives that were planning to descend on us for the festive season.

'Don't forget my concert's tomorrow night,' Josh warned. 'And can you please not be late this time.'

'I am never late.'

'Well, okay, but don't be the last to arrive. It means you always have to sit at the back and then you can't see properly. Scarlet Broadwell's mum is always early which means she gets the best seats at the front. It's not fair!'

'Scarlet Broadwell is an only child,' I reminded him curtly, but he was unimpressed.

'That's not my fault!' Josh was indignant as he swept out of the door.

At that moment Mac arrived in the kitchen.

'God, what a mess,' he said unnecessarily as he surveyed the chaos that was generally breakfast time in our house. 'Try and get it a bit tidier before tonight, will you? I hope you haven't forgotten that it's our annual bash at the office. I suggested to Charlie's wife, Karen, that she gets to you around six thirty. You don't mind driving her in again, do you?'

'Not again! How come she never gets to take me?' I was appalled at the suggestion. 'It's bad enough trying to escape the mayhem here, without having to give the impression to your client's wife that I am even vaguely organised at that time of night.'

'I'm sure you'll manage,' he grinned, giving me a peck on the cheek. 'Remember, seven fifteen at the Metropole and don't be late. Oh, and why not go and buy yourself a smart outfit for the occasion. If you turn up in that little black number again, people will start to think I'm too mean to buy you anything new!'

'Don't be late!' I repeated angrily under my breath as I hurled the cereal bowls into the washing up bowl. 'Now what could possibly delay me, I wonder?'

Having dropped the children off at school, I vaguely toyed with the idea of heading into town to see what the smart, new dress shop on the high street had in stock. But remembering my large bottom and scruffy mop of hair, I decided the idea of trying to squeeze into some sexy little number alongside people half my age and size was too depressing to contemplate. So instead of turning right into town, I signalled left and headed to Judy's.

Over a large cup of coffee, I vented my feelings.

'It's not that I don't want to go to this 'do' this evening. It's just that these things are not the same now that I've got children. Long gone are the days when you could relax in a bath and paint your toenails prior to going out. Nowadays I'm lucky if I get the chance to dip my toes in Archie's dirty bathwater by the time I've fed and sorted everyone! And I'm amazed this Karen lady is prepared to come with me again. Last time, we left in such a rush that we were halfway to the event before I realised I'd left the tickets to the parking area and the arena on the kitchen table. It was only my complete ineptitude that got us in. One look at the filthy car with two scruffy car seats and a load of toys on the back seat, confirmed my identity as an incompetent mother rather than potential terrorist. I was through all the security checks before you could blink.'

Judy nodded sympathetically.

'And it was even worse a couple of years ago. I'd not long had Archie so my figure was even worse than it is now. Complete disorganisation prevented me from checking my only outfit before it was too late. I tell you, 'tight' wasn't the word! Anyway, I somehow managed to squeeze myself into it before I realised there was a mark on the front. I sponged it off as best I could and, throwing a large shawl over my shoulders to cover up at least some of the damage, I drove into town.

To my horror, I walked into the reception to discover Mac's sexy young secretary wearing the same dress. I had to stop myself from turning round and running out screaming.'

'So how did Mac react?'

'Oh, he was hopeless. When I told him what had happened, he looked across the room at his glamorous assistant in her dress that loosely hung from her shoulders. He then looked at mine and said: 'Darling, I shouldn't worry. No one would ever guess!'

Judy sighed. 'Mind you,' she said, 'it's still not as bad as my experience at James' Christmas 'do' earlier this week.'

'Go on.'

'It started well enough. Miraculously, I got to the station in plenty of time and bought a magazine to read on the train. By the time I got into town I felt pretty relaxed. James was there to meet me and, when we arrived at the hotel, I was almost looking forward to it. It was only when he was introducing me to his boss that I noticed that the free ultra-thin panty liner I'd peeled off the front cover of the magazine and thought I'd buried beneath someone's discarded newspaper, had somehow managed to attach itself to the side of my skirt! I tell you, it doesn't get much more embarrassing than that.'

I sighed sympathetically. 'What's happened to us, Judy? Before I had the children, I loved a good party. I think I still could if I could just organise myself well enough beforehand.'

'Well, it's quite straightforward then.'

'How do you mean?'

'I tell you what we're going to do my girl. You're going to finish that coffee and then we'll both go into town and buy that outfit for tonight. By the time I've finished with you, you'll be the 'belle' of the ball!'

'You're joking!'

'No I'm not. I'm sick and tired of running around after everyone, especially at Christmas. It's high time we changed things a bit.'

\*    \*    \*    \*

The 'do' turned out to be rather better than I'd expected. The little red number Judy had persuaded me to buy did much to disguise many of my unwanted lumps and bumps and a quick trip to the hairdressers meant that I had a style that would at least see me through the evening, even if any attempt to recreate it myself was destined for disaster.

But despite the delicious food and drink, I couldn't entirely relax. True, I'd got to grips with one Christmas event, but the deadline on the others was fast approaching. I was going to have to make a monumental effort over the next few days if I was to stand any chance of getting on top of things.

## PINS AND NEEDLES!

'Kate, this is not going to work.' Victoria had been watching me try to sew pipe cleaners on to an old mouse costume of Claire's for the best part of an hour and the sheer futility of the project was beginning to annoy her.

'Where was that hedgehog in the Nativity story? That's what I want to know,' I looked accusingly at Victoria for an answer.

Ignoring the question, she picked up the half finished article and shook her head. 'To be honest, Kate, she'd have to be insane to put this on. Apart from anything else, I don't think it's safe. If she bumps into someone, she could take their eye out.' She pointed to a pipe cleaner whose metal prong had already viciously poked its way out of its woolly sheath.

'But I have to have something for her to take to school tomorrow,' I said defiantly. 'You don't understand. They're doing a costume check. If she doesn't have something to show the teacher, I'll look completely hopeless…again!'

'And what happens if you don't pass the test?'

'We go immediately to 'Plan B' which is to ring the lady who runs the costume shop in town and offer to pay any money for her to make me one.'

'Why on earth didn't you do that in the first place?'

'Because I have to be seen to make the effort. It's…it's like taking a bought cake for the 'bring and buy'. You're not a proper mother unless certain things are home-made. I must have told you about my hideous experience at the village fete. You should have seen Lady Henrietta's face when I confessed that my fruit pie had come from the local farm shop. I thought she was going to have a fit.'

'And whose problem was that? Yours or hers?'

'Oh, hers probably. But that didn't make it any less mortifying.'

'And do the children mind if the costume is made by you or someone else?'

'Actually, no. In fact Lizzie is desperate to get hers from the shop in town, even if she never wears it. Owning it will be quite enough for her.'

'Do you have to make Claire's cow outfit too?'

'No, thank God. That's got to be hired. It has to have all kinds of clever contraptions inside it to make it work.'

Having successfully auditioned for a part in the village pantomime, Claire had just learned, to her delight, that she was not to be part of the children's dance troupe. Instead, she was to be the back end of the pantomime cow, an honour that Josh had found hard to come to terms with.

'Oh Yuk! You'll be stuck for hours with your head pressed against someone else's bottom.'

'No I shan't. Anyway, the pantomime cow is one of the best parts. I even get to dance.'

'I think it's great,' I defended. 'As parts go, it's head and shoulders above being in the kids dance troupe.'

'Actually, it's head and shoulders below most of the parts if you think about it,' Josh replied, his mind still full of bottoms!

'Honestly Josh you're obsessed by people's rear ends. You're far too old for that sort of humour. I'm beginning to think you'll never grow out of it.'

'Like father, like son,' Victoria smiled knowingly as she disappeared into the kitchen.

Just then, the sound of a car in the driveway heralded the return of Lizzie who had been out to tea with Hatty, a friend from school and church. A few moments later the door opened and she burst in.

'Mummy, if you don't sign the permission slip to go to the Christmas concert in town by tomorrow morning, Mrs Brightman says I'll have to stay behind.'

Excellent timing, Lizzie. Yet another thing to add to my long list of inadequacies. Behind her, Hatty's mum, gave me a comradely smile.

'If you can't find the form, scribble something on a piece of paper. They just want written evidence that if she chokes to death on a lolly stick, you agreed to take the risk.'

But more worrying than that....what Christmas concert? And what permission slip? It was the week before the end of term and I feared I knew exactly where the vital information lay. That morning, whilst making a feeble attempt to clear up, I had moved a pile of papers from the corner of the kitchen which, for some days I had been unable to face. No doubt, lurking somewhere within it would be the piece of paper I needed now along with some unpaid bills, the overdue library book, and a pile of unfinished Christmas cards –one to an aunt which required a letter and a family picture or my mother would kill me, and several to families who had moved during the year and I had never quite got round to transferring their new address into my book.

As I had no intention of revealing that particular 'mess' to the gathering, I simply stared at Lizzie apologetically.

And it had been even worse that morning when I'd taken my overseas cards to the post office.

'Am I in time?' I'd asked helplessly.

'Well,' the post master had replied with a smirk, 'that rather depends on which Christmas you had in mind?'

At least I'd got the Christmas tree up. But even that hadn't been straightforward. After the cramped conditions in the cottage, I'd surveyed the collection of trees at the nursery and plumped for the biggest one I could find. With a lofty ceiling in the main room, I felt it could justify an impressive spruce.

But when the man delivered it later that evening, I realised I'd slightly over-estimated the size of the space.

'Do you want it dropped off here or shall I take it straight to Trafalgar Square?' the man said sarcastically as he and his mate tried to heave it off the back of the van. 'Presumably it's for outside.'

'Yes,' I lied. Mac was going to have to have his Christmas present of an electric saw a little earlier than I'd planned.

'Do you always get this flustered at Christmas time?' Victoria asked, once Lizzie had left the room.

'Yes....well no. Never quite this bad.'

'So what's so different about this year?'

'Living here. When we were at the cottage, we always went away for Christmas. We didn't have the space to invite hoards of relatives to stay. This year is payback time. I've got a houseful, and they don't all get on. And besides that, everyone's expectation of me seems to have gone up since we moved. I feel I can't get away with a shoddy tree or lousy decorations in the same way. And we're expected to host a party.....or at least it seems as if we are. It's as if I've suddenly had to grow up.'

'And how does Mac feel?'

'It's not the same for Mac. He's felt at home here from the start. It's as if he's always belonged here. He was born in a place like this in the middle of the countryside and, although he's lived all over the place, it's as if he always knew that one day he'd come back. I am trying to be more sophisticated now, for his sake. But somehow I always seem to muck it up. All around me in this village I see people like you, the church wardens, the flower ladies, the people who care for the churchyard and others tirelessly working to keep everything going like clockwork. And I do try and keep up but I don't always seem to manage it very well. And, well, now that it's almost Christmas, and I've got the most efficient sister-in-law in the world coming, the feeling of hopelessness just seems much, much stronger.'

'You're doing fine.'

I grunted. 'Ask me again next week after the carol singers have been.'

'What's so difficult about a few carol singers?'

'Wait and see.'

## CAROL SINGERS

We were sitting at the kitchen table enjoying a late night coffee. While Mac was idly looking through some Christmas cards, I was scrutinising a long, much altered list.

'Just remind me again what you've agreed to this time.' There was a note of resignation in Mac's voice.

'We are just continuing a village tradition.'

'Which is....?'

'To invite the carol singers in for mulled wine and mince pies when they tour the village next week. The Campbell's did it for years and, besides, the children will love it.'

'Sounds okay to me,' Mac sounded almost enthusiastic. 'I rather like the idea of having a small choir sing to me in my own house. It also means that we have a great excuse not to join them on a freezing night in December.' Clearly Mac thought this was a good result. I took a deep breath before filling him in with some of the finer details.

'I don't think the choir's that small,' I hesitated.

'Well, it can't be that big,' Mac reasoned. 'There are only about three hundred or so in the whole village.'

'And about fifty of them sing.'

Mac paused. 'You're joking!'

'No, I'm not. Which is why I'm planning a list of people to invite round to hear the carols with us. A choir that size can't be expected to perform to just the six of us.'

'Don't tell me. You've invited the rest of the village for supper?'

'Oh no. I can't do that. Louisa's in charge of the choir and she's made that quite clear. We can't invite anyone from the village because otherwise they will have no one to carol sing to before they get here.'

'So who are you planning to invite?'

'Well, I thought we could invite people who live too far off the 'beaten track' to be carol-sung to. That would mean the couple who live in the cottage in Marden Wood, the family that owns Brockhole Farm, Deirdre who owns the kennels, Jerry, the man who sells the vegetables from his garden at the end of the village and, of course... now what's their names? Oh yes, Edwina and Ted from the Caravan park.

'Excellent!' said Mac. 'So we're hosting a party for a group of strangers!'

'It's neighbourly,' I defended myself, 'and, besides, you might really like these people when you meet them.'

'And then again, I might not!' he muttered darkly. 'Of course we could have invited close friends to share a Christmas party with us, but I suppose that would have been 'un-neighbourly'.'

'Oh they're coming as well.' I smiled brightly.

'So how many will we end up with, assuming they all accept?'

I stared critically at my list for a moment. 'I reckon, including the carol singers, about eighty five.'

'You're joking?'

'But they won't all accept. And even if they do, I'm only feeding the guests. The carol singers just get mince pies and mulled wine, remember?'

'Oh that's alright then,' he muttered. But I could detect the heavy sarcasm in his voice as he stomped outside to gather yet more holly.

So, I sent out my invitations. But as the day grew nearer I began to panic. Clearly country folk were reluctant to commit.

'It sounds a lovely idea,' Sandra Benton from the cottage in Marden wood was on the 'phone. 'I've pencilled it in the diary. Can I confirm nearer the time?'

'My sister-in-law and her family will have arrived for Christmas by then,' Deirdre from the kennels was trying to calm four dogs and a tangle of leads on our doorstep. 'Her children would just love something like this. You don't mind if we bring them along too, do you?'

'Don't look for sympathy from me,' Mac looked irritated. 'This is all your fault. They see you coming.'

By five o'clock on the day, I was in a state of complete panic. The food was cooked but the kitchen looked like a bomb had hit it. Nothing particularly unusual about that but I wanted so badly to give the impression that this was an orderly household. Fat chance, judging by the noise that was coming from upstairs. Against my better judgment, my agreement to allow each child to have one friend round seemed to have been extended to an invitation for half the village children to join my lot for the afternoon. With strict instructions to keep out of the kitchen, and a warning that if the rest of the house wasn't kept tidy, my children would be adopted, I'd managed to close my ears to the noise until it was too late. When I surveyed the devastation in the lounge a few moments later, my murderous expression was enough to spark even the slowest child into immediate action.

A blitz on the kitchen produced a reasonable result and by quarter past six, with all visiting children dispatched from the house, I was beginning to feel a little more optimistic. There was just one important element missing - the mulled wine. That was Mac's responsibility. The trouble was….he was missing too! Presumably he was on his way home and had the matter well in hand. But, why hadn't he 'phoned? Not even he could forget that one…..or could he?

So, I tidied the remainder of the kitchen, thoughtfully laid out the ingredients for him on the table and went upstairs to get changed.

At around six thirty a screech of brakes outside indicated that the master of the house had finally returned. Ignoring my sarcastic tones and insisting that he was *not* late, he grabbed some oranges and started chopping enthusiastically. Within seconds sticky juice was covering the table, the floor, his jacket and any child foolish enough to get too close. Opening bottles at speed he then transferred the 'too full' bowl to the hob adding a generous helping of red wine to the mess on the floor and the cooker. Over-enthusiasm with the cinnamon shaker meant that the lid came off and before he could blink, the entire contents of the packet had emptied themselves into the pot …..delicious! Lots of swearing, more wine to dilute the now extraordinary taste and a rather large 'slug' of Cointreau later and he was ready. Muttering darkly about this being the one and only time we do this, he then stomped off to check the fire.

But later on he ate his words. When the choir appeared in the driveway singing 'Once in Royal David's City' and then gathered round the fire to the sounds of 'O Little Town of Bethlehem' and 'Hark the Herald Angels Sing', even the most cynical husband would have been hard pressed not to enjoy it. When the children gathered round the piano for a verse or two of 'Away in a Manger,' I even thought I saw a tear in his eye. But, then again, maybe not.

*     *     *     *

It was midnight and Mac and I were alone in the kitchen.

'That was lovely,' I reflected. 'All that hard work paid off. I think everyone enjoyed themselves. I thought the singing was wonderful.'

'I agree. Now you can put your feet up and relax a little.'

I muttered something but Mac didn't catch it.

'What was that?'

'Just Christingle and the Nativity play,' I mumbled again.

Mac picked up a tea-towel and with a dramatic sweep wiped the top of the breakfast bar.

'You know, for someone whose job requires them to speak clearly, you can be very difficult to understand sometimes.'

And with that he went to bed.

## CHRISTINGLES

As I trawled through the mountains of wrapping paper, gift tags and sticky tape in the supermarket, I was beginning to panic. Where on earth was the ribbon? I needed forty feet of the red variety and nothing else would do. I looked down into my trolley and did yet more rapid calculations. If I got this wrong, I'd be in trouble.

I was on a mission. Less than twenty four hours away was the annual Christingle service in the church. At one point during the proceedings, every child would solemnly receive an orange covered in sweets and red ribbon with a candle on the top. At least they would if I got my act together. Fully assembled, the idea was that the orange represented God's world, the red ribbon wrapped round the middle was the blood of Christ, sweets on four cocktail sticks attached at regular intervals around the centre became the fruits of the earth in the four seasons of the year and a lighted candle stuck in the top was 'Jesus Christ the Light of the World'. So with cocktail sticks sticking out of all sides and flames leaping out of the top, the question was 'symbolic object' or, 'lethal weapon'. Given that the congregation would include around fifty children, there was a strong case for the latter!

So, I checked again. To be on the safe side I'd got sixty oranges, two hundred and forty cocktail sticks, around a thousand tiny sweets (at least sixteen for each orange), and sixty candles. But still no ribbon. I looked again. Every colour except red. But with half the churches in the area running a similar service in December, that was hardly surprising. Like many other tasks at Christmas, I should have done it earlier, but it didn't quite work out like that.

Three shops later, and I'd sorted it. Just one more tiny little job to do……..making them.

At our other house, I'd made them all myself and, by the time I got to the church, I generally had as much seasonal spirit as a turkey awaiting execution. As I carried them across each year, the kitchen I left behind would always have a floor covered with very sticky orange juice. With three or more fingers covered with sticking plaster as a result of unsuccessfully trying to attach 'Jellytots' to cocktail sticks (they won't), I was often as 'prickly' as the Christingle and as hot and bothered as the candle on the top!

But in this village the system was different. The next morning, as I tipped the contents of my carrier bags onto the table, Mac came in. He stared at the table and then gave me a withering look.

'I thought you said you weren't making these this year.'

'I'm not. At least, not on my own. I've got help. Claire's quite keen and Judy and Moira should be arriving any moment. And to ease our pain at this traumatic time of the year, they're bringing a bottle of wine. We should get it done in no time.'

And we did. And by the time we'd finished the Christingles and the wine, we weren't too sure that all the bits were on in the right places. But then we didn't much care either.

Later that afternoon, and by then completely sober, I took them across to the church. Together on the table by the altar, they looked lovely. Clever little objects really. Even I could see how symbolic they were.

But then my eye caught sight of the buckets of water strategically placed round the aisles and I was reminded once again of their full potential.

'Expecting an inferno?' the organist laughed as I checked for the umpteenth time that I'd got my numbers right.

'Before or after they've choked on the cocktail sticks or removed their neighbour's eyes with them? I tell you, when they parade around the church this afternoon remembering Jesus Christ the Light of the World, I shall be praying that they get back to their parents without igniting the child in front's coat, hair or the whole church and its congregation!'

I turned to see Mac behind me with yet another tray.

'Why didn't you ask more of the mums to help you? Then you'd have got them done in a fraction of the time.'

'Well, I tried but they all said they were busy.'

'Well it's just lucky we're not!' was all he could say. And with that, he helped himself to a stray Jellytot, and went back to the house to get ready.

\*     \*     \*     \*

Two hours later and about half an hour into the service, things weren't quite going according to plan. I was standing alongside Moira and Vicar Vic, the unlit Christingles lined up in front of us. We had several tapers but no means of lighting them. Lined up in front of us were around fifty children, all waiting impatiently to receive their gift.

'Matches? Match what?' Mac mouthed at me vaguely as I gesticulated at him wildly from the altar.

Suddenly light dawned. Mac had remembered. As we'd left the house, I'd shouted back to him to bring the matches that now sat on our kitchen table. It was the only thing I had asked him to remember all day, but now wasn't the time to remind him of that. I would save that one for later!

Like a dart he shot past the queue of children, knocking several of them sideways as he went. A moment later he was back carrying the missing link.

'It would have looked a bit odd singing 'Shine Jesus, Shine' whilst holding an unlit candle,' I hissed at him as he handed them over. 'Christingle means 'Christ Light' remember. You know, 'Jesus Christ the Light of the World'. Seeing as I went to all the bother of buying and making these things, it's a pity that you couldn't be bothered to remember we needed to light them.'

But Mac refused to be needled. Instead he re-joined a highly excited Lizzie and Archie as they stood patiently in the queue waiting their turn.

It was lovely to watch the children parade round the church, the candles lighting up their excited faces. As they returned to the chancel, they lined up in three rows so that the congregation could see them all together. As they sang 'Away in a manger,' I could see that many of the mothers had tears in their eyes. But, sadly the peaceful scene was short-lived.

\*     \*     \*     \*

'She could have killed him,' Mac exclaimed as he joined me at the end of the service. 'I tell you Audrey and her precious daughter aren't safe to be let out!'

'You do exaggerate,' I replied. 'There were far too many adults on hand to allow Josh to come to any serious harm. Besides, the coat was only smouldering. Once I'd pulled it off his back, it stopped smoking in a second. Scarlet only singed his hood.'

'It could easily have been an inferno,' Mac continued, 'Think of all those wooden pews. All the other children were distracted by that child's scream. It was only luck that their own little time bombs didn't add to the potential disaster!'

'Nonsense! In the unlikely event of the flames taking hold, Moira would have doused them in a second with one of her many buckets of water.'

'What on earth possessed Audrey to take a picture? It was bound to distract the children,' Mac wondered. 'There are notices everywhere that say flash photography is forbidden in the church.'

'It wasn't the flash that caused the problem. It was the sight of her mother waving at her to get her attention that made Scarlet lose concentration. I saw the poor girl dying of embarrassment a second before she set light to Josh's hood, but I was too far away to do anything about it.'

My moans were suddenly interrupted by an over-excited Josh.

'Mum, Scarlet's mother thinks she caught the moment my hood caught fire on her photograph. She's going to let me have a copy.'

'There you go, I said that woman was mad. She's obviously not remotely embarrassed by the incident. Kate, when she's got over the excitement, remind her she owes us for a new coat.'

'Oh, don't be so ridiculous. Actually, if you must know, there's hardly any damage done.'

'Well, I disagree. Apart from the flames, Josh has also had to deal with the image of you hurling yourself at him from across the aisle. That alone would be enough to give most people post traumatic stress. We need to keep a close eye on him over the next few days. I must say that you certainly surprised me. I never realised you could move so fast!'

'Scarlet's mum says it's a pity she took a photograph rather than a video,' Claire sighed. 'Then she could have sent it to 'You've Been Framed' under the title 'You've been inflamed!'

'And you say she isn't mad?' Mac sighed. 'I rest my case!'

\* \* \* \*

It was cold outside as I staggered across the dark graveyard back to the Vicarage, precariously balancing several trays and a handful of half eaten Christingles. As I opened the gate to our driveway, I was vaguely aware of the heavy footsteps of Lady Henrietta behind me. Resolving there and then to refuse to do whatever she suggested, I braced myself for the inevitable request for last minute help. And it came, but not in the way I'd expected.

'Kate, dear, I'm so glad I caught you. It's just that..... as you appear to have been relieved of your normal duties this month, I was wondering if you had the time to organise some sort of entertainment for the children at the Village Hall party next Sunday?'

I reeled backwards, almost dropping my entire cargo on the ground in the process. 'What, exactly, do you mean by 'being relieved of my normal monthly duties'?' I queried acidly. I could see that she'd realised that she may have made a tactical error.

'Well,' she said rather awkwardly, 'as we weren't treated to one of your little plays at the Christingle service, I assumed you'd decided to take a bit of a 'back seat' for the Christmas season.'

It was tempting to slug her one, but luckily, an armful of trays and oranges prevented me. Instead, with an enormous effort I summoned my dignity and set about putting her straight on a few matters.

Raising myself to my full height I began: 'Lady Henrietta,' I said crisply, 'for your information, during the last seventy two hours, I have played host to the village carol singers, bought and helped assemble around sixty Christingles, assisted in their distribution, put out the odd fire, and now I am helping to clear up the mess. Furthermore, far from being relieved of my duties, this evening I shall be putting the finishing touches to my own version of the Nativity, a job which also involves organising costumes and carols. All that is in addition to the huge responsibilities I seem to have as a mother and wife at this time of year.'

Hoping she'd feel suitably chastened by my outburst, I stood back awaiting her reply. However, when it came, it wasn't quite what I'd expected.

Patting me gently on the shoulder she said: 'Kate, dear, you're letting all these little events get on top of you. Calm down before you make yourself ill. It's only Christmas you know. When you get to my age, you'll let these things wash over you. Experience will teach you not to get so excited about everything. Now what's this about a Nativity Play? That shouldn't be too difficult now, should it? Everyone knows the story. I'm sure you'll get it done in no time.'

I looked at her with desperate eyes but I didn't trust myself to speak. With an effort, I simply said 'Thank you, I'll bear that in mind.'

'Good. I hope my little 'pep' talk has helped you. Good luck dear, and keep smiling!' And with that she turned and marched back to the church.

'Patronising cow!' I blurted out to Mac as I relayed the story to him a few minutes later. 'I hope she burns in hell!!' He was on his hands and knees by the altar picking out bits of candle wax from the carpet. He handed me a half melted candle in an orange as he stood up.

'Now, now, has the nice Lady Henrietta upset you,' Victoria winked at me as she marched up the aisle. 'She's just told me about the conversation she had with you. I've come to give you my deepest condolences and to say that I agree with your sentiments entirely!'

I smiled weakly.

'There's just one thing, though. Next time you feel like mouthing off like that, don't do it by the altar. If you're not careful, God might send a thunderbolt down and we've only just had the chancel roof repaired.'

'I doubt if he'll bother to try that one,' I laughed. 'The pace I'm moving at the moment, there's not a chance one could catch me!'

\*     \*     \*     \*

It was about ten o'clock that evening. Mac was sitting contentedly in his favourite chair, a large glass of wine in his hand. I was on the floor trying, unsuccessfully to straighten a large pair of angel wings.

'Why are you bothering to fiddle with those when Lizzie has any number of perfect ones in her dressing up box?'

'The ones in the box are fairy wings,' I explained.

'You're not telling me there's a difference?'

'There certainly is. Angel wings are bigger.'

Mac laughed. 'Says who?'

'Lizzie, of course. If anyone's a 'wings' expert, she is.'

'So, I take it she's after the part of the Angel Gabriel.'

'I daresay she is, but she won't get it on two counts. Firstly she's too short and secondly the Angel Gabriel was a boy.'

'I doubt you'll find a boy in our church to play that part.'

'You're probably right. But I'm not too worried. I'm expecting lots of children to turn up tomorrow in all kinds of Nativity costumes, so I'm sure I'll have plenty to choose from.'

'I wouldn't like to be in your shoes when you cast it.'

'Oh, I'm sure it'll be fine. Apart from my lot, most of the kids are quite sensible.'

'It wasn't the children I was thinking of, it was their mothers!'

## PREPARATIONS

'Okay, just to recap. You don't want any bedding. You'll be bringing it all yourself.' My tone was crisp, but Sue, who was in full flight on the other end of the 'phone, didn't seem to notice.

'Yes, that's right. I'll pop our special mattress protectors on the beds as soon as we arrive. It seals them in, you see.'

'Seals what in?'

'Your house dust mites. Surely, you remember my problem with dust!'

'How do you know I have house dust mites?'

'Oh everyone has them. Obviously some people have more than others,' she added darkly. 'It depends on the age of your mattresses. We change ours very regularly and use the protectors... just to be doubly safe!'

Trying to ignore the awful vision of our family asleep in bed with millions of mites swarming beneath us, I hastily wrote 'BUY NEW MATTRESSES' in big letters across my pad and then took a deep breath. 'So, if you're bringing mattress protectors, shall I leave the bedclothes in the room so that you can put them on yourself.'

'Oh no,' Sue sounded horrified, 'I'll be bringing *all* our own bedding and towels. I'm afraid I'm not very good with those biological products you use. We all have very sensitive skin, you see. So, I only use natural soap powders. Not as convenient, I know, but I just feel it's so much healthier than sleeping next to all those chemicals.'

'Lovely,' I replied through gritted teeth.

'Oh, and I'm hoping there'll be room in your freezer for some of our food. As you know we eat organic whenever possible. So I've taken the liberty of preparing several casseroles in advance so that we can all enjoy them during our time with you. I've also arranged for our local organic supplier to deliver to your house during our stay. And, if it's alright with you, I'll order a large turkey from the same place. I'm hoping you'll let me do the Christmas lunch for you. It will be part of my contribution. I know how trying you find these things and, as you know, I just love cooking good, healthy food for everyone. You really will taste the difference when you try it.'

'I'm sure I will!' I spat. 'So, I don't really need to do anything, then. You seem to have it all under control.'

'Oh but you are providing us with a home when we most need it,' she assured me. 'My little contributions are nothing compared to your generosity. Believe me, we are so grateful. The boys, in particular, are thrilled. You see, we don't allow television at home. But I have told them that they may watch certain programmes during our stay and they are beside themselves with excitement. I don't think a little indulgence now and again does anyone any harm. After all, it is Christmas.'

'I've made a cake.' I blurted out. It sounded pathetic.

'Oh well done,' Sue gushed. 'One job already off the list then.'

'And I've made some pickles and some jam,' I added before I could stop myself.

'Excellent. What a clever girl. Gosh this is so exciting. I'm sure we're all going to have a really lovely time!'

\* \* \* \*

'Why on earth do you think you have to change your mattresses just because you sister-in-law is coming to stay?' Most people just change the sheets, you know.' Judy was studying the pages I'd marked in the Argos catalogue in disbelief.

'She's worried about the dust.'

'And why should your mattresses be more dusty than anyone else's?'

'Because they're old. The bed in the spare bedroom used to belong to my grandfather.'

'But that doesn't mean the mattress is as old as the bed.'

'Well, to be honest, it might be. Mind you, the mattress wasn't marked in any way when we inherited it, just a bit frayed at the edges. So, I simply put a large blanket over it and then made it up as normal. It's actually very comfortable.'

'But if it's just dust she's worried about, why don't you vacuum it?'

'It's not just the dust she's worried about. It's the mites that eat it! I think they're what make her sneeze! She says the older the mattress, the bigger the problem. If that's the case, I'm amazed the army of livestock in it haven't marched it off the bed years ago!'

'And is that all that's bugging you?'

'Apart from her insistence that she brings her own bedding and food, yes. One way or another, she's obviously convinced I'm going to poison her!'

'If you ask me, you're looking at this the wrong way. You've got a family coming for Christmas who are hell bent on organising it all for you! What could be better? It could be the most relaxed Christmas you've ever had. I tell you what, if it doesn't work out, send her round to me.'

'It's just that she makes me feel so hopeless all the time.'

'Once you realise that it's her problem and not yours, you'll feel heaps better. Mac's right. Deep down Sue envies you. She'd love to be able to take a more laid back attitude to housework but she simply can't do it. That's why she's so 'stick' thin. She burns it all up in nervous energy. As soon as you accept that she's the one with the neuroses, you'll probably like her a lot more. If I were you, I'd let her help as much as she likes this Christmas. Offer to help by all means but, for God's sake, take the opportunity to have a good rest.'

'The way things are going at the moment, I'm going to need it. This afternoon when I should be doing last minute present shopping, I shall be in the church for the first rehearsal of the Nativity play. In a moment of madness, I suggested the children wore costumes, partly because, last week, I noticed three beautiful crowns in a cupboard in the vestry that were obviously used in a previous performance. However, if the rumours I've heard over the past few days are anything to go by, I may have made a big mistake.'

## THE NATIVITY

'It's really very simple,' my patience was running out. 'We can only have one Mary in this play.'

In front of me were three indignant little girls. Two of them were clutching Mary outfits as if this, somehow, added weight to their argument.

'To be honest, I don't understand why you're all fighting over her. I don't ever remember a time when she had any lines. You'd all be far better off as angels. They get around. First with Mary, next with Joseph, then at the stable for the birth. And after a quick trip to see the shepherds, they're back at the stable again for the grand finale. What's more, they get to stand on stools looking beautiful where everyone can see them.'

I could see that my gang of three were wavering.

'It's the same with Joseph,' I continued warming to my task. 'You're far better off being an innkeeper or a King. In fact, the very best part is Herod. There's nothing to beat being the villain. Once they get to the stable, all Joseph has to do is stand still next to Mary, doing nothing for ages!'

The rehearsal for the Nativity play had got off to a bad start when Simon, a king, had dropped his 'frankincense' all over the aisle. As the contents of a bottle of shampoo poured all over the carpet, I cursed, not for the first time, that the nearest water supply was back at home.

'Is it real frankincense?' Scarlet looked horrified as she watched me clear up the mess. 'They told us at school that it's very valuable.'

'What do you think?' I replied with more than a hint of sarcasm. I was beginning to think, not for the first time, that I wasn't the right person for this job.

'If it had been frankincense,' Josh was keen to stick his oar in, 'it wouldn't have poured out of the bottle like that. 'It's a perfumed resin burned in honour of a God.'

Not to be outdone, Claire was keen to add her bit.

'Myrrh's even stickier. It's a gum used to prepare bodies for burial.'

'Yuk. Why on earth would you give that to a baby?'

'Because,' I added patiently, 'it showed that Jesus was human and would die just like anyone else.'

'Well, that's a cheerful thought when you've only just been born,' Mike, Simon's older brother, reflected. 'I'd have preferred a train set.'

'Probably a bit hard to get hold of one of those way back in the first century,' I argued. But I feared my sarcasm was wasted on the majority of the cast.

The idea of staging the Nativity story on the Sunday before Christmas had not, initially, seemed terribly challenging. Everyone knows the story and, as most of the children had already done it the previous week at school, costumes were generally not a problem. And we hadn't been stupid enough to do what the neighbouring village had done and import a real donkey. Given what that had done to their carpet, I was more than happy to mop up a bit of shampoo.

'Are you expecting a good 'turn out' this afternoon?' Mac asked as I was serving up lunch.

'Yes, I reckon the church will be packed. Everyone I've bumped into over the past few days says they're coming along. Actually, dare I say it, I'm quite looking forward to it. For a start, we don't usually have costumes for our plays and this morning, at the rehearsal, all the little angels looked really cute. It's amazing how a pair of wings and a halo can make the naughtiest child appear angelic. And it was easy to rehearse. They all know the lines, so there's far less chance for things to go wrong.'

But, as usual, I spoke too soon.

\*     \*     \*     \*

'It was all Audrey Broadwell's fault......again!' I moaned to Mac later that evening. 'I told her not to make Scarlet's wings so big, She sent Lizzie flying when she turned round suddenly during the stable scene!

And why did Herod's sword have to fall apart so spectacularly as he removed it from its sheath? It should have been one of the most dramatic scenes in the play. Instead I had an audience helpless with laughter and a very bemused child. It quite ruined the moment.'

'Well, I thought it was great,' Mac said loyally. 'But, for me, the best bit was when the star peeled itself off the wall. Your Kings had no idea where to point or what to follow. I thought the moment when one of them started to crawl along the aisle looking for it was quite the best in the whole play. To be honest, the audience love it far better when it all goes wrong.'

I grunted and carried on wrapping presents. 'Actually the best bit of the day happened this morning. You'd have loved it.'

'Go on.'

'We were putting the decorations on the tree and I was asking the children how they planned to spend Christmas Day. Laura told us that she would be coming to Church and then going home with her family to check the crib. It sounded so touching and so different from the mayhem that goes on in our house that I asked her to tell us more about it.'

'Oh,' she said brightly. 'We have to check the crib because last year while we were at church, our cat ate Jesus!'

## CHRISTMAS CRACKERS

'Wake up sleepy head. It's the 23rd December. Only two more shopping days to Christmas. Lots to do!' Mac, who was finishing work that lunchtime and was only going into the office for a drinks party, was clearly in holiday mood.

I groaned and turned over, trying to work out why I was so unbelievably tired. Then I remembered.

In an attempt to beat the rush, the previous evening, I had made a bold, or as it turned out, stupid decision. To avoid the inevitable hoards at the supermarket, I had announced to my family that I was going to buy my food at midnight.

'Wicked,' Josh leapt at the idea. 'Can I come?'

'Don't be ridiculous,' I retorted, 'that's the whole point. No screaming, over-excited children, no queues in the car park, and empty checkouts. This is going to be the way forward. Festive, stress-free shopping. I shall relish the peace and quiet.'

'Hold on a minute, I thought that Sue was having all the stuff delivered by that organic farmer friend of hers.'

'Yes. But he only does meat, fruit and vegetables. Sue's list is far longer than that. So, she rang me and asked if I'd mind getting the rest from the supermarket. To be fair to her, she's in chaos at home and she's also working until Christmas Eve.'

'And was midnight shopping the brilliant idea you thought it would be?'

'Funnily enough, it wasn't! I arrived at the store just before twelve, and as I stood outside, freezing cold on a Sunday night, to my horror I was far from alone. There I was thinking I was going to beat the rush but, unbelievably, half the town was there with me …. some had even brought the kids! What sort of Christmas treat did they call that!

As the doors opened there was, thankfully, no rush to get inside. Everyone was too sleepy, too bewildered by the reality of this crazy idea.'

'But, hold on a minute, does our local supermarket actually sell the kind of things Sue eats?'

'You'd be amazed. Last night I found myself in parts of the store I never knew existed. Did you know they have an entire section devoted to organic products? I got the organic milk and organic tomato sauce there! Next I found the soap flakes and finally, with some help from the deputy manager I located the 'low salt' products, some of which, in my opinion, should have a 'completely tasteless' warning on them. By the time I'd got to the checkout, I had a trolley full of stuff I hardly recognised. The only thing she'd allowed me a free rein on were the napkins and the crackers! But it was while I was paying for the stuff that I realised my second mistake.'

'Which was?'

'I'd forgotten that if you buy your food at midnight, you won't be able to dump the stuff on the kitchen floor at one o'clock and dive into a warm bed. Oh no! While you were fast asleep I was downstairs trying to cram the perishables I'd bought into our already overflowing 'fridge' and 'freezer'. Which reminds me, I need to ask Victoria if we can decant some of our stuff into her freezer today. She's coming here for Christmas lunch, so, with a bit of luck, she may have some spare space. It's the only chance we've got of accommodating Sue's delivery.'

'So does that mean we've got everything now?' Mac was sounding naively optimistic.

'I wish. There's a list somewhere. No I lie, there are several lists somewhere that I've made and re-made over the past few days. If we could find those, it would be a good start.'

'But we've got all the main presents, surely?' Mac was beginning to look concerned.

'What's with the 'we' suddenly? I don't remember you getting involved in any of this. Now let's see. I've sent the cards, bought and wrapped most of the presents, chosen the tree, fixed the lights, hung the decorations and last night at midnight sorted what remained of the lunch. And you???'

'Okay don't start that again. I'm offering to help now. Who still needs a present? Have you finally sorted Archie's milk float?'

'Yes, thank God. Late on Saturday I was hurrying past Argos and I suddenly spotted one in a corner of the window. I'd convinced myself it didn't exist – a wild figment of his imagination. So I rushed in and bought it. It was the only one they had. I can't tell you what a relief it was to find it. It felt like I'd won the lottery.'

Archie had been going on about a milk float for as long as we could remember. It was Mr Milko from his Noddy books that had first got him going. While other two year olds longed to be super-heroes or pirates, our simple little soul had recently taken to going round the house all day with a cardboard box full of plastic skittles balanced precariously on the back of his brick trolley. No matter where you were standing or what you were doing you'd suddenly find a delivery at your feet. 'Two pints!' he'd announce triumphantly and he was off to the next customer. It was as if he was practising now so that he would be certain to get it just right on Christmas Day. More than once I'd tripped over a large delivery by the kitchen door or been rebuked for forgetting to cancel.

'Talk about pressure! I'd told him that Father Christmas doesn't always get you what you want, but he really believes he will. It wouldn't have been so bad if he'd had other presents on his list but it was the only one. I can't tell you what a relief it was to get it sorted. The whole affair was beginning to give me nightmares.'

'So are we done now?' Mac wondered, surveying the numerous carrier bags scattered carelessly around our bedroom.

'I think so.'

'Good. So you can finally put your feet up and relax, can you?'

I looked at the bags, the pile of wrapping paper and the empty stockings in the corner and gave a derisive laugh.

\*   \*   \*   \*

But, by the following evening, Christmas Eve, we'd finally cracked it.........
or so I thought.

'Do you think Aunt Lucy's alright?'

'Why shouldn't she be?' Mac, who was balanced precariously on a step ladder securing mistletoe to the ceiling, didn't sound overly concerned.

'Well, I thought she'd be here by now.'

'If I were you, I'd be grateful for the extra time I had without her. Based on our experience this year, she's hardly likely to be helpful when she arrives. Quite the opposite, more likely!'

But at that moment a screech of brakes in the driveway put my mind at rest. Mac grimaced.

'Doesn't that mad woman realise it's icy out there? I tell you, she'll kill the lot of us one of these days.'

'Mac, it's Christmas. Please try and make a serious effort to be civil. It's only for a couple of days.'

Outside in the driveway, Aunt Lucy was already unloading an odd selection of packages from the back of the car.

'Another load of junk from the second-hand emporiums of the world, no doubt,' Mac sighed. But resigned to his fate, he strode outside to lend a hand.

'Happy Christmas, Aunt,' he called, staring at the huge pile of presents she was amassing on the ground. 'How on earth did you squeeze this lot into your car?'

'Careful with that one,' she warned as Mac bent down to pick up an interesting looking box. 'It's fragile.'

'Oooh, how exciting,' I exclaimed, trying to lighten the atmosphere between aunt and nephew. 'Who's that one for?'

'Josh.'

'You've brought Josh something fragile. Is that wise?'

'I've simply got him what he asked for,' she replied. 'I thought it was about time he learned some responsibility. If he's careful, no one will come to any harm.'

'What do you mean by that?' Mac was on his guard. 'It's not a weapon of any sort, is it? Oh my God, it's moving. What on earth is it?'

'Rats,' she replied with a look of triumph on her face. 'A pair of gorgeous white rats. He told me he wanted them more than anything else in the world but that you had refused him.'

'I did.' Mac was crisp. 'And having refused, what made you feel that my decision could be so shamelessly over-ruled?'

'Mac dear, the boy needs to grow up. Taking responsibility for two young lives by feeding them and keeping them clean will be a great way for him to start. You let Lizzie have her hamster, and she's doing very well with it. It's only fair to let Josh have a go too.'

'I hardly feel that you, of all people, are in any position to start teaching others about responsibility,' Mac retorted.

'Aunt dear, you shouldn't buy animals for the children without asking us first. Who's going to look after them when we go on holiday? It's one thing to ask someone to care for a hamster, but not everyone likes having a couple of rats in their house.'

'I will care for them in your absence. I like rats.'

'And what about Claire?' Mac reminded her. 'Have you forgotten her allergies? Or had you planned for her to live outside?'

'Don't talk nonsense, Mac dear. Of course I hadn't forgotten about Claire and her over sensitive nose. To that end, I have bought her these goldfish,' she explained placing a large plastic bag containing two tiny fish in Mac's other hand. 'And the rats will be perfectly happy in the cellar. Honestly, I thought you'd be pleased with my choice of gift. Far too much rubbish comes into your house each Christmas. The children play with it all for five minutes and then it's abandoned. This will be a present Josh can enjoy for years.'

With a look of resignation, Mac took the loosely wrapped cage and the goldfish into the house. As he disappeared down the cellar steps, he peered into the package and smiled.

'I can't wait to see what Sue says when she realises she's spending Christmas in a rat-infested house.'

'Don't tell her till the morning,' I cautioned. 'Better to break the news in daylight.'

Mac looked surprised. 'The Christmas spirit has obviously got to you. I'd have put money on you breaking the news about our unexpected visitors as she crossed the threshold, thereby ensuring the shortest stay on record.'

By eight o'clock that night I was exhausted. But, helped by a large glass of mulled wine, I finally began to relax. Judy and her gang had called round to deliver their presents and, with the children up in the playroom, I sat down in the large chair by the fire and heaved a deep sigh.

'All set then?' Judy queried.

'I guess so. You know every year it's the same. I see the stuff arrive in the shops and I start off looking forward to Christmas. Then December arrives and it all seems to go horribly wrong. Before I know it, I'm frazzled by the queues in the shops, harassed by the endless round of Christmas fayres, frustrated by tree lights that never work and flustered by my constant inability to find the right presents for anybody. If I could only remember what a nightmare it all is, I wouldn't end up quite so disappointed.'

'Well, you can relax now. You've done it.'

'Actually I do have one more job to do. But I can't do that until Mac goes to the pub.'

'What's that?'

'The snooker table! Mac's always wanted one but we never had the space before.'

'Oh God.'

'Precisely! It's still in a large box in the Wendy House. Somehow I've got to get it up to the house and assembled without him realising.'

'You're mad to try it on your own. Can't you let Mac help you in the morning?'

'Oh no, that would spoil the surprise. Anyway it's not that heavy. It's only half-size, so shifting it shouldn't be too bad.'

'You'll start Christmas Day with a slipped disc if you're not careful,' Judy warned. 'Why don't you give me a ring when he's off the premises, and I'll come and give you a hand.'

'Don't be silly. If I'm really stuck, I'll ask Terence, Sue's husband.'

'Gosh I'd forgotten about them. Where are they?'

'The boys are upstairs watching a video and, at Sue's insistence, Terence is cleaning my oven. I thought it was fine but it obviously didn't match up to her impeccable standards! Sue's now gone to bed with a headache. She says it's because she's exhausted. But I know it's because her brother's upset her.'

'Oh God! So soon. She can only have been here a couple of hours.'

'Precisely. Mind you, it was partly her fault.'

'What did she do?'

'Well, her family arrived in two cars earlier this afternoon. Both were crammed to the gunnels with stuff. First she spends a good half hour unloading it all and then spends another hour and a half sorting it. She then sits down in a chair and announces to Mac that she forgot to mention that her children would be needing somewhere quiet to practice their wind instruments each day. When Mac snorted and explained that if her children wanted to practice, he'd be the one needing the quiet room, she took the huff and went to bed. I think she was over tired and his remark just tipped her over the top!'

*     *     *     *

It was nine thirty when Judy's lot finally went home. With a few glasses of wine already safely tucked away, Mac came into the room smiling broadly.

'Still no sign of Sue then?' he queried absently.

'No. I think we won't see her now until the morning.'

'It's probably all the dust,' Josh surmised as he kissed me goodnight.

'Or maybe she's smelt a rat,' Mac whispered. 'Well if there's nothing more I can do, I'm off to the pub with Terence. Don't wait up. I may be late!'

'You may see Aunt Lucy down there. If you do, please try and be polite.'

'Okay. And I'll also remind her that if she gets home without a key again, she'll be sleeping the night on the doorstep.'

As Mac set off down the driveway, I stared out into the garden. Not only was it extremely dark out there, it was also extremely cold. But there was no turning back. It was now or never.

As Judy had warned, the snooker table was much heavier than I'd imagined. As I opened the door of the Wendy House and stared at the large package, I realised that it would be no easy task to pull it through the small door, let alone drag it uphill to the back door. With a great deal of huffing and puffing, I somehow managed to negotiate it through the small opening and out onto the lawn. Then, centimetre by centimetre, I dragged it over the damp grass, pausing every few seconds to catch my breath. Not only was this extremely hard work, I was also freezing. Looking up, I could see a dim light shining out of the landing window. Everyone inside the house was asleep, all blissfully unaware of the madness that was taking place just a few feet from their bedroom windows. The garden could have been full of burglars with machetes but they wouldn't have noticed a thing!

Little by little, I worked my way towards the back door. At this rate it was going to take me all night. After a lot of moaning and groaning, I managed to heave the vast package onto the paving stones alongside the house. Progress became easier now as I was on the 'flat'. Just a few more feet and I would make it to the back door. Phew!

Ten minutes later and the table was finally in the house. Luckily, assembling it was easy and soon I was potting balls to my heart's content. What a great present and nobody suspected a thing.

## CHRISTMAS MORNING

It was just before half past six the following morning when Lizzie burst into our bedroom trailing a full stocking behind her.

'Happy Christmas,' she shouted excitedly. Then her face fell.

'Oh Mummy. Oh my poor, poor Mummy.'

'Darling, what on earth's the matter?'

'No Mummy, don't look. It's just that....that ....Father Christmas has forgotten to fill your stocking!'

I pulled myself up and stared at the end of my bed. My empty stocking lay exactly where I had left it the night before.

From somewhere beneath the duvet beside me a voice could be heard.

'Oh my God, I completely forgot. Give me five minutes.'

Well, if you only get back from the pub at one o'clock, what can you expect?

'So it's you, Daddy,' wailed Lizzie. 'Does that mean that Josh was right and there really isn't a Father Christmas?'

'Oh well done!' I spat at him. 'What a great start to Christmas morning!'

But luckily, in the next room, 'doubting Josh' was about to save the day.

'He is real, he is real!' he exclaimed excitedly as he burst into the room.

'Of course he is,' I agreed, much relieved that the magic hadn't been lost for ever. Why are you suddenly so sure?'

'Look outside,' he screamed excitedly. 'His sleigh marks are on the lawn.'

As we all crowded round the window to look, we could see quite clearly the 'sweep' of flattened grass across the middle of the lawn made by me and the pool table the previous evening.

'Who did that?' Claire was bewildered.

'Father Christmas, of course!' I beamed round at everyone.

For a moment, Mac stared at the lawn. Then shaking his head, as if to clear it, he went into the bathroom. Clearly he'd drunk more than he thought the night before.

The next half hour passed in a flurry of excitement as the contents of stockings were torn apart.

'Our four are like a bunch of animals,' Mac lamented. 'Look at the mess! I've just popped a tray of tea into our guests' rooms and it is all so different at the other end of the corridor. Aunt Lucy, unbelievably, was sitting quietly in her chair with her headphones on listening, I presume, to the morning service from Kings College Cambridge, whilst in the next room Sue and Terence were sitting up reading, their teenage children still dead to the world on their camp beds. In both rooms, the stockings you'd so carefully compiled lay untouched at the bottom of every bed, almost as if they've forgotten what day it is. Okay, so they might be lacking a bit of Christmas spirit, but compared to the mayhem in our room, it all looked so deliciously civilized. Do you think there is any chance that, one day, we'll have a Christmas morning that starts like that?'

'I rather think we'll have died of exhaustion long before that happens.'

'Yep. That's just what I was thinking.'

But despite the early start, it wasn't until around nine thirty that everyone finally gathered in the kitchen for tea and toast. With eleven of us divided between the table and the breakfast bar, it was a little crowded, but somehow we managed. At the far end, I could just hear Sue muttering to Terence that, in her opinion, stockings for adults were a complete load of nonsense and didn't Kate know that she never used bath oil as it could easily cause her to fall over in the bath and break her neck.

Yes, I did realise that!

It was just at that moment that Josh burst into the room.

'Hey, guess what, I've just discovered two rats in the cellar! Aunt Lucy just asked me to go down there to get a new light bulb and there they were, their pink eyes staring up at me.'

'I thought we weren't allowed in the cellar without an adult?' Claire queried inadvertently fanning the flames that were now emerging from Mac's nostrils.

'Quite right. But, sadly, he was under the influence of a serial rule-breaker,' Mac replied crisply, glaring at Aunt Lucy. 'Had it not occurred to you, Aunt, that as he hurtled excitedly down those rickety steps, he could have broken his neck? As I have said all too often, we have rules in this house for a reason. You have been here less than twenty four hours and managed to break at least two of the most important ones.'

But Aunt Lucy refused to be moved by the rebuke. 'As I said yesterday, the boy needs to start taking some responsibility. I told him to be careful and, as you can see, he's absolutely fine. No damage done.'

But she was wrong, on the other side of the table, Sue was as white as a sheet.

'Mac, do something, I can't get through the day with the thought that you have vermin no more than twelve feet away from us.'

Clearly relishing the moment, Mac addressed his elder sister slowly. 'Sue dear, given that you live in the centre of town, statistically, you are probably never more than ten feet away from a rat. So, on that basis, you're probably safer here with our rat infested cellar than you would be at home.'

'Stop this at once,' I intervened. 'Sue, the rats are actually white rats and are Aunt Lucy's Christmas present to Josh. I can assure you that they are safely behind bars.'

In a second, Sue's anguish turned to anger. She turned on Aunt Lucy, her face contorted with rage. 'What a daft present, if I may say so. But no less than I'd have expected. Well, if that really is the case, can I have some assurance that they will remain incarcerated for as long as I am in this house. It is the only basis on which I am prepared to stay.'

It was tempting to refuse but, after all, it was Christmas.

'Yes,' I said glaring at Josh, 'of course you can.'

For a moment there was silence.

Suddenly, Sue gave a little scream and pointed dramatically towards the window.

'Good God, don't tell me one's escaped already,' Mac groaned. But it wasn't a rat, it was Bert Moggins, gesticulating wildly at us through the glass. Hastily Josh leapt up to let him in. As Sue looked on, her eyes wide, I noticed a wicked glint appear in Mac's.

'Bert. Welcome. Happy Christmas!' Mac generally ignored the wild man of the village, but clearly the opportunity to goad his sister was irresistible. Across the table, her face was a picture of abject horror!

'Sue, this is Aunt Lucy's friend, Bert.' Wiping his hand on his filthy coat, Bert smiled a toothless smile and offered Sue a greeting. Gingerly Sue returned it. 'Did Kate tell you he's joining us for lunch? The more the merrier, don't you think?'

Clearly that was not what she thought.

For a few seconds, there was awkward silence. Then Bert spoke.

'I was wondering if I could have a quiet word with Luce....in private, like? It won't take a minute.'

'Certainly!' Mac replied with a little too much enthusiasm. 'Aunt, dear, you are excused.'

Aunt Lucy's eyes lit up. 'Why of course,' she replied coyly and pushing back her chair, they both left the room.

Mac, noting his sister's anxious expression, patted Sue on the back. 'Rest assured, they'll be planning something dreadful!'

For a few moments peace reigned then I glanced up at the clock.

'I say, if we want to open some more presents before church, we'd better get a move on.'

The children didn't need to be told twice. As chairs were hurriedly pushed back, they charged, as one, into the lounge where a huge pile of presents sat seductively under the tree. Terence, Mac and I followed at a slower pace. Only Sue remained at the table.

'Not tempted to join us then?' Mac wondered.

'It is barely ten o'clock and, so far, you have managed to torment me with rats and a vagrant. Quite frankly, much as I love your children, right now the prospect of watching your hysterical offspring create mayhem in the lounge is not altogether attractive.' She paused to take a handful of herbal remedies from her handbag. 'Perhaps, in a few moments, I may be able to join you. But for now, I don't think my shattered nerves could stand it!'

'Suit yourself,' Mac replied with deliberate indifference. 'You know where we are.'

As Sue had predicted, the scene in the lounge was not good. As six excited cousins battled for position under the tree, I noted two neat columns of presents lined up beside the piano. All identically wrapped in silver paper and tied with velvet ribbon, Sue's contribution to the festivities were topped by a silver fountain pen and a leather bound book with 'Present list' embossed in gold lettering on the top.

'That says it all,' I sighed to Mac. And with that I grabbed a couple of post-it notes and a blunt pencil, and dived in to join the chaos. It wasn't long before my voice was the loudest of them all.

'Lizzie, who gave you that?' I yelled above the excited babble. Clutching my present list I shouted at Claire. 'No, don't open another present yet. I haven't written down Josh's present from Auntie Mary yet!'

'Calm down Kate,' Mac looked concerned. 'It's Christmas Day. You sound like a referee at a football match.'

'Don't you tell me to calm down while you're sitting there smugly with a glass of Bucks Fizz.' I barked. 'If I don't sort out who gave what to whom, we'll be in a right muddle, you see.'

Mac sighed. Then he gently took two pens and some paper from the desk and handed them to Claire and Josh. He then removed one of the post-it notes from my hand and sat down beside me.

'Claire and Josh are quite old enough to list their gifts. I'll look after Lizzie and you concentrate on Archie. There, that's better, isn't it?'

I looked gratefully at Mac and then, suddenly the tears welled up.

'Hey, stop that,' he said gently putting a protective arm around me. 'I thought you usually looked forward to the 'present opening' bit.'

'I do,' I blubbed. 'It's just that this year, living here, I seem to have had far more to do. I think all the extra responsibilities have finally got to me. If you must know, I think, deep down, I just want to be a child again and enjoy all the good bits without all the endless worry.'

Mac gave me a hug. Then he pointed across the room. 'Look.'

I turned my attention back to the muddle, in time to watch the magical moment of the day. Archie had just pulled the wrapping paper off the large parcel in the corner and was now beaming at his new acquisition.

'Is that the one you wanted?' I asked gently. He nodded as he lovingly fingered his milk float then each of the shiny plastic bottles on the back.

'Did you see one at a friend's house?' Mac was curious to know.

Archie shook his head and toddled out into the kitchen. He returned a few minutes later and put a large book into my lap.

'Cat book,' he said triumphantly. He had given me the latest Argos catalogue.

'My 'cat' book.....my catalogue...my Argos catalogue!' God, how on earth did I miss that one?'

'Why didn't you tell us that before?' Mac moaned. 'It would have saved us an awful lot of trouble.'

Archie looked puzzled. Claire gave us a despairing look.

'He didn't think that you needed to know, did he? He thinks some chap with a red coat and white beard sorts these things out.........duh!'

## AND FINALLY...

'Tell me, Kate, how is it possible to lose Aunt Lucy between our house and the church? It can't be more than thirty yards! She can't have done a 'runner' with Bert, can she? I'd have thought there was far too much going on here for her to want to miss anything.'

'Don't panic, she's over there. Look, she's sitting in the back row. And Bert's with her. By the look of them both, they're obviously hatching some kind of plot.'

'Why doesn't she want to sit with us?' Josh was clearly upset that his new ally had abandoned him.

'Cheer up,' Mac looked relieved. 'Look on the bright side. If she wants to sit in that dark corner, let her. At least it'll give us the chance to have a bit of peace.'

'You haven't said anything else to upset her?' I demanded, not liking the glint in my husband's eye.

Mac screwed up his face trying to remember. 'No, not as far as I can recall. Since my justifiable outburst at breakfast, I've been my usual charming self.'

'That's what worries me. Look, you stay here a moment. I'm going to check she's alright.'

'Well don't encourage them to come down and join us. If they're happy where they are, please leave them there.'

Aunt Lucy looked up enthusiastically as I approached.

'Kate, dear, guess what? Bert and I have just discovered another reason why we're kindred spirits.'

'In what way, Aunt dear?' I asked, fearing the worst.

Lowering her voice for dramatic effect, she whispered. 'Neither of us likes this 'shaking hands' business in the middle of the service.'

'What on earth are you talking about?'

'You know. That bit in the communion service when we're all expected to embrace and wish one another the 'Peace of the Lord'. Well, we think we're too old for that sort of thing. So, today we're going to try an experiment. When it comes to that part of the service, we're going to keep our hands firmly on our laps and shut our eyes. That way everyone should leave us alone. Bert has always found it most intimidating.'

'Aunt Lucy, I wasn't aware that you found anything intimidating.'

'Oh I don't. That's not why I object to it. I just dislike the assumption that I should wish to have peace. To be honest, it's something I've never sought!'

When I told Mac what she'd said, he laughed. 'Let her get on with it. Whatever happens, it's going to ensure that we get some peace, even if she doesn't!'

A tap on my shoulder heralded the arrival of Lady Henrietta Caldwell.

'Merry Christmas, dear,' she gushed proffering me a kiss on both cheeks. 'Tell me, are the children going to be performing one of your plays today?'

'Oh no. Not during a Holy Communion service on Christmas Day,' I replied. 'I don't think my chaotic offering would be appropriate.'

'No indeed,' she replied. I felt she looked relieved.

Feeling somewhat chastened, I took my seat alongside Lizzie. Next to her, Josh was looking annoyed.

'How come Cosmo's doing a reading?' he complained. 'I thought it was my turn to do one.'

'I wouldn't complain if I were you. When you hear what he's got to read, you'll be delighted you're not doing it.'

'What do you mean?'

'He's got to describe Mary's reaction when she hears she's going to give birth to the Son of God.' It's from St Luke's gospel. At some point Cosmo will have to cry out… 'How can this be, I am a virgin?' Somehow, I couldn't see you wanting to say that.'

'No, I wouldn't,' Josh replied looking horrified.

'Precisely. Mind you, remembering how Cosmo reacted to the line 'Do you love me?' in the Ascension service, I don't think he's going to be too keen either.'

'Mum, look at Scarlet. She's got the job of lighting all the candles,' Claire announced jealously as she watched Scarlet balance herself precariously on the end of a pew to light a nightlight on a window ledge.

'Ye Gods, whose mad idea was that?' Mac exclaimed. 'She'll incinerate the lot of us. Doesn't anyone remember her performance at the Christingle service? Why on earth isn't she being supervised? Or has everyone forgotten that, only a few days ago, she very nearly ignited my son and half the congregation.'

From the pew in front, Audrey, far from looking concerned, looked on wistfully. 'It is so much more meaningful to see the real flames than the artificial lights, don't you think? And seeing a child light them….it's enchanting.'

'Frightening, more like,' Mac muttered under his breath.

A nudge from Lizzie distracted me for a moment.

'Mum, why's Hatty carrying the baby Jesus?'

'I beg your pardon?'

'Look. She's got him on her lap.'

'Ah yes,' I explained, 'that's because she's going to place him into the crib at the start of the service. It's very symbolic.'

'That's not fair. Our family haven't been given any jobs to do.'

'Well, of all the jobs on offer, you certainly wouldn't have got that one,' Mac pointed out bluntly. 'Given that the baby Jesus is made of china, it's highly likely that you'd have dropped him on the stone floor on the way to the crib. Somehow, seeing Jesus break into a thousand pieces on Christmas morning isn't quite the symbolism we'd be looking for.'

'Mum, Judy's arrived,' Claire exclaimed excitedly. 'And that must be Erica.'

I turned to see a young girl with a bubbly face holding Fred and a large wooden fort.

'Do you think she made that?' Claire said enviously. 'How wicked to have an aunt who makes toys for a living.'

'And what do we have?' Josh added bitterly. 'An aunt who ignores her great-nephew on Christmas Day and another who's a solicitor and doesn't like television or chocolate!'

'Do look at Eddie,' Lizzie interrupted. 'He's wearing a Darth Vader costume.'

'Odd thing to come to church in?' Mac reflected. 'And on Christmas Day, too.'

'No, it's not odd,' Claire explained. 'Vicar Vic asked all the children to bring their favourite present to church so that everyone could enjoy them.'

'So why didn't my family bother?' Mac sounded surprised. 'We don't normally miss an opportunity to make an exhibition of ourselves.'

'Oh, but we did,' Claire sounded hurt. 'Haven't you noticed Lizzie's new fairy costume?'

Mac stared critically at his younger daughter and shook his head. 'You know, over the past few months, I've barely seen Lizzie without some kind of fairy costume. In fact, there have been days when, if I didn't know her better, I'd have sworn she'd grown wings. Come to think of it, if I saw her wearing normal clothes for any kind of outing, I'm not sure I'd recognise her.'

Claire sighed. 'You do say some ridiculous things sometimes. Now, have you noticed Archie's uniform?'

Turning his attention to his youngest offspring, again he looked puzzled. 'What do you mean by uniform? What job requires a Noddy T-shirt and peaked cap?'

'I'd have thought that was obvious,' Claire hissed as she gave a rather hurt looking Archie a reassuring pat. 'It's his milkman's outfit. He did it himself. Ask him. He's got two bottles of milk in his bag to prove it.'

'For goodness sake, who on earth allowed him to do that? Get them off him immediately. Does no one around here have any common sense?'

'It's not real milk, silly. They're plastic ones from his milk float,' Claire explained with a giggle. 'I've got my 'Game Boy' to show everyone, which will be especially useful if the sermon's a bit long and Josh has brought ......' she tailed off suddenly as Josh gave her a sharp nudge.

'And what has Josh brought that he's suddenly so secretive about?' Mac queried, staring fixedly at the small box Josh was clutching tightly to his chest. 'And why has it got holes in the top? Oh my God, Kate, he's brought the rats. Josh, have you not remembered one word of the clear instructions Aunt Sue gave to you this morning?'

'Yes I did. Aunt Sue said that the rats had to remain locked up as long as she was in the house. Well, she's not in the house now, is she? She's here.' He finished with rather less conviction than he'd started. It didn't take a genius to work out that his father was very unimpressed.

'Well, you can take them back to their cage right now. And don't be surprised if both of them are back in the shop on Boxing Day.'

'I didn't bring them both. I only brought the little one,' Josh explained defensively. As if to demonstrate, he lifted the lid of the box a fraction to reveal two pink eyes and some rather sharp teeth. But, before he could close it again, the rat had seized the moment. As quick as a flash, he'd shot through the small gap and scurried along the pew to the aisle.

'Ye Gods, the damn thing's escaped,' Mac exploded. 'After him Josh, quick.'

As the rat turned east and headed for the Chancel, Aunt Sue took the westerly route down the aisle and outside to the graveyard, followed at a discreet distance by her husband, Terence. A few other nervous members of the congregation were quick to join them. The rest stayed, keen not to miss any of the excitement.

'You're going to have to go and help him,' I hissed to Mac. 'He's never going to catch it on his own. Oh look, it's climbed up the altar cloth. For heavens sake, do something before Josh pulls the whole lot onto the floor.'

'I swear I'll murder him the second I catch him,' Mac muttered to a rather surprised looking lady as he eased himself along the pew. 'And,' he added, in case there was any possible misunderstanding, 'I'm not talking about the rat.'

'Okay, so where's the damn thing now?' Mac demanded of his son when they met a moment later.

'Dad, you mustn't swear in church, especially by the altar,' Josh urged, remembering Vicar Vic's recent stark warning to his mother after the Christingle service, and clearly expecting a thunderbolt to appear at any point and strike his father dead. 'I think he's under the chair.'

With a look that made it clear that any thunderbolt would be targeted at his son rather than him, Mac moved into position. 'We'll have to corner him,' he announced. 'You frighten him out and I'll pounce. Right, after three.'

With a yell of fury, as Josh banged the chair, Mac hurled himself at the tiny animal. But to no avail. The rat slipped through his fingers and sought refuge under the Christmas tree.

The congregation was agog. By now several of the men had moved forward to help. Instructing them to encircle the tree, Mac once again moved into position. This time he was in luck. As Josh shook the branches, showering the assembled crowd with tinsel and pine needles, the rat shot out and, somehow, Mac managed to grab it by its tail. As he held it triumphantly aloft, any reaction from the congregation was curtailed as the rat twisted round and sank its teeth deep into his hand. With a yell of pain, Mac dropped it.

There was a groan from the congregation but, as the rat fled down the aisle, a large black object flew through the air. It was a coat and, as it fell to the floor, it stopped the rat dead in its tracks. As if from nowhere, Bert appeared and threw himself on top of it. As he gathered up the jacket, the rat's tail could just be seen peeking out underneath it. A moment later, Bert, his coat and the rat disappeared into the graveyard to the accompaniment of a large round of applause. Some way behind him, Mac and a somewhat subdued Josh followed. They reached the door just as Vicar Vic emerged from the vestry ready to start the service. Muttering apologies for his blood-stained hand, Mac slunk out through the door leaving her momentarily dumbstruck. As she walked down the aisle to the strains of 'O come all ye faithful', she was left wondering why the sight of Mac at the door had sent several members of the congregation scurrying in all directions round the churchyard.

Not knowing what else to do, I turned to face the front and put a protective arm around my remaining children. Behind me, I could feel the angry stares of my two teenage nephews. I could tell exactly what they were thinking: 'Relatives simply couldn't come much more embarrassing than that!'

It was halfway through the third carol that I heard the church door open. Turning, I saw Mac enter, his arm now bandaged and supported by a strangely benevolent looking Sue. Behind them followed Terence and Josh, the former with a comforting hand on his nephew's shoulder and, finally, a rather smug looking Bert. As they sidled into the back pew, I watched as a now humbled Aunt Lucy mouthed 'sorry' to her nephew. Reeling from the shock, I gasped as Sue leant across and gave Bert a quick peck on the cheek. Clearly Christmas had worked some magic after all.

*   *   *   *

'I didn't realise I was only the supporting act,' Vicar Vic laughed as I approached her in the graveyard after the service. 'I've just heard some of the gruesome details. No one told me that you were planning some last minute entertainment to liven things up!'

'Don't say such things,' I implored. 'I don't think I've ever been so humiliated in my life.'

'Nonsense,' Victoria giggled. 'Most of the congregation thought it was the best bit of the service. They'll be talking about it for years!'

'We got our little bit of chaos after all,' Lady Henrietta smiled. 'Bert and your husband quite stole the show.'

'Those two ought to be in the village rugby team,' James, Judy's husband, commented. 'I haven't seen tackles like that in a long time.'

'I could do with both of them to solve my rat problem in the stables,' Jim, the farmer from the end of the village, added. 'Best pest control I've seen for years!'

'Do you think we'll ever live this one down?' I wondered.

'No chance,' Victoria was not consoling. 'They'll be expecting something similar every Christmas now. Quite an act to follow really!'

I groaned again. 'Are you still prepared to brave Christmas lunch with us, rats and all?'

'I wouldn't miss it for the world. But don't you think it's time you got back and took control before Aunt Lucy initiates her final act of the year and burns your house down? She's probably the only one of the congregation who minded playing second fiddle to a rat.'

'Oh she won't feel left out. At least not after Mac's spoken to her. Believe me, he holds her entirely responsible for the incident.'

As Victoria went off to change, I turned to stare at the Vicarage. I had no idea what I expected to see but it wasn't the serene image of Aunt Lucy sitting by the tree in the drawing room, her feet up and what looked like a glass of whisky in one hand. Beside her, Archie and Lizzie were playing happily with their new toys. Through the next window Mac, Terence and the three older male cousins were trying out Mac's new pool table, and in the kitchen at the far end of the house, Sue was smiling broadly as if glad, finally, to have a firm hand on the proceedings. Helped by Claire and what looked like a large glass of champagne, she seemed as happy as I'd ever seen her. It was as if the rat had finally saved the sinking ship.

Behind me, the last of the congregation were making their way to the gate, most shouting 'Merry Christmas' to everyone as they left.

Then, as if from nowhere, I heard bells. I turned to see a smiling Bert coming up our lane. Beside him was his old pony, covered with tinsel and pulling a cart full of presents.

'Just a little surprise for everyone to thank you for allowing me to share your day,' he whispered. 'Hope you don't mind.'

'Bert,' I replied quite overcome by it all, 'you're wonderful!'

As Bert turned into our driveway, I watched as the children rushed to the window their eyes wide with excitement. And as I stood alone, staring at the twinkling lights of our tree shining out of the drawing room window, I took a moment to reflect on our first chaotic year at The Old Vicarage in Lower Hadbury and realised, not for the first time, how lucky we were to be part of such a remarkable community.

## A VERY IMPORTANT ACKNOWLEDGMENT
## TO ALL VICARS... ESPECIALLY MY OWN

We didn't buy our house from the Church of England. As far as I know, we are the fourth family to live here since it was sold off in the 1970s.

Had we lived in a different era, our house would have been the vicar's home. Today locals still call it 'The Vicarage' just as they call the cottage down the road 'Jim's' house, even though he died more than twenty years ago and two families have lived in it since then. It is a nostalgic name for a house that is now just a family home. So, while we may affectionately call it 'The Vicarage' or 'The Old Vicarage', the simple truth is, it is a Vicarage no more.

Since the Church of England sold off so many of its valuable assets, the real Vicarages in many towns and villages have often become smaller, modern buildings. Free from draughts and the damp and cold, they are far easier to heat in the winter. And with fewer rooms, keeping them clean and tidy is less of a challenge, if you care about that sort of thing.

But I know which I prefer.

Ironically, I know a vicar who was ordained late in life. He gave up his city job and his beautiful country 'Old Vicarage' to be a priest in a small village. His wife hated the modern 'box' she was offered in the parish, so they bought a tiny old cottage and quickly brought to it much of the charm of their former home.

Today, many priests, including our own, are part-time because the Church of England can no longer afford full-time priests for many of their smaller parishes. Ours, like most, manages to cram more than a full week's work into a few days. He has a home many miles from here and only stays in the modern Vicarage in our parish when he's at work. That should make me feel better about living where I do, but it doesn't.

As a family we try, probably not nearly hard enough, to open our doors to other people in our community. Certainly we provide the village with a constant source of amusement as we stumble through our daily lives.

So, thank you to the church for giving people like me the opportunity to live in such a lovely home, but many apologies to the vicars everywhere who have missed out.

Jill